THE ILLUSTRATED
ENCYCLOPEDIA OF
COMMERCIAL
AIRCRAFT

THE ILLUSTRATED ENCYCLOPEDIA OF
COMMERCIAL AIRCRAFT

Editor-in-chief BILL GUNSTON

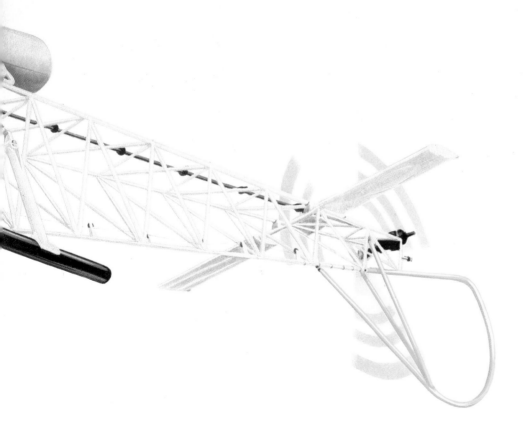

NEW YORK

in association with Phoebus

Contents

Jet Airliners

Nene Viking, Vickers-Armstrong	1
Lancastrian jet, Avro	2
Tay Viscount, Vickers-Armstrong	3
Jetliner, Avro Canada	4
Comet 1, de Havilland	6
Boeing 707	10
Boeing 720	18
XCG-20A, Chase	21
Tu-104, Tupolev	22
Tu-110, Tupolev	25
Tu-124, Tupolev	26
Caravelle, Aérospatiale	28
Comet 4, de Havilland	34
DC-8, Douglas	38
BB-152, VEB	44
CV-880, Convair	45
CV-990, Convair	48
VC10/Super VC10, BAC	50
Trident, Hawker Siddeley	54
Boeing 727	60
One-Eleven, BAC	65
DC-9, McDonnell Douglas	70
Boeing 737	76
Tu-134, Tupolev	82
Tu-154, Tupolev	86
Il-62, Ilyushin	90
F28 Fellowship, Fokker	92
VFW 614	97
Yak-40, Yakovlev	98
Yak-42, Yakovlev	100
Mercure, Dassault-Breguet	102
An-72, Antonov	104
Il-76, Ilyushin	106
Concorde, Aérospatiale/British Aerospace	111
Tu-144, Tupolev	118
DC-9 Super 80, McDonnell Douglas	122
BAe 146, British Aerospace	124
Boeing 757	126
F29, Fokker	128
L-1011 TriStar, Lockheed	129
Boeing 747	138
DC-10, McDonnell Douglas	148
A300B, Airbus Industrie	158
A310, Airbus Industrie	170
Il-86, Ilyushin	174
Boeing 767	181
SST Projects and Advanced Transports	186
Hydrogen-fuelled Airliners	190
Slew-winged Airliners	192

General Aviation

Po-2AP, Polikarpov	193
FC.2, Fairchild	194
Robin, Curtiss	195
Bellanca AirCruiser	196
Norseman, Noorduyn	197
Widgeon, Grumman	198
Aerovan, Miles	199
Beaver, de Havilland Canada	200
Drover, de Havilland Australia	201
An-2, Antonov	202
DHC-3 Otter, de Havilland Canada	203
Twin Beech, Beechcraft	204
Courier, Helio	206
Fletcher, Aerospace	207
E.P.9, Edgar Percival	208
AG-Cat, Gulfstream American	209
JetStar, Lockheed	210
Sabreliner, Rockwell	211
Turbo Commander, Rockwell	212
BAe 125, British Aerospace	214
P.166, Piaggio	216
Falcon 20, Dassault-Breguet	217
Falcon 10, Dassault-Breguet	218
Falcon 50, Dassault-Breguet	219
Learjets	220
Gulfstream I, Gulfstream American	222

Xingu, Embraer	249
Challenger, Canadair	250
Dromader, PZL	251
Kruk, PZL	252
IAR-827	253
Commander 700, Rockwell	254
ST-600, Foxjet	255
M-15, PZL	256

Civil Helicopters

Bell 47	257
Hiller 360	258
FH-1100, Fairchild Hiller	259
Bristol 171	260
Bristol 173	261
S-51, Sikorsky	262
S-55, Sikorsky	263
S-58, Sikorsky	264
S-61N, Sikorsky	266
Yak-24A, Yakovlev	268
Whirlwind Series 3, Westland	270
Lama, Aérospatiale	271
Alouette III, Aérospatiale	274
Mi-1, Mil	275
Mi-2, Mil	276
Mi-6, Mil	277
Mi-8P, Mil	280
SA 321F Super Frelon, Aérospatiale	281
Brantly	282
Hughes 300	283
Hughes 500	284
Bell 204	285
Bell 205	286
Bell 214B	288
Bell 206 JetRanger	290
Boeing Vertol 107	292
LongRanger, Bell 206L	293
Bell 222	294
Ka-25K, Kamov	296
Ka-26, Kamov	297
A 109A, Agusta	298
Enstrom	300
Puma, Aérospatiale	302
Gazelle, Aérospatiale	304
AS 350 Ecureuil, Aérospatiale	306
BK 117, MBB/Kawasaki	308
S-76 Spirit, Sikorsky	310
Kania, PZL	312
Dauphin, Aérospatiale	314
R22, Robinson	315
V-12, Mil	316
Boeing 234	318
Mk II, Spitfire	320
Index	321

Wilga, PZL	223
Turbo-Porter, Pilatus	224
Navajo, Piper	225
Super King Air, Beech	226
AL.60 Conestoga, Aermacchi/Lockheed	227
MU-2, Mitsubishi	228
HFB 320 Hansa, MBB	230
Skyvan, Short	231
An-14, Antonov	232
CL-215, Canadair	233
Westwind, IAI	234
Gulfstream II, Gulfstream American	235
Bandeirante, Embraer	236
Arava IAI	237
Pawnee, Piper	238
Thrush Commander, Ayres	239
Airtruk, Transavia	240
Air Tractor AT301	241
Citation, Cessna	242
Corvette, Aérospatiale	244
Nomad, GAF	245
Cheyenne, Piper	246
Conquest, Cessna	247
Skyservant, Dornier	248

Introduction

The Jet Age, in civil aviation, is generally considered to have begun on May 2, 1952, when a Comet jetliner of the British national airline BOAC left London on a scheduled flight with fare-paying passengers to Johannesburg. At that time the Comet was regarded by most of the world's airlines as an interesting technical achievement but not as possible equipment. They found plenty of reasons for preferring the known quantity of slow, relatively low-flying piston-engined aircraft that thumped and vibrated on their established routes.

This book shows how totally the gas-turbine engine, in both its jet and shaft-drive forms, has swept the piston engine away from civil aviation except in the field of small private-owner aircraft. Even the helicopter, which began to switch to turboshaft power in 1955 after a few earlier prototype experiments, was so transformed by the new type of engine that the large piston-engined helicopters were soon extinct. Basically, the gas turbine offered lighter weight, less drag, more power, greater reliability, reduced maintenance costs, cheaper fuel and improved safety.

Today the gas turbine has penetrated far into the last stronghold of the piston engine, general aviation. Usually defined as all aviation except that of armed forces and airlines, GA includes such groups as private owners, training schools, clubs, agriculture, business and executive transport, survey and mapping, and offshore patrol, search and rescue. Despite high costs, the jet has practically taken over the upper range of the business and executive market, and now the turboprop and even the jet are for reasons of power, reliability and safety invading the unexpected realm of 'ag-aviation'. This is no mean market, for farmers around the world use an estimated 36 000 aircraft.

Though this book includes general aviation aircraft and civil helicopters its main content is made up of the vast fleet of jetliners that today carry 70% of all airline passengers, 85% of the flying holidaymakers and 100% of those making intercontinental journeys. The early jetliners sold on the strength of their passenger appeal. People reached their destinations in half the time, and arrived relaxed after a smooth flight high above the rough air and turbulent clouds. But in some ways these aircraft were a retrograde step. Though some found them exciting, their thunderous noise was if anything worse than that of the lumbering piston-engined airliners, and their sooty jet trails a particularly visible form of pollution (though a relatively harmless one).

What the early jetliners did accomplish was to enable airline traffic to grow at an unprecedented rate, and – to the amazement of some who predicted financial disaster – make the airlines basically profitable. New equipment from 1960 accelerated the process and gradually cured the noise and smoke. The newest of this group, the British Aerospace 146, will be the most socially acceptable transport aircraft yet when it enters service in September 1982.

Also included in this book are the advanced jetliners, which deal mainly with what the airlines call the wide-bodies. The first of these was the Boeing 747, better known to the public as the Jumbo Jet. Never before had so many advances been offered in one vehicle: more than twice the number of passengers, dramatically reduced fuel consumption per passenger, higher speed, greater range and noise slashed by about one-hundred-fold. Key to these advances was a new kind of gas turbine, the high-bypass-ratio turbofan, which though looking totally unstreamlined in fact brought a new high level in efficiency. Today virtually all the long journeys are made in wide-bodies, and the fact that they have been made to fit the world's airports means that air traffic has been able roughly to double, with no extra flights and dramatically reduced noise – though the airports themselves are often overcrowded.

This book also takes a look at the future. Instead of seeking more speed or more passenger seats, the designers are trying to find answers to two severe problems: one is the escalation in costs, especially in the price of fuel; the other is the fact that today's aviation fuel derived from petroleum is soon going to become not only costlier but scarcer, and in the lifetime of most people alive today the oil wells will almost run dry.

Bill Gunston

Contributors: Cliff Barnett, Chris Chant, Peter G Cooksley, Will Fowler, Bill Gunston

Color illustrations: Jim Bamber, Jeremy Banks, John Batchelor, Tony Bryan, Nick Falmer, Terry Hadler, Frank Kennard, David Mallott, Peter Sarson, David Staples, Michael Trim
Line illustrations: Terry Allen Designs Ltd, Arthur Bowbeer, Ray Hutchins, Abdul Aziz Kahn, David Mallott, Martin Woodford (research by Arthur Bowbeer)
Cutaways: © Pilot Press Ltd
Three-view drawings: © Pilot Press Ltd, © Phoebus Publishing Company

© 1980 Phoebus Publishing Company/BPC Publishing Limited, 52 Poland Street, London W1A 2JX

First published in USA 1980 by Exeter Books
Distributed by Bookthrift, Inc New York, New York

Phototypeset by Tradespools Limited, Frome, Somerset, England

Printed in Great Britain by Redwood Burn Limited, Trowbridge, Wiltshire

ISBN 0-89673-077-8

Nene Viking, Vickers-Armstrongs

FIRST FLIGHT 1948

WHILE the first Nene-Lancastrian can be dubbed 'the world's first jet airliner' only in that in 1946 it took passengers for rides in an uncanny near-silence, and with a total lack of the vibration to which airline travellers were then used (with its surplus piston engines switched off). It could not really be called an airliner at all but only an engine testbed. The Nene-Viking was a different proposition. It has also been called 'the first jet airliner' but with much more justification.

It was a true airliner, designed from the start as a civil transport and in its normal form, powered by piston engines. At an early stage in the programme the Ministry of Supply, then the government procurement agency for aircraft, decided to order one Viking with turbojets instead of the usual Hercules sleeve-valve radial piston engines. This was partly in order to assist general development of jet airliners, and see what problems might arise, and partly to furnish ministers and officials with a comfortable executive transport.

The 107th airframe on the Weybridge production line was set aside, and the designers schemed a series of major changes. The existing nacelles were replaced by completely new jet pods each housing a Rolls-Royce Nene, with the trailing edge of the wing extended at the rear to fair smoothly into the top of the pod. The Vickers main landing gears were of a totally new type, designed only for this aircraft, with four separate short legs each carrying a wheel which retracted to lie on each side of the jet pipe inside the nacelle. Unlike other Vikings the elevators were skinned with metal, and the metal skin on the wings and tailplane was made thicker than normal. There were also changes to the cockpit, fuel system and other items.

Chief test pilot J 'Mutt' Summers flew the Type 618 Nene-Viking from Wisley on April 6, 1948. At different times it bore civil registration G-AJPH and Ministry serial VX856. On the 39th anniversary of Blériot's crossing of the Channel, on July 25, 1948, the Nene-Viking loaded with passengers (24 was the usual maximum) at London Heathrow and flew them in great comfort to Villacoublay, Paris, in 34 min 7 sec, less than half the regular scheduled time and faster than a previous record set by a Spitfire. Six years later it was sold to Eagle Aviation and rebuilt as an ordinary Viking IB freighter, with Hercules engines, and put into service as *Lord Dundonald* on September 24, 1954.

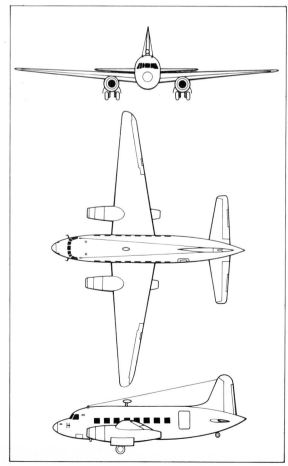

Above: The Nene-Viking with civil registration number. It became the world's first all-jet airliner when it made a record-breaking trip to Paris on July 25, 1948. After trials it reverted to a conventional powerplant with Hercules engines

618 Nene-Viking

Type: twin-jet experimental transport
Maker: Vickers-Armstrongs (Aircraft)
Span: 27.2 m (89 ft 3 in)
Length: 19.86 m (65 ft 2 in)
Height: 5.94 m (19 ft 6 in)
Wing area: 81.93 m² (882 sq ft)
Weight: maximum 15 196 kg (33 500 lb); empty 9548 kg (21 050 lb)
Powerplant: two 2268-kg (5000-lb) st Rolls-Royce Nene I turbojets
Performance: maximum speed 753 km/h (468 mph); cruising speed 632 km/h (393 mph); range at 3050 m (10 000 ft) 555 km (345 miles)
Payload: normally equipped for instrumentation but cabin same size as 36-passenger Viking IB
Crew: 4
Production: 1

Lancastrian jet, Avro

FIRST FLIGHT 1946

THE Lancastrian, a high-speed transport derived from the Lancaster bomber, was an ideal vehicle for testing the new jet and turboprop engines that were becoming ready for flight testing from the end of World War II. Some of these engines were for combat aircraft, but even so needed endurance flying to enable them to mature quickly and become reliable and well developed before being fitted to new civil machines.

First to fly was Lancastrian VH742, delivered to the Rolls-Royce flight development airfield at Hucknall in October 1945. Its outer Merlin engines were removed and the nacelles were also taken away, while the fuel system was completely rebuilt to carry both gasoline for the inner engines and kerosine for the new jets. In the outer positions were added completely new nacelles housing Nene turbojets, then the most powerful jet engines in the world. It flew again on August 14, 1946 with two Merlins and two Nenes.

On September 19, 1946 this aircraft acted as the world's first jet airliner by making three passenger flights carrying representatives of the Press as well as Ministry officials and other passengers (who were all most impressed and suggested that an airline that could offer jet travel would be the talk of the world). Rolls-Royce also flew a second Nene-Lancastrian, VH737, and two Avon-Lancastrians, VM732 and VL970. The latter was used for almost six years, its later flying being concentrated on the Avon 502 civil turbojet for the Comet 2 airliner.

The original engine for the first jet airliner to enter service, the Comet 1, was the de Havilland Ghost 50. This was tested in the outer positions of Lancastrian VM703, first flown with the jets on July 24, 1947. As the original intention with the Comet was to use rockets to boost thrust on take-off, VM703 was also used to test the only rocket then available, the captured German Walter 109-500, two of which were fixed under the fuselage. A second Ghost-Lancastrian, VM729, handled the final development and certification flying of the Ghost 50 for the Comet 1 so that Comet development from July 1949 began with a reliable and mature engine.

Among other jet Lancastrians were VM733 with Armstrong Siddeley Sapphires, and various test-beds with the Canadian Orenda, Swedish Dovern and the British ASX, Adder and Viper. Turbo-props included the Dart, Mamba and Python.

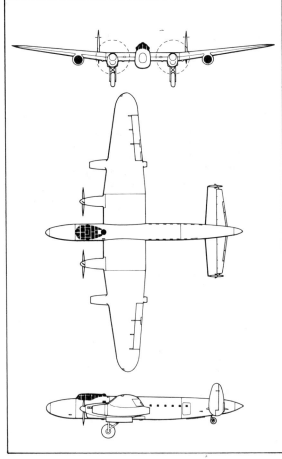

691 Lancastrian (jet)

Type: jet engine testbed and research transport
Maker: A V Roe Company
Span: 31.09 m (102 ft)
Length: 23.42 m (76 ft 10 in)
Height: 5.94 m (19 ft 6 in)
Wing area: 120.495 m² (1297 sq ft)
Weight: maximum 29 484 kg (65 000 lb); empty (typical) 13 517 kg (29 800 lb)
Powerplant: 2 R-R Merlin piston engines (various marks) and 2 Rolls-Royce Nene or Avon, or DH Ghost or AS Sapphire or other turbojets
Performance: not released
Payload: usually comprised instrumentation and special equipment, with 3 to 10 passenger seats
Crew: 3 to 9
Production: jet conversions, 6

Above: Avro jet Lancastrian VM732, powered by Rolls-Royce Avons, was converted from the famous Lancaster bomber of World War II
Left: VM733 had Armstrong Siddeley Sapphires. It bears the prototype letter 'P' by the tail and did much to ensure that the Hunter, Victor and Javelin began life with reliable engines

Tay Viscount, Vickers-Armstrongs

FIRST FLIGHT 1950

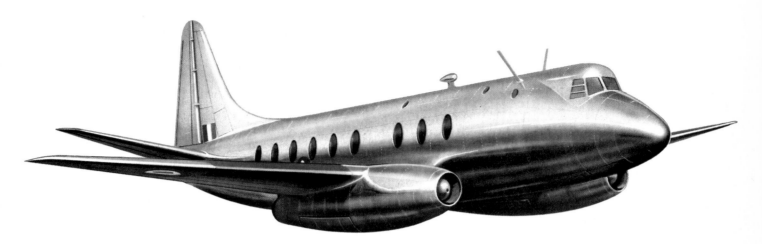

LAST of the prototype and experimental jetliners built in Britain in the immediate postwar era, the Tay-Viscount was an aircraft of great technical interest which went on to carry out many important research programmes. It came about because of Rolls-Royce's ability to wring more power from the Dart turboprop, which in turn enabled Vickers-Armstrongs (Aircraft) at Weybridge to enlarge the Viscount. This left the second of the original small-size V.630 Viscounts redundant, and the Ministry of Supply took it under its wing as a twin-jet for special research.

With company designation V.663, it was kept the same size as the original first prototype but completed with new turbojet engine pods and four separate main landing gears retracting on either side of the jetpipes as on the earlier Nene-Viking. Each engine was the Rolls-Royce Tay, a slightly larger and more powerful development of the Nene which, by chance, never flew in any other aircraft (though similar engines were made under licence in the USA and France). Thanks to the advanced high-speed design of the Viscount nothing much had to be done to the airframe to clear it for high-speed jet flight, though the interior was fitted out for instrumentation instead of passengers.

Originally allocated civil registration G-AHRG, the Tay-Viscount was completed in Ministry markings with serial number VX217. It first flew at Wisley on March 15, 1950, and caused a sensation at the 1950 Farnborough show by appearing to be even faster than the Comet. Its first major task was to help develop the Boulton Paul-powered control system for the Vickers-Armstrongs Type 660 bomber (later named Valiant). Based at Seighford, it then went on to become the first aircraft in the world to fly with an electrically signalled flight-control system. Still with Boulton Paul (a company later absorbed into the Dowty Group) it carried out several years of research on electrically signalled flight-control systems which are only now coming into use.

Weights and performance figures for the Tay-Viscount were never published, and once it had finished its early spell of display flying and gone to Boulton Paul it was hardly ever seen in public and conducted its important missions in an atmosphere of secrecy. In general take-off, climb and manoeuvrability it exceeded all other early jetliners, despite its design being settled in 1945–46.

Above: A pilot stands by the Tay-Viscount during its trials. The four wheels of the main undercarriage are housed in the engine nacelles. Note the instrumentation antenna above the cockpit

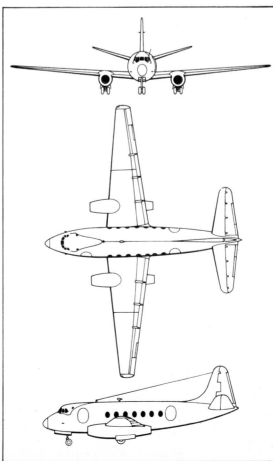

663 Tay-Viscount

Type: twin-jet research aircraft
Maker: Vickers-Armstrongs (Aircraft)
Span: 27.13 m (89 ft)
Length: 22.71 m (74 ft 6 in)
Height: 8 m (26 ft 3 in)
Wing area: 82.22 m² (885 sq ft)
Weight: maximum 18 144 kg (40 000 lb); empty 12 746 kg (28 100 lb)
Powerplant: two 2835-kg (6250-lb) st Rolls-Royce Tay RTa.1 turbojets
Performance: not released but considerably higher than either standard Viscounts or Nene-Viking
Payload: normally equipped for instrumentation but cabin same size as 32-passenger Viscount 630
Crew: 3 to 8 depending on tasks
Production: 1

Jetliner, Avro Canada

FIRST FLIGHT 1949

THE first jetliner built in Canada was designed, built and very successfully demonstrated by a new multinational team, the A V Roe Canada Company. It was a team to rival that of the world's largest aircraft companies, with brilliant talent and the ability to work fast. But with the Jetliner it worked too fast and began too early. The world was simply not ready for such a product.

Under chief engineer Eric H Atkin and chief designer Jim Floyd work went ahead on the C.102 as a company venture, alongside the big twin-jet night and all-weather CF.100 fighter ordered by the government. As Britain's de Havilland Comet was aimed at fairly long routes the C.102 was designed for shorter inter-city sectors such as those carrying the bulk of traffic in the United States and Canada. It was felt the best design would be one similar in most respects to the very latest and best conventional airliners but powered by turbojets instead of piston engines.

The fuselage diameter was fixed at 3.048 m (10 ft), the same circular section as the Comet; but, because flight times would be shorter, more of the cabin was given over to seating, the total being 40 to 52 in 10 to 13 rows of four. The interior was fully pressurized, to maintain sea-level conditions to 6700 m (21 000 ft) and 1830 m (6000 ft) conditions to 10 675 m (35 000 ft). Windows and other cut-outs were made circular or elliptical to avoid the fatigue problems that later hit the British jet.

Dowty provided the landing gears, with twin-wheel units retracting forwards and upwards.

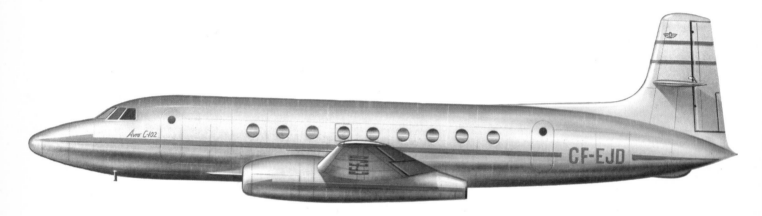

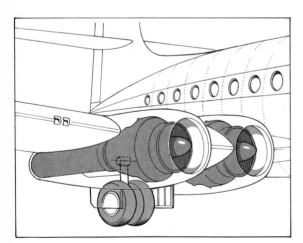

Top: The Avro Canada C.102 was Canada's first jetliner. It remains an example of how a talented and motivated team could work together to produce a unique aircraft in record time
Above: The Rolls-Royce Derwent turbojets of the Jetliner with main landing gear which retracted between the jet pipes
Right: The Avro Canada Jetliner prototype CF-EJD-X which first flew on August 10, 1949 – only two weeks after Comet 1

Engines were four Rolls-Royce Derwent 5 turbojets, each rated at 1588 kg (3500 lb), in paired nacelles mounted low on the inner wings. Main gears were housed between each pair of jetpipes.

The wing was as thick as that of a Lancaster and had the same NACA-23000 series profile. There were simple split flaps, and the leading edge was fixed. The whole leading edge had thermal (hot gas) anti-icing, however, and the tail was anti-iced by electric heater strips in a very advanced way. Another modern feature was that all fuel, a total of 10 350 litres (2300 Imp gal) or more than a Lancaster, was contained in integral tanks in the outer wings. An even more modern feature was the flying control system. The ailerons had hydraulic power boost, the elevators were aerodynamic-tab operated, and the rudder comprised a rear section with manual operation hinged to a front section with hydraulic power for use if an engine should fail at low speed.

Despite starting about two years later, the Avro Canada team got the prototype C.102 into the air only two weeks later than the Comet, on August 10, 1949. The prototype was a fine-looking aircraft, with a stylish paint scheme, registered CF-EJD-X. Test flying showed up no more than minor problems which involved details of systems rather than basic aircraft qualities. By 1950, with a few extra items and modifications visible, CF-EJD-X had a provisional certificate for passenger carrying.

Probably the only thing a modern observer would quarrel with is that the Derwent was a primitive engine, descended in 1943 direct from Whittle concepts of 18 months earlier, and by 1950–51 no longer in the front rank technically. In particular it burned more fuel and had a rather shorter life than more modern turbojets, but Avro always intended replacing it when possible with a newer engine. Its own Orenda, a modern axial used in the CF.100 fighter, was well suited to the Jetliner, but this would have made it a twin and 30 years ago airline presidents wanted four engines. Inability to offer an engine fully developed for airline use, with the right power and economy, did more than anything else to kill the Jetliner.

Hundreds of airline executives studied this pioneer machine and were extremely impressed but nobody bought it and the C.102 was abandoned ten years ahead of its time.

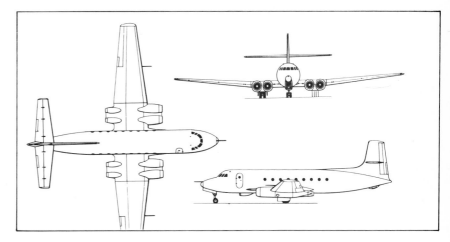

C.102 Jetliner

Type: short-haul transport
Maker: A V Roe Canada Ltd
Span: 29.9 m (98 ft 1 in)
Length: 25.2 m (82 ft 9 in)
Height: 8.065 m (26 ft 5½ in)
Wing area: 107.49 m²
(1157 sq ft)
Weight: maximum 27 216 kg
(60 000 lb); empty not
released
Powerplant: four 1588-kg
(3500-lb) st Rolls-Royce
Derwent 5 turbojets
Performance: maximum
cruising speed 805 km/h
(500 mph); range with full
payload, approx 1996 km
(1240 miles)
Payload: seats for 40 to 52
passengers; cargo holds
behind flight deck and behind
main cabin, all above floor
Crew: 2 to 3
Production: 1

Comet 1, de Havilland

FIRST FLIGHT 1949

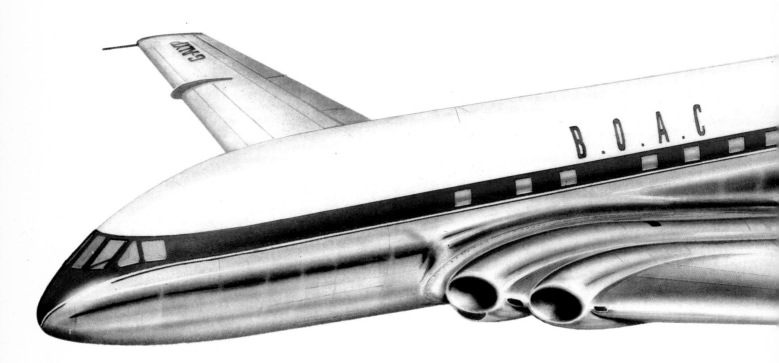

WHILE all the aircraft that carried passengers on jet engines in the immediate postwar period might be considered in some way to be jet transports, the Comet was indisputably the first jet airliner. It was the first to be conceived, the first to fly, and (by more than four years) the first to enter service.

In May 1943 the Second Brabazon Committee deliberated on the details of the types of postwar airliners to be built. The so-called Type IV was planned as a jet-propelled transport, the first in the world.

In 1944 the first outline drawings of the DH.106, later named Comet, showed a tailless aircraft with an unspecified number of de Havilland Ghost turbojets in the rear fuselage. By 1945 the size had been increased to seat 14 passengers over fairly short ranges, but the main effort was on increasing the range and the design began to harden at the start of that year as a transport carrying only a few sacks of mail, and possibly one or two VIP passengers, over the North Atlantic. Three Ghosts provided power, and the DH.108 research aircraft were built to prove the tailless configuration. In February 1945 the design team under R E Bishop at Hatfield was authorized to go ahead with detailed design.

Fortunately at this time the de Havilland management agreed with the designers that the design should be modified in two major respects. The unconventional layout was abandoned in favour of a conventional configuration with a tail, and the basic size was scaled up to seat 24 to 32 passengers

in a normal unrestricted cabin. It was still thought that the type would be able to operate on the North Atlantic routes, and the predicted cruising speed was an impressive 813 km/h (505 mph). On January 21, 1947, BOAC placed a preliminary order for eight Comet 1s, later increased to nine, and the detail design and manufacturing programme went ahead.

The first prototype, G-ALVG, flew on July 27, 1949. The engines were installed inside the wing roots, fed from inlets in the leading edge and discharged through nozzles just behind the trailing edge. Between each pair of nozzles was a bulge containing a de Havilland Sprite rocket, a self-contained unit fed with high-test peroxide and used to boost thrust on take-off. Features included the

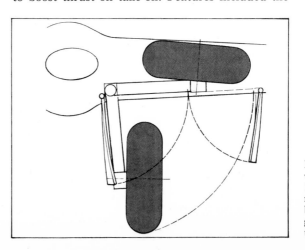

Above: DH.106 Comet 1 G-ALYP which was the first production aircraft. It first flew on January 9, 1951 but after delivery to BOAC in early 1952, it crashed into the sea off the island of Elba on January 1, 1954. The accident was traced to an explosion caused by decompression

Left: The original single-wheel main gear of the Comet 1 prototype; it was later replaced by a four-wheel bogie. This new four-wheel gear was accommodated in the original wheel bay

6

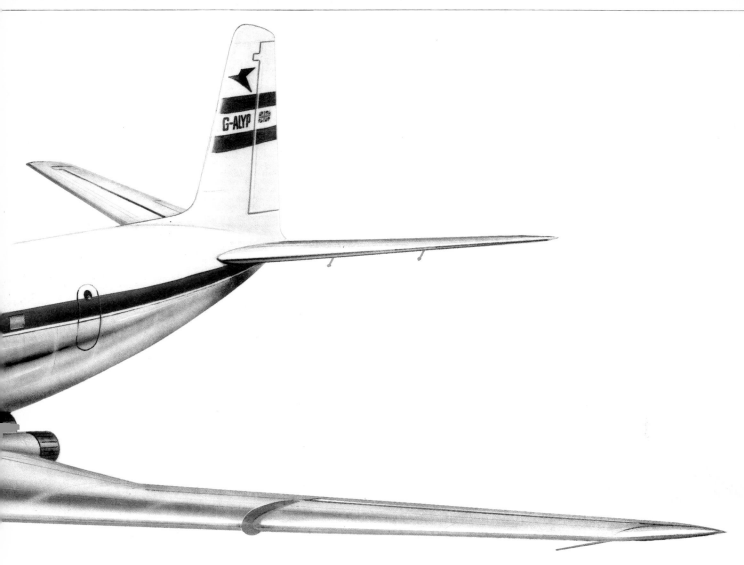

exceptional cabin pressure differential of 0.58 kg/cm² (8.25 lb/sq in), giving the same interior conditions, equivalent to 2438 m (8000 ft) at the planned cruising height of 12 200 m (40 000 ft), as in a Constellation or other rival airliner at half this height.

Flight trials from Hatfield were impressive, and soon included overseas flights which approximately halved the previous record times between important cities. Careful measurements of the performance of the second prototype showed what de Havilland had long known, that the aircraft would not be a practical proposition on the extremely long North Atlantic routes, but that it would be admirably suited to BOAC's African and Eastern routes, and to the needs of many other airlines.

The first production aircraft flew on January 9, 1951, in BOAC livery. Jet airline travel began on May 2, 1952, when G-ALYP (*Yoke Peter*) left London on a regular scheduled flight to Rome, Beirut, Khartoum, Entebbe, Livingstone and Johannesburg. Subsequently the nine BOAC Comet 1s opened up jet services throughout the corporation's routes to Africa and the Far East.

While production switched to the heavier Mk 1A, de Havilland also developed the more advanced Comet 2, with Rolls-Royce Avon axial engines and many engineering refinements, as well as a slightly lengthened fuselage with normal BOAC seating increased from 36 to 40 or 44. A Mk 1 re-engined aircraft with civil Avons flew on February 16, 1952 and as the airlines were by this

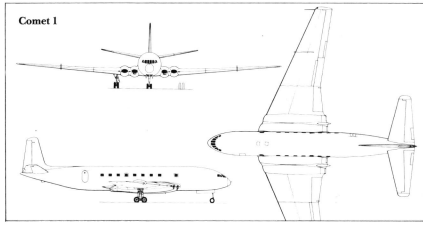

Comet 1

Comet 1

Type: medium-range passenger transport
Maker: de Havilland Aircraft Company
Span: 35.05 m (115 ft)
Length: 28.35 m (93 ft)
Height: 8.65 m (28 ft 4½ in)
Wing area: 187.2 m² (2015 sq ft)
Weight: maximum 47 628 kg (105 000 lb); empty not released but approx 27 200 kg (60 000 lb)
Powerplant: four 2019-kg (4450-lb) st de Havilland Ghost 50 Mk 1 turbojets, plus (first prototype) two 2268-kg (5000-lb) thrust de Havilland Sprite I rocket motors
Performance: maximum cruising speed 789 km/h (490 mph); cruising altitude 10 668 m (35 000 ft); range with full payload and no reserves intended to be 5710 km (3540 miles)
Payload: 36 passengers
Crew: 4
Production: 11

Comet 1A

Specification similar to Comet 1 except in following particulars:
Weight: maximum 52 164 kg (115 000 lb)
Powerplant: four 2268-kg (5000-lb) st de Havilland Ghost 50 Mk 2 turbojets; no rocket motors
Performance: cruising altitude 12 192 m (40 000 ft); range with full payload considerably greater than Mk 1, suitable for practical sector distances of just over 3200 km (2000 miles)
Payload: 44 passengers

time beginning to take the jet seriously the Mk 2 was ordered by BOAC, Canadian Pacific, UAT, Air France, British Commonwealth Pacific, Japan Air Lines, LAV (Venezuela) and Panair do Brasil. Even more impressive was the swift design of the Mk 3, with much more powerful Avon 16 engines, extra fuel in pod tanks projecting ahead of the leading edge, and a fuselage stretch of no less than 5.64 m (18 ft 6 in) to seat 58 to 78 passengers. By 1954 the Comet seemed certain not only to be the first jetliner but also the most successful.

All had not been plain sailing, however. One of the first Comets to be lost was the first Mk 1A for CPA, which crashed on take-off at Karachi on its long eastbound delivery flight to Vancouver. The trouble was traced to lifting the nose too early,

causing the engine inlets to lose efficiency, thus reducing engine thrust at the most crucial time. Then a BOAC Comet crashed near Calcutta, but it was discovered it had broken up in a storm of exceptional ferocity which would probably have destroyed most other airliners flying through it at high indicated airspeed.

On January 10, 1954 the first Comet 1 in service, *Yoke Peter*, disappeared a few minutes out of Rome, over the Mediterranean. Then on April 8, 1954 precisely the same thing happened to *Yoke Yoke*. The Certificate of Airworthiness was withdrawn.

This was the end of the Comet's sweeping worldwide success. Had the rectification of the problems been more positive and rapid, as was done with the equally fundamentally faulty Electra

Comet 1

1 Nose cone
2 Nose construction
3 Windscreen frame panel
4 Instrument panel shroud
5 Rudder pedals
6 Windscreen wiper
7 Cockpit roof construction
8 Co-pilot's seat
9 Control column
10 Pilot's seat
11 Engineer's control panel
12 Swivelling engineer's seat
13 Navigator's seat
14 Navigator's work table
15 Nosewheel bay construction
16 Nose undercarriage leg
17 Twin nosewheels
18 Nosewheel door
19 HF grid aerial
20 Navigational instrument rack
21 Engineer's work table
22 Radio and electrical rack
23 Observation window
24 Crew's wardrobe and locker
25 Crew entry door
26 Forward luggage and freight hold
27 Hydraulic equipment bay
28 Control cable runs
29 Maintenance access hatch
30 Ice inspection window
31 Galley
32 Aft-facing seats (one row)
33 ADF loop aerials
34 Dining table
35 Smoke room seating (eight passengers)
36 Emergency escape window
37 Air-conditioning plant
38 Air-conditioning distribution duct
39 Partition door to main cabin
40 Right inner wing fuel tanks
41 Outer wing fuel tanks
42 Leading-edge wing fence
43 Pitot tube
44 Right navigation light
45 Static discharge wicks
46 Right aileron
47 Aileron tab
48 Flap outer section
49 Airbrake (upper and lower surfaces)
50 Fuel jettison pipe
51 Flap inboard section
52 Undercarriage bay upper panel
53 Fuselage frame construction
54 Cabin floor construction
55 Wing centre-section fuel tank bays
56 Window frame panels
57 Fuselage main frame
58 Aft luggage and freight hold
59 Floor beam construction
60 Air-conditioning outlet vents
61 Cabin trim panels
62 Overhead coat rack
63 Main cabin seating (36 passengers)
64 Emergency escape window
65 Luggage and freight hold loading door
66 Drinking water fountain
67 Book and magazine rack
68 Aft cabin door
69 Wardrobe
70 Official stowage locker
71 Aft radio rack
72 Toilet compartment partition with curtained doors
73 Ladies powder room/wash room
74 Toilet
75 Rear pressure dome
76 Fin root fillet
77 Right tailplane
78 Dielectric tailplane tip aerial
79 Right elevator
80 Fin leading-edge de-icing
81 Fin construction
82 Dielectric VHF aerial cover
83 Rudder
84 Tailcone
85 Tail navigation light
86 Left elevator
87 Elevator tab
88 ILS aerial
89 Tailplane construction
90 Leading-edge de-icing
91 Elevator controls
92 Tailplane attachment
93 De-icing air distribution ducts
94 Tailfin/fuselage frame
95 Rear fuselage construction
96 De-icing air supply
97 Tailplane control rods
98 Elevator servo control unit
99 Main passenger door
100 Stewardess' seat
101 Wing root fillet
102 Water injection tank
103 Inboard tailpipe duct
104 Rocket assistance motor housing
105 Dinghy stowage
106 Outboard tailpipe duct
107 Engine exhausts
108 Flap inboard section
109 Flap construction
110 Fuel jettison pipe
111 Flap jack
112 Connecting links between flap sections
113 Airbrake (upper and lower surfaces)
114 Flap outboard section
115 Aileron tab
116 Aileron control jack
117 Aileron construction
118 Static discharge wicks
119 Aileron balance weight
120 Left navigation light
121 Outer wing construction
122 Outer wing fuel tank bays
123 Wing stringer construction
124 Wing outer section joint
125 Leading-edge wing fence
126 Wing rib construction
127 Leading-edge de-icing
128 Main wing fuel tank bays
129 Undercarriage well
130 Retraction control mechanism
131 Main undercarriage leg
132 Four-wheel bogie
133 De-icing air duct
134 De Havilland Ghost 50-1 engine
135 Inboard engine bay
136 Engine bay bulkhead
137 Engine mounting
138 Intake duct construction
139 Engine air intakes
140 Air-conditioning intake
141 Ventilating ram air intakes

Above: The Comet 1 G-ALVG which first flew in July 1949 and received its certificate of airworthiness in April 1950. It was scrapped at Farnborough in July 1953
Above right: The de Havilland Ghost 50 engines of the Comet 1. The de Havilland Sprite rocket motors are located between the tail pipes. They were thought to be necessary for extra thrust at take-off, but were not fitted to production models. The buried engines with their twin air intakes gave an attractive and characteristic shape to the wings

five years later, the programme could probably have been restored but with a loss of six months. As it was the Comet 1 was never again used by the airlines, the Comet 2s were completely rebuilt and used by the RAF (the Royal Canadian Air Force continued to use its 1As after local anti-fatigue modifications) and not even the Mk 3, first flown on July 19, 1954, was put into production as had been planned. Instead many Comets were used up in extended fatigue tests in giant water tanks, while others were flown unpressurized as laboratories or RAF electronics platforms. There was even a strong body of opinion that the whole programme should be abandoned, and even in the de Havilland company many thought the name should be rejected.

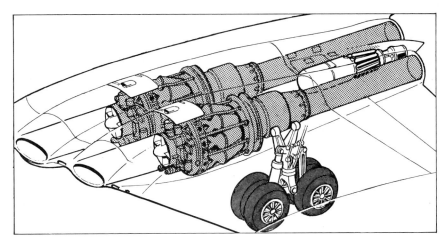

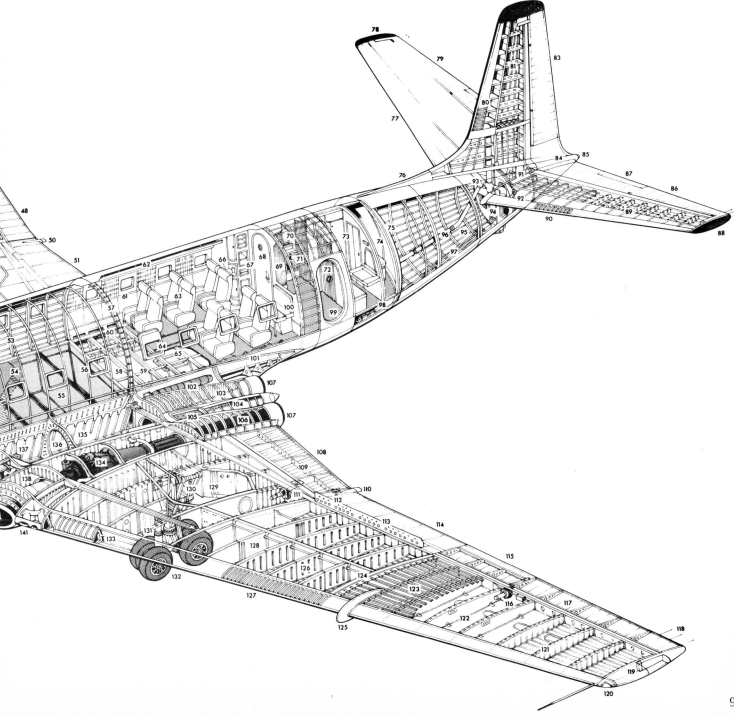

Boeing 707

FIRST FLIGHT 1954

BOEING, in 1949–50, concentrated its future transport studies on advanced jet or turboprop versions of the Stratocruiser, and a few C-97s were flown with turboprop engines. But the success of the Comet gradually convinced Boeing the answer had to be a jet, and a design much more advanced than any improved Stratocruiser. Studies were given the same Model number, 367, as the C-97, though they increasingly departed from it in shape.

By late 1951 all the 367-series studies were centred around the use of four Pratt & Whitney JT3 turbojets, civil version of the J57 used in the company's B-52 heavy bomber. But neither the B-52 nor the earlier B-47 was any good as a basis for a jetliner. Studies continued from 367-40 to 367-80 searching for the right arrangement of wing,

engines and landing gear. The one fairly constant feature was the body cross-section, larger than that of the C-97 and with the sides of the 'double bubble' or figure-8 section filled in to give an approximately oval form.

In early 1952 the 367-80 configuration appeared to be the best that could at the time be achieved. The wing was swept at 35°, had a thick root that filled the space under the cabin floor where the spar box crossed the fuselage, carried the engines in separate widely spaced pods hung well forward and below the wing, and rested on two four-wheel trucks that retracted inwards from pivots on the wing to occupy large bays in the fuselage. In continuing discussions with the USAF the company secured acceptance of the design in principle,

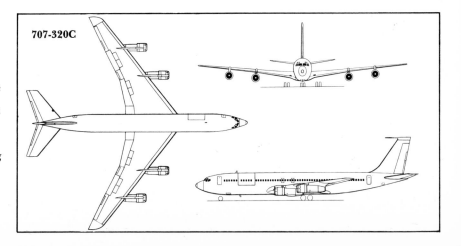

Boeing 707-120

Type: medium-range passenger transport
Maker: Boeing Airplane Company
Span: 39.87 m (130 ft 10 in)
Length: (except 138) 44.04 m (144 ft 6 in); (138) 41 m (134 ft 6 in)
Height: as originally built 11.68 m (38 ft 4 in); later many given taller vertical tail
Wing area: 226 m² (2433 sq ft)
Weight: maximum varied with sub-type from 108 860 kg (240 000 lb) to 116 120 kg (256 000 lb); empty typically 54 432 kg (120 000 lb)

Powerplant: four 5896-kg (13 000-lb) st (with water injection) Pratt & Whitney JT3C-6 2-shaft turbojets
Performance: maximum cruising speed 946 km/h (590 mph); typical long-range cruise 869 km/h (540 mph); cruising height up to 11 885 m (39 000 ft); range with full payload and no reserves 5177 km (3217 miles)
Payload: maximum 23 590 kg (52 000 lb); seats for maximum of 181 passengers
Crew: 4
Production: (civil) 141

707-320C

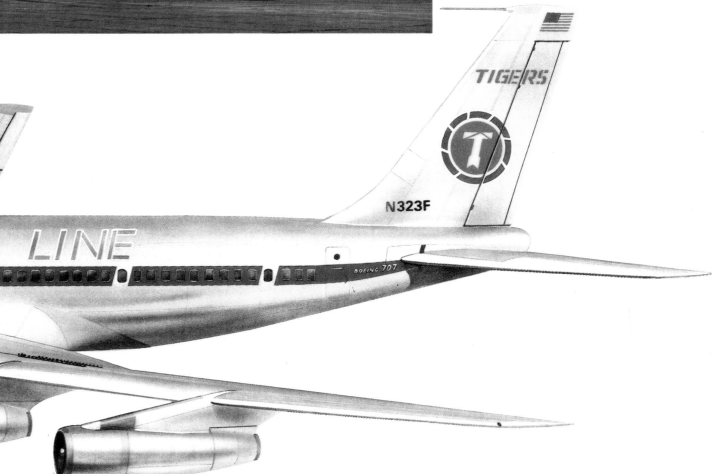

Left: A Fast Air 707 cargo carrier being loaded by a scissors lift
Below: A 707 of the Flying Tiger Line, Los Angeles, California. The company specializes in freighting operations and was formed in 1946

Boeing 707-320

Type: long-range passenger and cargo transport
Maker: Boeing Airplane Company
Span: 43.41 m (142 ft 5 in)
Length: 46.61 m (152 ft 11 in)
Height: 12.7 m (41 ft 8 in)
Wing area: 268.68 m² (2892 sq ft)
Weight: maximum 141 520 kg (312 000 lb); empty 61 235 kg (135 000 lb)
Powerplant: four 7167-kg (15 800-lb) st Pratt & Whitney JT4A-3 2-shaft turbojets; later re-engined with 7620-kg (16 800-lb) JT4A-9s and finally 7945-kg

(17 500-lb) JT4A-11s
Performance: maximum cruising speed 969 km/h (602 mph); economical cruising speed 876 km/h (545 mph); range with maximum payload 7700 km (4784 miles)
Payload: 24 950 kg (55 000 lb); seats for up to 189 passengers
Crew: 4
Production: 69

Boeing 707-320B and -320C

Type: long-range passenger and (320C) cargo or passenger/cargo transport
Maker: Boeing Commercial Airplane Company
Span: 44.42 m (145 ft 9 in)
Length: 46.61 m (152 ft 11 in)
Height: 12.93 m (42 ft 5 in)
Wing area: 279.64 m² (3010 sq ft)
Weight: maximum 151 315 kg (333 600 lb); empty 63 740 kg (140 524 lb); (320C) all-cargo 60 725 kg (133 874 lb)
Powerplant: four 8165-kg (18 000-lb) st Pratt &

Whitney JT3D-3 or -3B 2-shaft turbofans or 8618-kg (19 000-lb) JT3D-7s
Performance: maximum cruising speed 966 km/h (600 mph); economical cruising speed 886 km/h (550 mph); range with maximum payload 9915 km (6160 miles)
Payload: 24 709 kg (54 476 lb); (320C) all-cargo 43 603 kg (96 126 lb); seats for 189 passengers or, with 2 extra emergency exits, 202
Crew: 4
Production: 188; (320C) 336

Boeing 707-420

Specification similar to 707-320 except in following particulars:
Height: 12.93 m (42 ft 5 in)
Weight: empty 60 330 kg (133 000 lb)
Powerplant: four 7945-kg (17 500-lb) st Rolls-Royce Conway 508 turbofans; some later uprated to 8165-kg (18 000-lb) Mk 508As
Performance: range with maximum payload 7830 km (4865 miles)
Payload: 25 855 kg (57 000 lb)
Production: 37

but itself chose to manage the programme and find the money. President Bill Allen announced on May 20, 1952 the decision to build the prototype, at a cost of more than $20 million, at that time the largest risk ever accepted by an aircraft manufacturer.

The new jetliner was proudly rolled out from the plant where it was built at Renton, near Seattle, in May 1954. By this time the company type numbers had entered the 700s (the 500 series being reserved for gas turbines and the 600s for missiles) and the jetliner became the 707.

First flight took place on July 15, 1954, slightly later than planned because of an embarrassing structural failure during taxiing in which one main landing gear broke clean upwards through the wing. Flight development on the still undeveloped JT3C engines went extremely well, and after trials with the new Boeing high-speed inflight refuelling boom the USAF ordered 29 KC-135 tankers very similar to the 707 prototype and with Boeing type number 717. Subsequently Boeing delivered no fewer than 820 of the KC-135 and C-135 family.

Engineering development and flight test occupied until mid 1955, by which time it was clear the 707 would be certificated. It had made a good impression on hundreds of airline personnel, many of whom had flown it or flown in it.

First to order was PanAm, which signed for 20 (and to the shock of world airlines and Boeing, 20 DC-8s as well) on October 13, 1955. It then emerged that Boeing had decided to make the civil 707 slightly larger than the Dash-80 prototype and the military versions. Amazingly, the major change of altering the body cross-section, by a mere 100 mm (4 in), was gladly accepted in order to ease the accommodation of a triple seat on each side of the aisle. Fuel capacity was increased, customers being offered a choice of range and gross weight by varying the number of flexible fuel cells in the centre section (the main tankage being integral compartments further outboard). The engines were fitted with water injection, an undesirable boosting system for use on take-off, to give the first production version, the 707-120, some hope of being able to take off within available runway distances. Finally, the wider upper lobe of the fuselage was offered in two lengths, the 707-120 having a length of 44 m (144 ft 6 in) and the 138 being 3 m shorter (134 ft 6 in).

In July 1955 the USAF had formally given consent to sales of a civil version, allowing Boeing to use some tooling for the tankers and the civil 707s. Later the demands for both types were so severe that tooling had to be expensively multiplied to increase combined output in the late 1950s to as much as 35 a month. At first the output of civil 707s was modest, and the first 707-121 for PanAm did not fly until December 20, 1957. Observers noticed its long row of small passenger windows, two to each seat row on each side, contrasting with the larger windows of all other airliners. Another new feature was the noise-suppressing nozzle on each engine, discharging the jet through 20 separate tubes which soon became covered with soot. Noise on a water-injection take-off was excruciating, and the aircraft climbed away leaving a thick

12

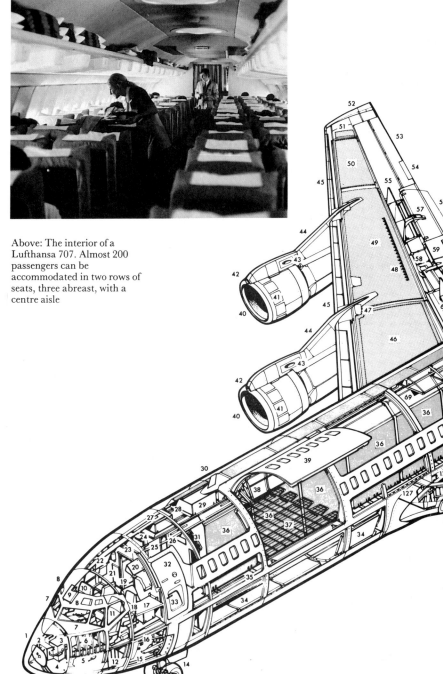

Above: The interior of a Lufthansa 707. Almost 200 passengers can be accommodated in two rows of seats, three abreast, with a centre aisle

707-320C

1 Nose cone
2 Weather radar scanner
3 Glide-slope aerial
4 Forward pressure bulkhead
5 Pitot head
6 Nose frames
7 Windscreen panels
8 Eyebrow windows
9 Overhead console
10 First Officer's seat
11 Captain's seat
12 Forward frame
13 Twin nosewheels
14 Nosewheel doors
15 Nosewheel box
16 Drag struts
17 Navigator's table
18 Observer's seat
19 Navigator's seat
20 Navigator's overhead panel
21 Flight Engineer's seat
22 Flight Engineer's instrument panels
23 Flight-deck entry door
24 Crew coat closet

25 Crew toilet
26 Crew galley/buffet
27 Spare life vest stowage
28 Radio (emergency) transmitter
29 Life-raft stowage (2)
30 VHF aerial
31 Smoke and fume-proof curtain
32 Forward entry door (61 cm × 183 cm [24 in × 72 in])
33 Escape slide stowage
34 Forward underfloor freight hold
35 Cabin floor level
36 Six cargo pallets (total 125 m³ [4424 cu ft])
37 Ball transfer mat (five segments)
38 Door actuator rams
39 Main cargo door (raised)
40 Engine intakes
41 Secondary inlet doors
42 Turbocompressor intakes
43 Turbocompressor outlets
44 Nacelle pylons
45 Leading-edge wing flaps
46 Main tank No 3 (15400 litres [3390 Imp gal])

47 Fuel system dry bay
48 Vortex generators
49 Main tank No 4 (8790 litres [1935 Imp gal])
50 Reserve tank (1660 litres [365 Imp gal])
51 Vent surge tank
52 Right wingtip
53 Right outboard aileron
54 Aileron balance tab
55 Right outboard spoiler (extended)
56 Right outboard flap
57 Flap tracks
58 Aileron/spoiler actuator linkage
59 Right inboard aileron
60 Control tab
61 Right inboard flap
62 Right inboard spoiler (extended)
63 Life-raft stowage (4)
64 Escape straps
65 Escape hatches/emergency exits (50.8 cm × 96.5 cm [20 in × 38 in]) (4)
66 Life-raft attachment clips
67 Inter-cabin movable bulkhead

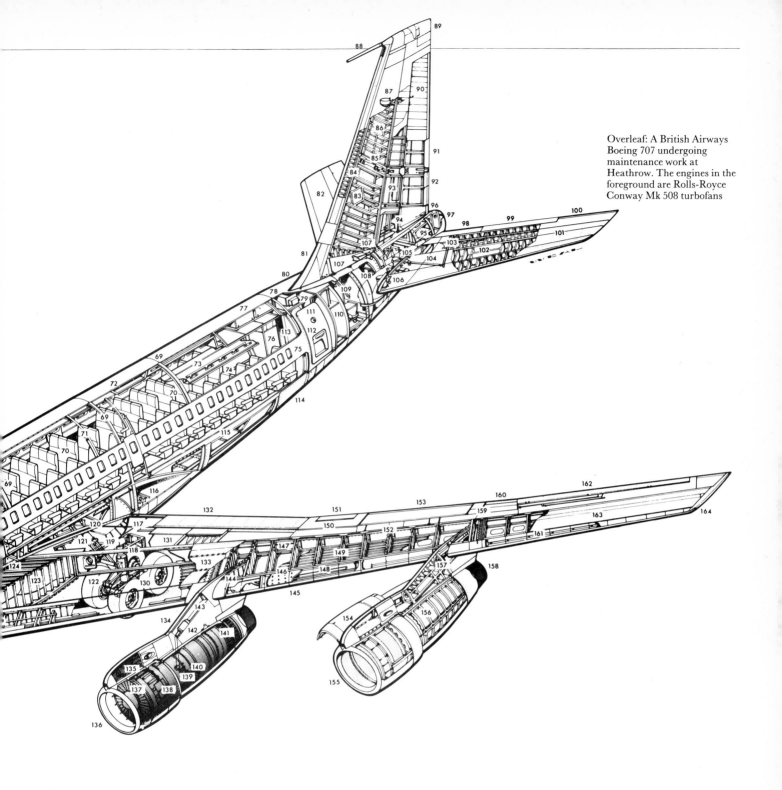

Overleaf: A British Airways
Boeing 707 undergoing
maintenance work at
Heathrow. The engines in the
foreground are Rolls-Royce
Conway Mk 508 turbofans

68 Access door (left walkway)
69 Fuselage frames
70 87-passenger tourist class cabin
   configuration (86.3 cm [34 in] seat
   pitch)
71 Four-abreast seating row
   (emergency exit stations)
72 Ceiling air conditioning
73 Passenger amenities
74 Rear cabin single-row seating
75 Cabin windows
76 Coat closet
77 Life-raft stowage (2)
78 Spare life vests (and machete)
79 First-aid kit
80 Aft service door (right)
   (61 cm × 122 cm [24 in × 48 in])
81 Fin fillet
82 Right tail plane
83 VOR antenna
84 Removable fin leading edge
85 Rudder control linkage
86 Tailfin construction
87 Rudder 'Q' bellows
88 HF probe antenna

89 LORAN antenna
90 Rudder
91 Rudder control tab
92 Rudder antibalance tab
93 Internal balance panel
94 Rudder flutter damper
95 Elevator torque tube
96 Rudder trim tab
97 Tail cone
98 Tail-plane actuator tab
99 Elevator control tab
100 Left elevator
101 Left tail plane
102 Internal balance panel
103 Elevator linkage
104 Crank assembly
105 Elevator quadrant
106 Autopilot elevator servo
107 Tailfin spar/fuselage joints
108 Rear pressure bulkhead
109 Aft toilets (2)
110 Coat closet
111 Aft entry door
112 Escape slide stowage
113 Vestibule

114 Fuselage skinning
115 Aft underfloor freight hold
116 Wingroot fairing
117 Fillet flap
118 Landing gear trunnion
119 Undercarriage shock strut
120 Main undercarriage well
121 Side strut
122 Torsion links
123 Fuel tank end rib
124 Wing rear spar/fuselage pick-up
   point
125 Inboard wing stringers
126 Wing front spar/fuselage pick-up
   point
127 Fuselage centre tank forward face
128 Landing lights
129 Front spar
130 Four-wheel main landing gear
131 Left inboard spoilers
132 Left inboard flap
133 Vortex generators
134 Nacelle pylon
135 Turbocompressor
136 Engine intake

137 Pratt & Whitney JT3D turbofan
138 Fan thrust reverser doors
139 Engine fuel pump
140 Starter
141 Primary thrust reverser cascade
   vanes
142 Wing anti-ice check valve
143 Wing anti-ice shut-off valve
144 Duct temperature sensor
145 Leading-edge wing flap
146 Dimpled inner skin
147 Rear spar
148 Leading-edge thermal anti-icing
   duct
149 Integral wing fuel tanks
150 Left outboard aileron
151 Control tab
152 Left outboard spoilers
153 Left outboard flap
154 Engine access doors (left and right)
155 Nacelle nose cowl
156 Nacelle structure
157 Strut/pylon attachment
158 Exhaust
159 Pylon/wing joint

160 Tab
161 Leading-edge anti-ice supply
   manifold
162 Left outboard aileron
163 Wing skinning
164 Left wingtip

13

pall of sooty smoke. But the world's airport authorities responded positively to the demanding 707 by spending fortunes on longer runways, and increased-capacity terminals.

PanAm opened jet service with a flight from New York to Paris on October 26, 1958. Ideally the new jet was a US domestic machine, entering service with National (using leased PanAm aircraft) on December 10, 1958, and with American on January 25, 1959. Only one customer, Australia's Qantas, selected the short-body 138 series. Boeing also offered a heavier 220 series with the larger and more powerful JT4A engine, and this again sold to only one customer, Braniff. In 1957 Boeing also offered a lightweight shorter-range version at first called 717 (the same as the military variants) and

16

707-020 but the aircraft finally sold as the 720.

Boeing had been hit by Douglas's decision to offer a long-range JT4A-powered model of DC-8 to meet the needs of PanAm. Boeing had said this could not be done, and later fitted the big engine to the 220 to improve field performance. But by 1956 it was clear a larger, long-range version would have to be designed to keep ahead of the DC-8. The result was the 707 Intercontinental, offered as the 707-320 with JT4A turbojets and as the 707-420 with Rolls-Royce Conway turbofans.

Compared with other versions the 320 was considerably larger, heavier, had greater fuel capacity and could fly much further with a larger payload. The first flew on January 11, 1959 and PanAm had the first in operation in August of that

Top: A 707 in British Airways livery takes off from Heathrow
Above left: British Airways 707s are powered by Rolls-Royce Conways or, as shown here, Pratt & Whitney engines
Above: An Air France 707-328 refuelling. After British suggestions improvements were incorporated into later marks, namely an increase in fin height and an additional fin area below the tail cone

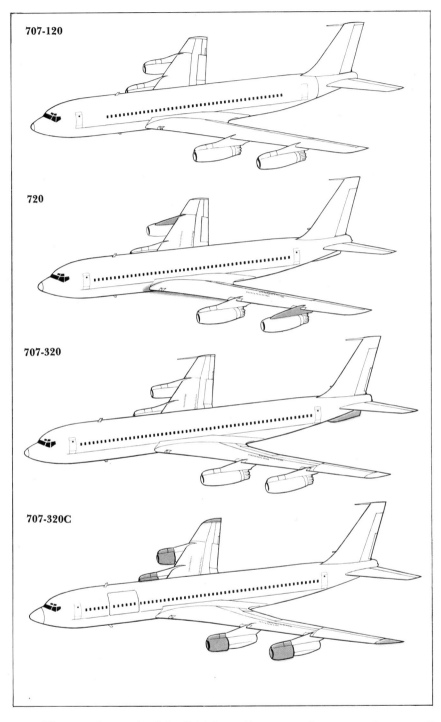

707-120

720

707-320

707-320C

Left: The Boeing 707-120. This aircraft was one of the earliest in the family and was shorter than the others with a smaller tail fin. The Boeing 720 was a short-range aircraft with a superficial resemblance to the 707-120 and was originally known as the 707-020. The full-span leading-edge flaps enhance the 720s field performance. The 707-320 was also called the Intercontinental. Though the 707-120 had flown the Atlantic, the -320 was the first proper long-range version. The underfin was a British Airworthiness requirement. The Boeing 707-320C was the cargo version (C stood for Cargo or Convertible). It had a strengthened floor to take concentrated cargo loads. Seats were often fitted but arranged to fold against the cabin walls, when the -320C was in use as a cargo carrier. The shaded areas show the progressive modifications made to the 707, culminating in the much larger 320 and more efficient 320C with JT3D turbofan engines and new wingtips

Above: Ground-running a Boeing 707; the engines have been fitted with baffles to reduce the noise and direct the exhaust fumes upwards. One of the complaints about the 707 was that it was noisy and also not very clean

year. To meet the needs of the British certification authority a large underfin was added. At about the same time the height of the basic fin and rudder was considerably increased, making the underfin unnecessary. Later this tall tail became standard on all models and was retrofitted to most of the aircraft already built, as well as military variants.

To meet the challenge of the Conway, Pratt & Whitney quickly redesigned the JT3C turbojet into the JT3D turbofan, offering much greater thrust, better fuel economy, less noise and water injection as an option. The new engines were neatly cowled, discharging the fan air through a short duct of distinctive appearance, and with the core jet issuing from a plain hole with no noise suppressor. Cabin air-conditioning services used ram inlets above two, three or all four of the engines, and complex but reliable reversers were fitted to brake the aircraft after landing. The JT3D transformed all versions of 707, making it a more environmentally acceptable vehicle as well as a safer one. But the chief result was the version that swiftly became the standard type, the 320B and 320C.

In this the basic Intercontinental airframe was further improved by a new wing with slotted leading-edge flaps, improved trailing-edge flaps of changed profile and increased area, and new long-span wingtips of streamwise shape. The 320B passenger and 320C convertible passenger/cargo versions have since 1962 been universally adopted, taking orders for all versions to what may be a final total of 930.

Boeing 720

FIRST FLIGHT 1959

WHILE the first commercial 707s were on the assembly line at Renton in early 1957 the Boeing Airplane Company, as it then was, began to refine the design of a slightly smaller and appreciably lighter version for US domestic and similar short/medium-range services. At first given the same 717 type number as the military KC-135, it was then styled 707-020 before finally hitting the market in 1958, prior to first flight, as the 720. This was a true type number, and the only one in the Boeing commercial jet series not to end in a 7.

Though it looked basically the same as the original 707s, in fact hardly any of the structural parts were common, and even the systems were in many respects dissimilar. Dimensionally it had the same fuselage as the short-body 707-130 series,

though the latter as built for Qantas was reduced by a further 0.51 m (20 in). The wing was dimensionally similar but lighter in construction, with considerably reduced fuel capacity, and with a major aerodynamic change in the form of a large 'glove' added on the leading edge inboard of the inner engines. This glove added area and chord at the root to increase the permissible cruising Mach number by 0.02, and resulted in the 720 being the only member of the 707 family to have a kinked leading edge. A further important change was that the lift-increasing Krüger flaps added inboard on other 707s were on the 720 added almost to the tips, resulting in the desired short field-length and sprightly hot-and-high performance (take-off and landing at high-altitude or tropical airfields).

Right: A Lufthansa 720 with call sign D-ABOL and named 'Stuttgart' by the airline
Below: A 720 in more colourful guise; one of the three 720s operated by Ecuatoriana, the national airline of Ecuador

Partly because of its extremely competitive price – known as the 'bargain basement jet' in the airline industry at the time – the 720 sold quickly, and in so doing doomed to failure the attempt by General Dynamics to make a major and sustained entry into the civil market. The first 720s were fitted with JT3C-7 or -12 engines, similar to those used on the first 707s but simplified by the removal of water injection, and reduced in weight. First flight took place on November 23, 1959 and commercial services were opened by United and American in July 1960. From the start the lightweight Boeing jet was popular, encouraging Boeing to sink the formidable capital needed to build a more efficient 'clean sheet of paper' short-haul jetliner. The fruits of this investment eventually matured into a vastly different aircraft, the 727.

In 1960 the vastly superior JT3D turbofan engine became available, and it was soon applied to all the Boeing jet subtypes then in existence, often as a retrofit to aircraft already delivered. To confuse the issue the first with the new engine, a 707-120B (the B suffix distinguished fan-engined models) first flown on June 22, 1960, was also retrofitted with the wing glove and outboard Krüger flaps of the 720, so that apart from a minor difference in length the main way to tell the two apart is to examine the structure. Production totals thereafter became confused, some 720 lists also including the 707-120B family. Even the Qantas 707-138 was modified to 138B standard and given certain 720 features.

The first true 720B, with JT3D-1 engines, flew on October 6, 1960. Certification of the agile aircraft followed on March 3, 1961 and American put the 720B into service alongside 120Bs nine days later. Most of the final 720s were completed as 720Bs and about half the existing aircraft were re-engined. Total production amounted to 154, not including any of the near-relatives more properly described as 707-120Bs or -138Bs. Of this healthy total just 100 were still in scheduled service in 1979, though only two operators – Western in the United States and Lebanon's Middle East Airlines – had fleets larger than seven. All 720s and 720Bs had suffix numbers, identifying aircraft for a particular customer, in the blocks from -020 to -099, unlike the 707s whose suffix numbers were all greater than 100.

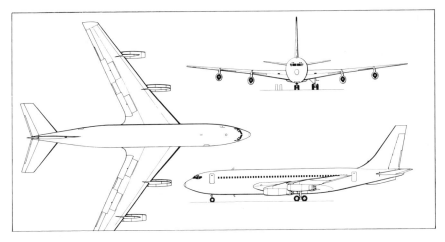

Boeing 720B

Type: short/medium-range passenger transport
Maker: Boeing Commercial Airplane Company
Span: 39.87 m (130 ft 10 in)
Length: 41.68 m (136 ft 9 in)
Height: 12.67 m (41 ft 7 in)
Wing area: 234.2 m² (2521 sq ft)
Weight: maximum 106 140 kg (234 000 lb); empty 52 163 kg (115 000 lb)
Powerplant: four 8165-kg (18 000-lb) st Pratt & Whitney JT3D-3 turbofans (a few still flying with 7718-kg [17 000-lb] JT3D-1s)
Performance: maximum cruising speed 978 km/h (608 mph); economical cruising speed 858 km/h (533 mph); range with maximum payload 6614 km (4110 miles)
Payload: 18 600 kg (41 000 lb); seats for up to 181 passengers
Crew: 4
Production: 154

Left: One of the three 720Bs operated by Monarch Airlines, Luton

XCG-20A, Chase

FIRST FLIGHT 1951

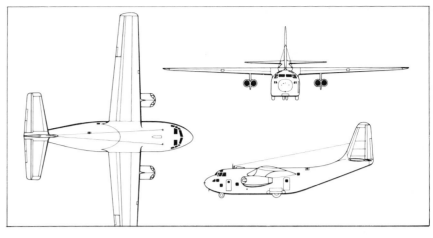

CHASE Aircraft Company was formed in New York in 1943 to design and build military assault gliders. On January 4, 1945 it flew the first XCG-14, a wooden 16-passenger glider, followed in October of that year by the 24-seat XCG-14A. In 1946 Chase switched to all-metal stressed-skin construction and a year later flew the 32-seat CG-18A. From this was derived the powered C-122 Avitruc for the US Air Force, with two 1425-hp Wright R-1820-101 Cyclone engines. Much later (1959) the Hiller X-18 experimental VTOL mated a C-122 with a new 90° tilting wing with Allison XT40 turboprops and a Westinghouse J34 jet in the tail for control.

Biggest of the Chase gliders, two airframes were built designated XCG-20, but neither flew as a glider. The first was finally completed with two R-2800-CB14 Double Wasp piston engines and became the prototype of the excellent C-123 Provider transport, which during the Korean war was ordered in quantity from Kaiser-Frazer who failed to deliver; finally 300 were built by Fairchild and the majority are still flying after a most successful career with the USAF and other operators.

The second XCG-20 was structurally modified for engine nacelles at about the time (October 1949) that the XC-123 first flew, but no piston engines were ever fitted. Instead, under USAF sponsorship and with the enthusiastic backing of Chase's president and chief engineer Michael Stroukoff, it was completed with two twin jet pods each housing two General Electric J47 turbojets. The pods were based on those used on the B-36D and B-47B and C bombers, with a prominent splitter fairing upstream of the two inlets and with pointed fairings on the front of each engine front hub projecting in the centre of each inlet. Unlike the B-36 pod, there were no air shutters in the inlets. The pod was carried well below the wing, and was not swept forward as in the jet bombers but mounted on a conventional vertical pylon.

The all-jet XCG-20A flew on April 21, 1951. Flight trials were excellent, and this somewhat oddball aircraft has a place in history as the first jet transport to fly in the United States and the first to fly with pod-mounted engines. Later, Chase's successor, Stroukoff Aircraft, rebuilt it as the XC-123D with boundary-layer control, and rebuilt it again as the 'pantobase' YC-134A.

XCG-20A

Type: experimental jet cargo transport
Maker: Chase Aircraft Company
Span: 33.53 m (110 ft)
Length: 23.5 m (77 ft 2 in)
Height: 10 m (32 ft 8 in)
Wing area: 113.6 m² (1223 sq ft)
Weight: maximum 24 495 kg (54 000 lb); empty 11 340 kg (25 000 lb)
Powerplant: four 2359-kg (5200-lb) General Electric J47-GE-11 single-shaft turbojets
Performance: maximum cruising speed 644 km/h (400 mph); maximum estimated range 4023 km (2500 miles)
Payload: 6350 kg (14 000 lb)
Crew: 3
Production: 1

Left: The XCG-20A as it later flew with swept-forward pylon struts. Although it was a jet transport it was still owned by the USAF

21

Tu-104, Tupolev

FIRST FLIGHT 1955

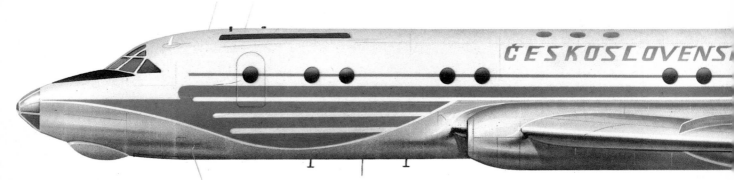

IN 1944 the Tupolev bureau was given the task of examining the B-29 bomber, preparing drawings and, in extreme urgency, putting it into production. From the resulting Tu-4 stemmed all postwar structural, systems and related technologies for large aircraft, strongly influencing the Tu-16 twin-jet strategic bomber of early 1952. It was logical then to produce a passenger transport version with a much larger fuselage mounted entirely above the wing. Other changes were kept to a minimum, though the nose landing gear had to be longer and the two Mikulin engines were derated in comparison with the Tu-16's.

The prototype Tu-104G was built at the Kharkov plant and flew on June 17, 1955 just after the first Caravelle flew in France. The suffix meant 'grazdhanskii' (civil), though as all Tu-104s were ostensibly civil this is seemingly superfluous. Production aircraft followed immediately, though at a low rate, and by early 1956 at least two were being used by Aeroflot for route-proving on several routes including Moscow-Novosibirsk. These early Tu-104s had seating for 48 passengers in 12 rows of four, and were an outstandingly economical way of getting a jet transport into service, though the aircraft itself was extremely primitive and suffered from various systems problems – for example, sudden changes in cabin pressure that were painful to passengers – and relatively short time between overhauls for the engines and most other items.

In April 1956 an official visit to London by Serov, head of the NKVD secret police, was chosen

Above: A CSA Tu-104A. Note the portholes in the roof of the galley
Below: The original Tu-104 on its 1956 visit to Heathrow. The airliner is finished in natural metal, although Aeroflot later adopted a blue and white livery

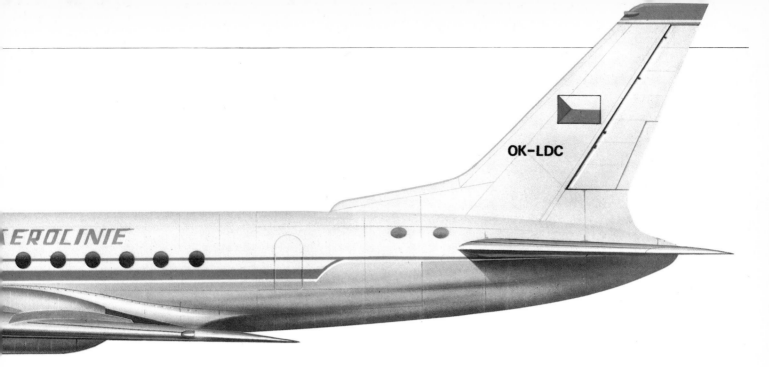

OK-LDC

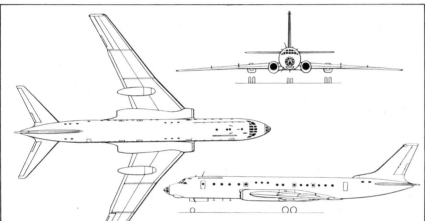

Tu-104

Type: short/medium-range passenger transport
Maker: Soviet state industry
Span: 34.54 m (113 ft 4 in)
Length: (104, 104A, 104V) 38.85 m (127 ft 5½ in); (104B, 104D) 40.05 m (131 ft 4¾ in)
Height: 11.9 m (39 ft)
Wing area: 174.4 m² (1877 sq ft)
Weight: maximum (104A) 76 000 kg (167 550 lb); empty (104A) 41 600 kg (91 710 lb)
Powerplant: 2 Mikulin AM-3 single-shaft turbojets, originally 6750-kg (14 880-lb) st AM-3s, then 8700-kg (19 180-lb) AM-3Ms, and

finally 9700-kg (21 385-lb) AM-3M-500s
Performance: maximum cruising speed 900 km/h (559 mph); economical cruising speed 800 km/h (497 mph); range with maximum payload at high altitude 2650 km (1647 miles)
Payload: normally 9000 kg (19 841 lb); seats for 50, 70 or 100 passengers depending on sub-type
Crew: 3 to 4
Production: minimum 200

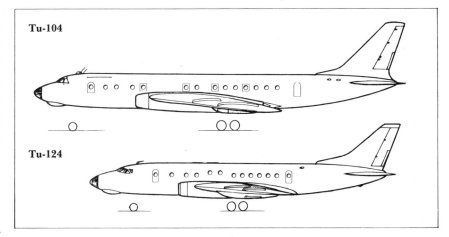

to disclose the new jetliner to an astonished world. It was clear even at that time that, while the military background was sufficient to speed development and avoid any severe problems, the Tu-104 would never be a really economical aircraft. Observers especially noted the glazed nose for traditional visual navigation by spotting surface landmarks, the radar being installed in a bulge under the nose. As in the Tu-16 bomber the bogie main gears folded into large fairings on the trailing edge of the wings.

Regular services began on the Moscow-Irkutsk route, with stops at Kazan, Sverdlovsk, Omsk and Novosibirsk, on September 15, 1956, followed by routes to Western capitals including Amsterdam and Paris. NATO called it the 'Camel', and believed it was also used as a military transport (if this was so, the number was small). In 1958 the much more powerful AM-3M engine was introduced, enabling the Tu-104Ye (104E) to set several world class records for speed with load; altogether Tu-104 versions set 22 FAI records. The Tu-104A, introduced in early 1958, accommodated 70 passengers in the original fuselage, while in September 1958 the Tu-104B (104b) with a slightly longer fuselage increased the seating to 100. In 1958 the Czech airline CSA received three Tu-104As to become the only foreign operator. In 1959 the final development was made possible by the even more powerful AM-3M-500 engine. The original Tu-104A with this engine was designated Tu-104V (104B), while the longer 104B with the new engine became the 104D.

Production at Kharkhov terminated in about 1960, by which time Aeroflot had received at least 200 of all versions and CSA five, with a sixth supplied from Aeroflot to replace one written off. Altogether the Tu-104 succeeded admirably in providing relatively trouble-free high-speed transport over a large route network with minimal development effort, though measured in terms of direct operating cost as is the case in the West – which is in fact a measure of energy efficiency as much as anything else – it was unattractive. By 1975 the general opinion was that only about 50 of the original production numbers remained in Aeroflot service, and it is believed now that the type has finally been withdrawn from secondary routes.

Tu-110, Tupolev

FIRST FLIGHT 1957

AT THE start of the Tu-104 project in 1953 the decision had to be taken whether so large an airliner could safely be designed to use only two engines. The choice of the same engine installation as the Tu-16 bomber was undoubtedly wise, but an alternative existed in the somewhat later and more advanced AL-5 turbojet by the design bureau of Arkhip M Lyulka, first run in 1951 and used in the Il-30, Il-46, La-190 and Yak-1000, and possibly in other military prototypes. In 1956 it was decided to fly at least one Tu-104 modified to have four AL-5 engines, and the result was the Tu-110, the only one of the Tupolev civil transports not to have a number ending in a 4.

Since the different engine installation called for a totally new wing it is certain that the Tu-110 was a separate parallel programme and not merely a modification to aircraft already constructed. As far as can be deduced from photographs, the Tu-110 was otherwise identical to the Tu-104A, though lacking the three small windows on each side in the pantry and service area above the wing box of the standard machine. The engines were housed in four separate bays each served by a circular-section inlet duct starting far ahead of the leading edge.

Some observers have insisted only one Tu-110 was ever built, though it seems probable that the Kharkhov plant constructed several. The first to be disclosed carried military markings, unlike the Tu-104s, and the serial number 5600. Later a Tu-110 was seen with military insignia but no number. The first flight took place in the spring of 1957, and at one time a Tu-110 was being used as a VIP transport, though so far as is known it never went outside the Soviet Union. NATO allotted it the name 'Cooker'.

It was first seen by Western observers at Vnukovo Airport, Moscow in July 1957. Aeroflot said it would be used on some domestic routes and for international services. It was said that the Tu-110 had better handling characteristics than the Tu-104 and Tu-104A.

There is no evidence that the Tu-110 was in any way faulty or a disappointment, and its performance was bound to be superior to that of any of the Tu-104 family. In the overriding interest of standardization, however, and with economics playing no part in the judgement, it was decided not to build the Tu-110 in quantity.

Bottom: Only one Tu-110 is thought to have been built, and it never carried Aeroflot markings. The fuselage had features of the 104, 104A and 104B

Tu-110

Specification similar to Tu-104 except in following particulars:
Powerplant: four 5500-kg (12 125-lb) st Lyulka AL-5 turbojets
Other details are not available

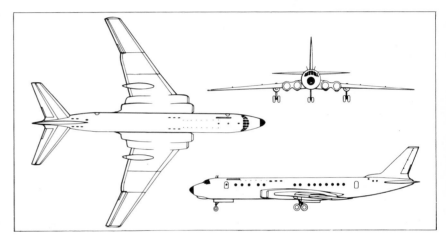

Tu-124 ,Tupolev

FIRST FLIGHT·1960

SUPERFICIALLY this neat airliner looks very much like a Tu-104, but in fact it is a totally new design with virtually no common parts except in the fuselage. The Tupolev bureau was, in 1958, instructed to produce a smaller version of the Tu-104 for use on Aeroflot services offering slightly less traffic and with shorter or poorer-surfaced runways. As a secondary advantage it was clear that the Tu-124 would be a valuable military transport, with field performance similar to that of the Il-14 and other widely used propeller aircraft.

As with most Soviet airliners, special attention was paid to the design so that it would have very good field performance and the ability to operate from runways in very poor condition and even from totally unprepared airstrips. To meet this require-

ment the standard aircraft has a very robust short-leg landing gear, double-slotted flaps (the trailing edge inboard of the gear pods being at right angles to the fuselage) and combined airbrake/spoiler/lift dumper surfaces hinged ahead of the flaps.

The engine bureau of P A Soloviev designed a new turbofan, the D-20P with a by-pass ratio of 1:1, for this aircraft. The prototype flew at Kharkhov in June 1960, and carried civil No 45000. Subsequently about 150 Tu-124 transports were constructed, the last in about 1966. As in the Tu-104 the cabin floor level had to be raised above the wing, resulting in an inefficient series of interior options most of which have three separate cabins. Early aircraft seated 44, and these entered service with Aeroflot on the Moscow-Tallinn route on

Above: The Tu-124 is used not only by Aeroflot, but East Germany, India and Iraq. Though it has the NATO reporting name 'Cookpot', as far as is known, it has not been used as a military transport for troop movement by the USSR

Below: A Tu-124 in the livery of the Czechoslovakian national airline, CSA

October 2, 1962. This has been described as the first scheduled use in the world of any aircraft with turbofan engines, but many aircraft with Conway and JT3D engines preceded it. By 1963 the standard version was the Tu-124V (124B), with three quadruple seat rows in the forward cabin, three in the centre cabin and eight in the rear cabin, a total of 56.

Almost all the Tu-124s were supplied to Aeroflot, though three were purchased by CSA of Czechoslovakia and two by Interflug of East Germany. A small number were supplied to the air forces of the Soviet Union, East Germany, India and Iraq.

In 1964 the Soviet export organization Aviaexport issued leaflets describing VIP versions designated Tu-124K and K2. In the Tu-124K the centre and rear cabins seat 8 and 24, respectively, with furnishing resembling the original civil version, but the forward cabin – which is somewhat quieter, as in all the Tupolev transports with wing-mounted engines – is arranged with just four large swivelling armchairs, together with various tables, cabinets and other furniture. In the Tu-124K2 the entire interior has VIP status: the centre cabin has two swivelling armchairs and a comfortable divan; the rear cabin has eight swivelling armchairs in two groups of four with tables between the pairs on each side of the central aisle; making a total of only 22 passengers. The K2 version is believed to have been used in the 1960s for officials of the Soviet Communist party central bureau and for domestic flights by ministers and senior military officers.

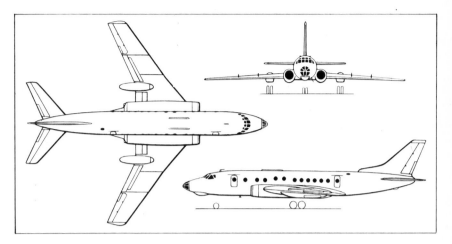

The Indian and other exported versions were equipped more closely to the 124K standard with a regular rear cabin for 24.

By 1969 at least some of the Tu-124s used by Aeroflot were fitted with lightweight seat units installed at much-reduced pitch giving a total capacity of 68. NATO called the Tu-124 the 'Cookpot', though it was never used as a military aircraft except for VIP purposes. By 1980 the Tu-124V was still an important Aeroflot aircraft, with at least 92 operating regular services on secondary routes. It had been withdrawn, however, from the other civil airline fleets, whilst continuing in service with the air forces of East Germany, India and Iraq, who continue to operate at least seven aircraft among them.

Tu-124

Type: short-range passenger or VIP transport
Maker: Soviet state industry
Span: 25.55 m (83 ft 9½ in)
Length: 30.58 m (100 ft 4 in)
Height: 8.08 m (26 ft 6 in)
Wing area: 119 m² (1281 sq ft)
Weight: maximum 38 000 kg (83 775 lb); empty 22 500 kg (49 600 lb)
Powerplant: two 5400-kg (11 905-lb) st Soloviev D-20P 2-shaft turbofans
Performance: maximum cruising speed 870 km/h (540 mph); economical cruising speed 800 km/h (497 mph); range at economical speed at high altitude with maximum payload 1220 km (760 miles)
Payload: 6000 kg (13 228 lb); seats for up to 56 passengers
Crew: 3
Production: fewer than 200

Caravelle, Aérospatiale

FIRST FLIGHT 1955

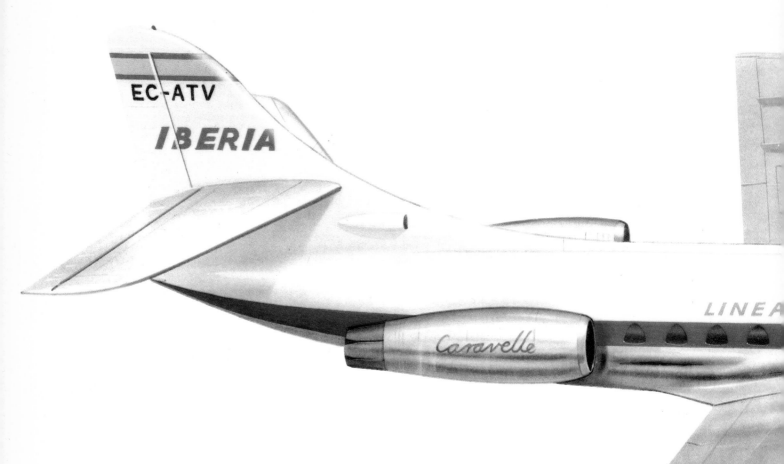

Above: One of the 19 Iberia Caravelles; the other major operators of the type were Air France, SAS and Alitalia. Though no longer used on main routes the Caravelle is a popular charter aircraft for holiday package trips

THIS attractive and innovative French aircraft was the first short-haul jetliner to go into production, and also the first aircraft in the world to fly with engines hung on the sides of the rear fuselage. It was designed by the former French national group SNCASE (the Sud-Est nationalized company) to meet a government SGACC specification for a short-haul jet written in 1951. At that time the very concept of a short-range jet transport was judged to be of doubtful value, since the saving in time appeared to be insignificant and the extra cost in fuel, compared with a modern propeller-driven aircraft, likely to be considerable – especially as over short sectors the aircraft could hardly cruise at the great heights where jet engines are more efficient. As finally issued in November 1951 the SGACC requirement called for a payload of 6 to 7 tonnes carried at 700 km/h (435 mph) over a range of 1930 km (1200 miles).

There were at that time numerous constructors capable of building jets in France, and at least eight submissions were received. In September 1952 the SGACC selected the X-210 produced by SNCASE, who were accordingly awarded a contract in January 1953 for two flying prototypes and two test airframes. Originally the X-210 was planned to use three SNECMA Atar turbojets arranged in the way common today on, for example, the Trident. By June 1953 it had been decided that to reduce risk the more developed Rolls-Royce Avon would be used, and this much more powerful engine allowed the centre engine to be eliminated. Risk was further reduced by using the entire front

28

Overleaf: One of the eight
Caravelles operated by
Swissair in the 1960s. SAS
and Swissair shared the costs
of maintaining their
Caravelle fleets

AÉREAS DE ESPAÑA **IBERIA**

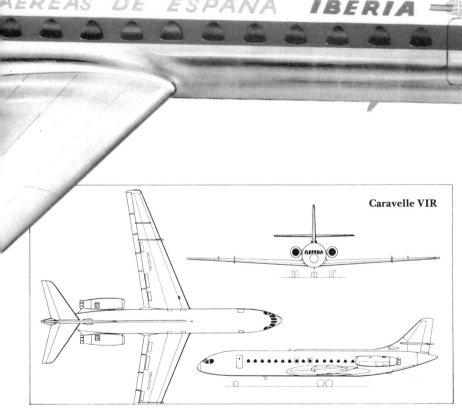

Caravelle VIR

Caravelle 10R, 11, Super

Specification similar to Mk
III except in following
particulars:
Length: (11) 32.71 m (107 ft
4 in); (Super) 33.01 m (108 ft
4 in)
Weight: maximum (10R)
52 000 kg (114 640 lb); (11)
54 000 kg (119 050 lb);
(Super) 56 000 kg
(123 460 lb); empty (10R)
29 075 kg (64 100 lb); (11)
28 841 kg (63 585 lb); (Super)
30 055 kg (66 260 lb)
Powerplant: two 6350-kg
(14 000-lb) Pratt & Whitney
JT8D-7 2-shaft turbofans
Performance: maximum
cruising speed (10,11)
800 km/h (497 mph); (Super)
835 km/h (518 mph); range
with maximum payload and
reserves (10R) 3455 km (2145
miles); (11) 2800 km (1740
miles); (Super) 2655 km (1650
miles)
Payload: (10R) 9400 kg
(20 720 lb); (11) 9095 kg
(20 050 lb); (Super) 9100 kg
(20 060 lb); seats for 80 (10R),
99 (11) or 105 (Super)
Production: (10R) 20; (11)
6; (Super) 22

Caravelle 12

Specification similar to Mk 11
except in following
particulars:
Length: 36.23 m (118 ft 10 in)
Weight: maximum 56 000 kg
(123 460 lb); empty 32 400 kg
(71 430 lb)
Performance: range with
maximum payload and
reserves 1620 km (1006 miles)
Payload: 13 200 kg
(29 100 lb); seats for up to 140
passengers
Production: 12

Caravelle III

Type: short-range passenger
transport
Maker: French state
industry, SNCASE, Sud-
Aviation, Aérospatiale
Span: 34.3 m (112 ft 6 in)
Length: 32.01 m (105 ft)
Height: 8.72 m (28 ft 7 in)
Wing area: 146.7 m² (1579 sq
ft)
Weight: maximum 46 000 kg
(101 413 lb); empty 24 185 kg
(53 320 lb)
Powerplant: original Mk I,
two 4763-kg (10 500-lb) st
Rolls-Royce Avon 522 single-
shaft turbojets; Mk III two
5170-kg (11 400-lb) Avon 527s

Performance: maximum
cruising speed 805 km/h
(500 mph); range with
maximum payload and
reserves 1700 km (1056 miles)
Payload: 8400 kg (18 520 lb);
seats for up to 80 passengers
Crew: 2 to 3
Production: 78, preceded by
20 Mk Is and 12 Mk IAs

Caravelle VI

Specification similar to Mk
III except in following
particulars:
Weight: maximum (VIN)
48 000 kg (105 822 lb); (VIR)
50 000 kg (110 230 lb); empty
(VIN) 27 330 kg (60 250 lb);
(VIR) 28 655 kg (63 175 lb)
Powerplant: (VIN) two
5535-kg (12 200-lb) Avon
531s; (VIR) two 5725-kg
(12 600-lb) Avon 533Rs
Performance: maximum
cruising speed 845 km/h
(525 mph); range 2350 km
(1460 miles)
Payload: 8200 kg (18 080 lb)
Production: 109

fuselage and flight deck of the Comet, for which the French government – which funded the whole cost of the programme – paid de Havilland a royalty. Front fuselages were constructed in France, largely with French instruments and equipment, though they were fitted with British windscreen panels and many other British parts throughout the functioning systems.

Structurally the design was clean and modern, with a three-spar wing with the modest sweepback of 20° and a high aspect ratio (unusual for jets at that time), a circular-section fuselage and extremely short landing gears with four-wheel main bogies of French Hispano design. The wings had fixed leading edges, with thermal de-icing, large Fowler flaps, prominent perforated airbrakes opening above and below and, in later versions, spoilers which also served as lift-dumpers after landing. The tail, with the horizontal surface mounted only a little way above the fuselage, again had thermal de-icing and like the ailerons had fully powered control surfaces using duplicated hydraulic power units by the British Lockheed (Automotive Products) company, similar to those used on the Comet. All fuel was housed in wing integral tanks, with pressure fuelling, and an unusual feature was that the passenger windows were of a rounded triangular shape to reconcile the need for a generous view downwards with small overall area and avoidance of stress-concentrating corners. Another bold innovation was a large hydraulically powered passenger stairway under the tail, forming a rear-fuselage support in the lowered position, as

was later fitted to several other jetliners.

In 1953 the designation changed to SE.210 and the name Caravelle was selected. The first prototype made a very successful first flight on May 27, 1955, powered by two Avon RA.26 engines very similar to the Valiant bomber engine and each rated at 4536 kg (10 000 lb). In November 1955 Air France placed an order for 12, and after the second prototype flew on May 6, 1956, the Caravelle became familiar at airshows and began to give rides to the media and prospective customers. A favourite trick was to climb to at least 11 km altitude (36 000 ft), close down the engines to flight idling and then glide half-way across France.

Gradually the favourable impression made by the two prototype Caravelles, allied with the

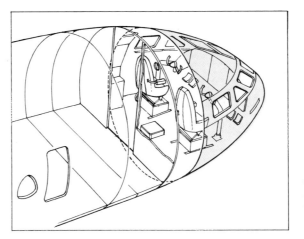

Left: The Caravelle employed the complete nose section of the de Havilland Comet 1 (shaded). This included the Captain's and First Officer's seats but the central console and instrument panels were modified for the Caravelle's twin-engine installation

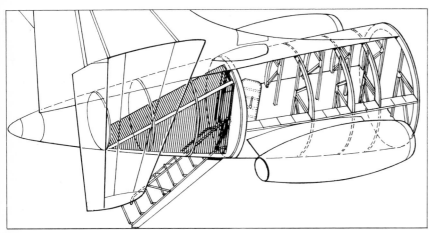

Above: The Caravelle had many innovations among which was the 'airstair' for entry via the rear. There was a door in the rear bulkhead with a 'tunnel' (shaded) of stiffened skin leading downwards
Right: The 'lace-edged' airbrakes on the Caravelle. They opened above and below the wing and were operated by hydraulic jacks. An airflow-straightening 'fence' can be seen in the foreground

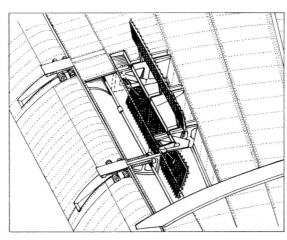

acceptance of the US-built long-range jets, resulted in a succession of orders led by such hard-headed operators as SAS and Sabena. Unlike the Tu-104, however, which rested on a bomber design and went into production from the start, the Caravelle took a long time to develop and though the first certification was in April 1958, Air France only put the Caravelle I into service on May 6, 1959.

Generally similar to the prototype apart from having a longer fuselage, more powerful engines, with zero-stages on the compressors, and avionics aerials housed in a long but shallow dorsal fin along the top of the fuselage, the Caravelle I was very popular with passengers and operators. The 20 of this type were followed by 12 Mk IAs with Mk 526 engines. Then on December 30, 1959, Sud-Aviation (as SNCASE had become) flew the Mk III, with Mk 527 engines allowing greater weights and higher speeds. One Mk III was re-engined with CJ-805-23 aft-fan engines by Douglas in an attempt to penetrate the US market (Douglas did not succeed and later built the rival DC-9). In addition to 78 Mk IIIs, all the earlier Caravelles were modified to this standard.

One US operator, United, did buy 20 Caravelles direct from Sud-Aviation in February 1960, launching the more powerful VI-N (53 built) and VI-R (56) with more powerful silenced and reverse-equipped engines, larger flight-deck windows, spoiler/lift dumpers and more powerful brakes. Meanwhile the fan-engined Caravelle VII sponsored by Douglas attracted a sale to TWA, which was cancelled in 1962. TWA specified the

Mk 10, with alternative name Caravelle Horizon, and though nothing came of this Sud-Aviation realized it had to update the Caravelle and on March 3, 1964 flew the first Caravelle 10B, later called Super Caravelle. This had JT8D-7 turbofans in a much modified airframe with longer fuselage, swept-forward wing roots, double-slotted flaps with greater operating angle, greater fuel capacity, bullet fairing ahead of a larger tailplane, constant-frequency electric power, an APU (auxiliary power unit) and seating for up to 104.

While building 22 of these work went ahead on the Mk 10R with JT8D-7 engines in a Mk VI airframe (20 built) and the Mk 11R (6) with longer body for passenger/cargo operations. These eked out production through the 1960s, though the assembly line at Toulouse was no longer impressive by 1969 when Sud-Aviation (which a year later merged with Nord to become Aérospatiale) announced the final version, the Caravelle 12. Essentially this was a Super Caravelle further stretched to seat 140 on Sterling Airways inclusive-tour operations, with the highest weights of any version and JT8D-9 engines. Apart from structural reinforcement the Mk 12 features larger emergency exits and a better interior layout. Final customer was Air Inter, which bought five to bring production to a close in 1972 at the 282nd aircraft.

This was by far the most successful jetliner ever developed by a single West European country. It did more than any other to make the jet familiar on short-haul and local routes, and by 1980 some 125 were still in use.

Below: A Caravelle of Scandinavian Airline Systems, which entered service in April 1959. The Caravelle was the first of a succession of rear-engined commercial transports

Comet 4, de Havilland

FIRST FLIGHT 1958

IN 1955 the protracted enquiry into the causes of the disasters that overtook the Comet 1 established beyond any doubt that metal fatigue had resulted in explosive decompression of the whole fuselage. The existing Comets, of which there were 22, could very quickly have been structurally modified to make them wholly safe for a long period of airline use. Instead nothing was done, and foolishly arguments raged over whether the whole programme should be abandoned. Late in 1955 BOAC, which preferred turboprops, rather reluctantly decided to order 19 of a completely redesigned Comet 4 type for use on the North Atlantic as well as the African and Eastern services.

This was a strange decision, because the Comet 4 was not really a transatlantic transport, and had no hope of competing successfully with the much larger, faster and longer-ranged 707 and DC-8 which had just been ordered by PanAm. The Comet 4 was in fact a good medium-haul aircraft, especially on routes with short or hot/high airfields, its ratio of thrust-to-weight being almost twice that of the 707, Caravelle and other jetliners and thus resulting in startling take-off distances and very steep climb. Instead its debut was polarized around the North Atlantic, even to the extent of trying to beat PanAm into service in a childish race presumably thought to offer some short-term gain.

During 1955 the Comet 3 continued intensive development, fitted with the so-called 'pinion

Below: Comet 4 G-APDO in BOAC service; it was transferred to Dan-Air in April 1971 after 12 years service with BOAC

Comet 4

Type: medium-range passenger transport
Maker: de Havilland Aircraft, Hawker Siddeley Aviation, Hatfield/Chester
Span: 35.05 m (115 ft)
Length: 33.99 m (111 ft 6 in)
Height: 8.97 m (29 ft 5 in)
Wing area: 197 m² (2121 sq ft)
Weight: maximum 70 762 kg (156 000 lb); empty 32 929 kg (72 595 lb)
Powerplant: four 4763-kg (10 500-lb) st Rolls-Royce Avon 525 single-shaft turbojets
Performance: maximum cruising speed 861 km/h (535 mph); range with maximum payload and no reserves 5697 km (3540 miles)
Payload: 11 612 kg (25 600 lb); seats for up to 81 passengers
Crew: 3 to 5
Production: 28

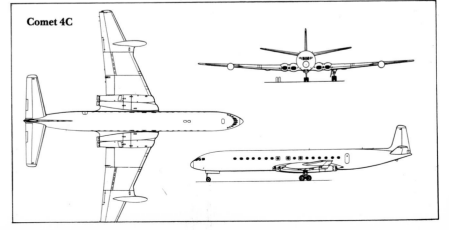

Comet 4C

tanks' of the Mk 4 and in December 1955 it made a complete round-the-world flight. In 1956 two of the Avon-engined Comet 2s were set aside from conversion for the RAF and eventually completed in 1957 as civil development aircraft designated Comet 2E, with the Comet 4 Avon 524 engines in the outer positions. They flew extensively on BOAC routes, including the North Atlantic.

The first of the BOAC Comet 4s, G-APDA, flew on April 27, 1958. This was the same size as the Comet 3 but heavier, with more powerful engines, more fuel, more passengers (63 to 81 instead of 58 to 78) and longer range at slightly greater speed and height. The airframe was greatly refined, and flight testing confirmed all predicted figures and indicated the Comet 4 was a first-class aircraft –

though not really one suitable for the North Atlantic. After hurried final preparations the first Mk 4 made an outstanding flight from Hong Kong to Hatfield in one day in 16 hours 15 min on September 14, 1958 followed by certification and delivery on September 30. The third aircraft, APDC, inaugurated services between London and New York, stopping at Gander, on October 4, 1958.

In 1957 British European Airways, which had previously poured scorn on jets and ordered a second-generation turboprop, the Vanguard, did a sudden U-turn and ordered six of a new version of the Comet, the 4B. Nearly a year earlier de Havilland had been pushed into the Comet's true market, that of busy domestic routes, by Capital

Below: The development of the Comet 4 from the Comet 1; Comet 4 had larger intakes, rounded windows and leading-edge fuel tanks; Comet 4B was further stretched for high density short-haul trips; Comet 4C has the same dimensions as the 4B but with leading-edge tanks is used for the medium-range routes

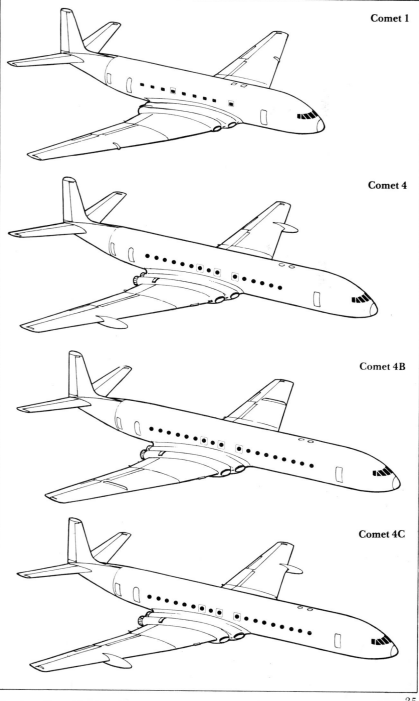

Comet 1

Comet 4

Comet 4B

Comet 4C

Comet 4B

Specification similar to Comet 4 except in following particulars:
Type: short-range transport
Span: 32.87 m (107 ft 10 in)
Length: 35.97 m (118 ft)
Wing area: 191.28 m² (2059 sq ft)
Weight: maximum 71 649 kg (157 960 lb); empty 33 483 kg (73 816 lb)
Performance: range with maximum payload and no reserves 4184 km (2600 miles)
Payload: 13 130 kg (28 950 lb); seats for up to 101 passengers
Production: 18

Comet 4C

Specification similar to Comet 4 except in following particulars:
Length: 35.97 m (118 ft)
Weight: maximum 73 482 kg (162 000 lb); empty 35 610 kg (78 500 lb)
Payload: 13 130 kg (28 950 lb); seats for up to 101 passengers
Production: 28

Airlines of Washington. James Carmichael, Capital's pro-British president, who previously had become the world's largest customer for the turboprop Viscount, ordered a special short-haul Comet designated 4A, with reduced wingspan and other structural changes to allow flight at greatly increased indicated airspeeds. This opened the way both to lower cruising altitudes and greater cruising speeds. The 4A seemed to be a winner, but for reasons unconnected with it Capital cancelled the order and later merged into United.

BEA's 4B was identical with the 4A except for minor structural changes and refined dimensions, including a considerably stretched fuselage with five-abreast seating for 92 to 99 passengers. On August 21, 1958 the Comet 3 flew as a 3B, with

Comet 4

1 Radome
2 Radar scanner
3 Front pressure bulkhead
4 Windscreen framing
5 Windscreen wipers
6 Instrument panel coaming
7 DME aerial
8 Rudder pedals
9 Cockpit roof construction
10 Co-pilot's seat
11 Control column
12 Pilot's seat
13 Engineer's control panel
14 Emergency escape hatch
15 Radio rack
16 Engineer's work table
17 Engineer's swivelling seat
18 Navigator's seats
19 Navigator's work table
20 Nosewheel bay construction
21 Nosewheel leg strut
22 Twin nosewheels
23 Nosewheel door
24 Crew entry door
25 Crew's wardrobe
26 Forward galley
27 Galley supplies stowage boxes
28 Radio and electrical equipment bay
29 Forward right toilet compartment
30 Forward left toilet compartment
31 Wash basin
32 Air-conditioning duct
33 Toilet servicing panel
34 Cabin window panel
35 First class cabin seats
36 Twin ADF loop aerials
37 Air-conditioning grilles
38 Floor beams
39 Forward freight and luggage hold
40 Freight hold door
41 Control cable runs
42 Fuselage keel construction
43 Overhead hat rack
44 Cabin dividing bulkhead
45 Air distribution duct
46 Emergency escape window
47 Air-conditioning plant
48 Hydraulics bay
49 Right wing integral fuel tanks
50 Flow spoilers
51 External fuel tank
52 Tank bumper
53 Fixed slot
54 Outer wing fuel tanks
55 Navigation light
56 Wingtip fuel vent
57 Static dischargers
58 Right aileron
59 Aileron tab
60 Flap outer section
61 Airbrake
62 Fuel dump pipes
63 Fuel vent
64 Flap inboard section
65 Inboard airbrake (upper surface)
66 Fuselage frame and stringer construction
67 Wing centre-section fuel cells
68 Emergency escape hatch
69 Aileron servo controls
70 Aft tourist class cabin
72 Rear freight hold/luggage compartment
73 Floor beam construction
74 HF aerial cable (left and right)
75 Overhead hat rack
76 Tourist class cabin seats
77 Aft galley
78 Right service door
79 Aft right toilet compartment
80 Aft radio rack
81 Rear pressure bulkhead
82 Anti-collision light
83 Dorsal fin fairing
84 Right tailplane
85 ILS aerial
86 Right elevator
87 Leading-edge de-icing ducts
88 Fin construction
89 HF blade aerial
90 Rudder balance weight
91 Rudder
92 Elevator hinge controls
93 Elevator tab
94 Left elevator
95 Tailplane construction
96 ILS aerial
97 Leading-edge de-icing
98 Tailplane attachment
99 Fuselage fin frame
100 Tail bumper/fuselage vent
101 Rudder and elevator control rods
102 Access hatch to control bay
103 De-icing air supply duct
104 Rear freight hold
105 Tailplane servo controls
106 Mail locker
107 Aft left toilet compartment
108 Passenger entry door
109 Door frame construction
110 Steward's seat
111 Tourist class passenger seating
112 Wing fillet construction
113 Life raft stowage
114 Inboard tailpipe duct
115 Exhaust silencer nozzles
116 Outboard tailpipe
117 Thrust reverser (outboard only)
118 Inboard flap section
119 Fuel vent
120 Fuel dump pipes
121 Flap jack
122 Flap connecting links
123 Left airbrake (upper and lower surfaces)
124 Outboard flap section
125 Flap construction
126 Aileron tab
127 Left aileron
128 Aileron hinge controls
129 Aileron construction
130 Static dischargers
131 Wingtip fuel vent
132 Left navigation light
133 Outer wing construction
134 Outboard fuel tank bays
135 Fuel tank access panels
136 Wing stringer construction
137 External fuel tank
138 Tank bumper
139 Fixed slot
140 Wing rib construction
141 Leading-edge de-icing ducts
142 Four-wheel bogie unit
143 Wing skin joint strap
144 Undercarriage well
145 Main undercarriage leg mechanism
146 Wing integral fuel tank
147 Rolls Royce Avon RA.29 engine
148 Inboard engine bay
149 Engine mounting frame
150 Intake duct construction
151 Landing lamp
152 Engine intakes
153 Ram air intake
154 Heat exchangers
155 Taxi lamp

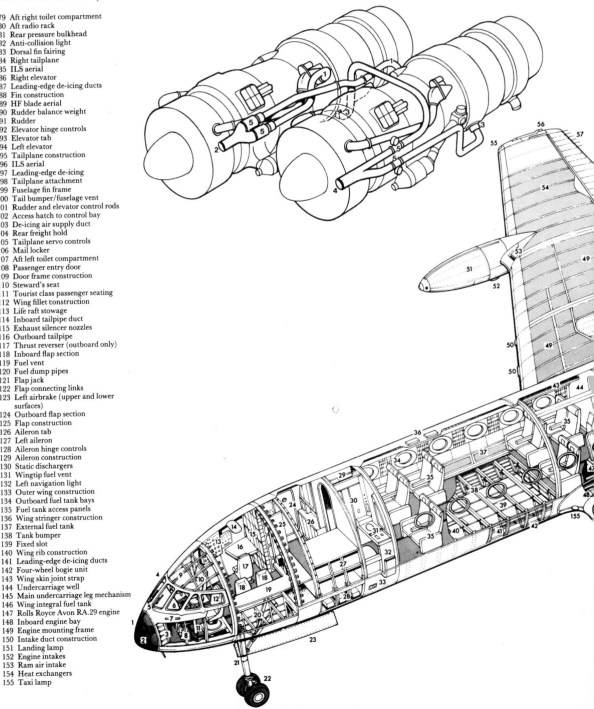

clipped wings and pinion tanks removed, and the first 4B, G-APMA, followed on June 27, 1959. Altogether 18 Comet 4Bs were built, and they proved to be excellent aircraft, though overpowered for the work they had to do.

The ultimate commercial Comet was a natural mating of the long fuselage of the 4B with the long wing and large fuel capacity of the 4. This version, naturally called the 4C, appealed to a number of customers, and had it matured in 1954 as should have been possible it would have sold in hundreds. As it was, 28 were built, the first flying on October 31, 1959 and the last coming off the line at Hawker Siddeley's Hawarden (Chester) plant in 1964. At that time two airframes remained unsold and these were greatly modified during construction to emerge as the prototypes of the maritime reconnaissance aircraft originally designated HS.801 and finally BAe Nimrod.

Throughout the 1960s the Comet 4, 4B and 4C gave excellent service on air routes in many parts of the world. In 1966 the then-small British inclusive-tour operator Dan-Air bought two ex-BOAC Comet 4s, and found them ideal for the packaged holiday market. Subsequently nearly all the 4s, 4Bs and 4Cs passed through Dan-Air's hands, operating from a base at London Gatwick and with engineering handled by the airline at Lasham. Dan-Air bought every Comet it could lay hands on, and in 1980 still had ten flying (four 4Bs and six 4Cs). They are popular with tour operators and are the last still in regular airline operation.

Above left: A Sudan Airways
Comet 4 photographed in
June 1975
Left: Air and heating in the
Comet 4
1 Tappings for the air supply;
2 Air-supply line; 3 Hot air
for anti-icing system; 4
Supply line; 5 Control valves

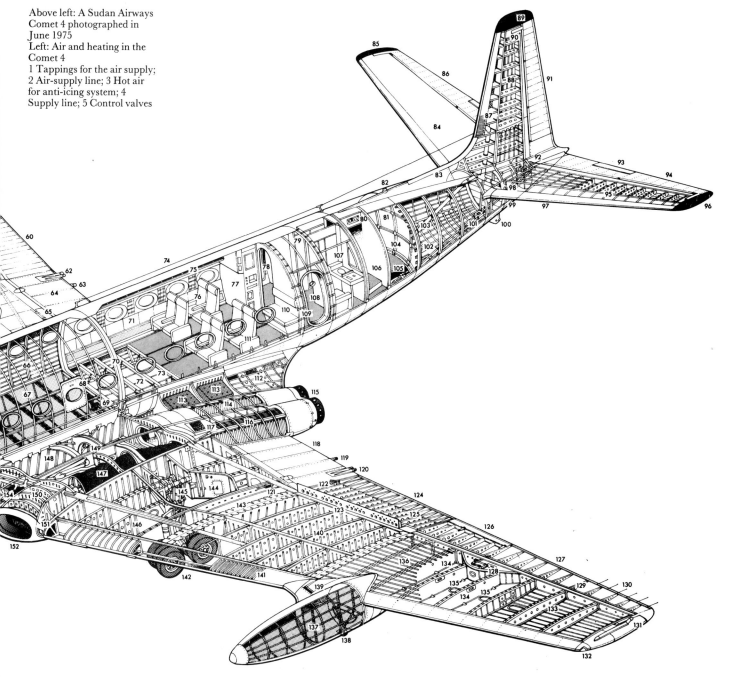

DC-8, Douglas

FIRST FLIGHT 1958

THROWN into a tough competitive situation by Boeing's decision in 1952 to build a jet transport, Douglas Aircraft Company began a long and careful series of studies into the best options for a successor to the DC-7. The piston-engined aircraft was selling well but clearly had a limited future, and much thought was given to the turbo-prop DC-7D and various completely new turbo-prop civil transports. Increasingly, however, the Douglas management were advised that Boeing had got it right, and there seemed no alternative but to come from behind with an almost identical aircraft and try to do it better.

Douglas announced its commitment to the new jetliner in June 1955, and two months later released preliminary specifications. The DC-8

Domestic was very close indeed to the 707, the only major differences being a reduced wing sweep, more conventional flight controls with outboard all-speed ailerons and full power operation throughout, continuous inboard flaps with a hinged segment to avoid the inboard jet wakes, nose inlets for cabin conditioning, and a small number of normal-size cabin windows, one per seat row. At first it was intended to use articulated bogie main gears with the front and rear pairs of wheels pivoted to the leg to assist ground man-oeuvring without scrubbing the tyres, but this was dropped in favour of conventional bogies with a rigid four-wheel truck. Another unusual feature was that the wing roots had an inverted profile, flatter on top and with most camber on the

Above: A DC-8 of Seaboard World Airlines; this US charter cargo line began operations in 1947 and now employs two Boeing 747s and 11 DC-8Fs

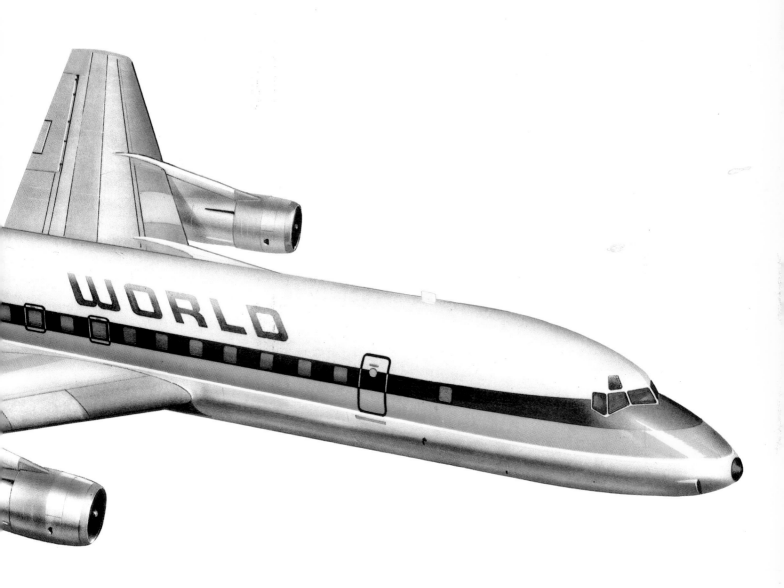

underside, to avoid excessive local airflow acceleration and suction at speeds close to that of sound.

On October 13, 1955 PanAm ordered 20 DC-8s
as well as the first 707s, demonstrating its willingness to ensure domestic competition. Douglas had
less money in the bank than Boeing, but just
managed to find the $25 million for the prototype,
and then used progress payments from a healthy
list of customers to fund the $250 million needed by
certification. Inevitably the DC-8 ran later than
the 707 in timing, but Douglas scored in their
marketing policy. The company announced its
willingness to build a heavier intercontinental
version with JT4A engines, with the radical new
British turbofan, the Rolls-Royce Conway, as a
customer option. At the same time it stated that all

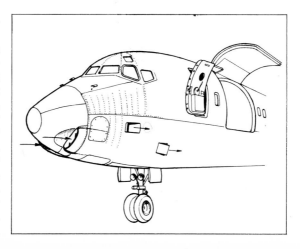

Left: The main cabin air-
conditioning in the nose of the
DC-8. The 'nostril' intakes
are indicated with the outlets
for the turbine and heat
exchanger a little to the rear.
The illustration shows a DC-
8F with a large cargo door on
the left side

planned DC-8s would have identical dimensions. Boeing countered by offering a JT4A aircraft but this had the same fuel capacity as previous 707s and only one airline selected it.

The first DC-8 Series 10 flew at Long Beach on May 30, 1958. In November the JT4A-powered Series 20 took to the air, and the Series 10 was certificated on August 31, 1959, entering domestic service with United and Delta the following month. By this time Douglas had sold over 160, to more airlines than Boeing had sold the 707; but the programme was still a year behind its rival and Boeing had even caught up on the heavy long-range model. The DC-8 Series 30, for PanAm, flew on February 21, 1959 and was certificated on February 1, 1960. To meet market demands the gross weight of all versions had climbed throughout the flight test period.

On July 23, 1959 Douglas flew the first Conway-engined DC-8 Series 40, an extremely attractive aircraft which, despite the greater power and economy of its engines, sold only to Air Canada, Alitalia and Canadian Pacific. It was one of this series that exceeded Mach 1, the only civil transport, other than an SST, to do this. The Series 40 was certificated on March 24, 1960. Last of the first generation of DC-8s was the Series 50, with the JT3D turbofan engine at various ratings and introducing various airframe improvements. The first JT3D-DC-8 was the original prototype re-engined and flown on December 20, 1960. Certification of the Series 50 followed on May 1, 1961.

In the course of production several improvements were introduced, some of them being retrofitted to aircraft already delivered. The most important was a new leading edge to the wing, adding a little to the area by increasing chord 4% and reducing drag, especially at high speeds. For a given fuel burn it gave about 5% extra range. All improvements were incorporated in the Series 54 Jet Trader, first flown on October 29, 1962. This was a flexible cargo/passenger aircraft able to carry its full payload of 43 219 kg (95 282 lb) non-stop in either direction across the North Atlantic. Schemes were included for up to 189 passengers, while a few customers bought Jet Traders with no windows for pure cargo operation. The Model 55, of 1964, had more powerful JT3D-3B engines.

On April 5, 1965 Douglas announced a completely new Super Sixty series to escape from what was very belatedly recognized as a competitive disadvantage in having only one size of fuselage. First of the new models, flown on March 14, 1966, the DC-8 Series 61 featured a record stretch of 11.18 m (36 ft 8 in) to seat up to 259 passengers. Naturally the underfloor cargo/baggage bays were also handsomely enlarged. Service with this aircraft began on February 25, 1967 followed by the Super 61F and CF (convertible) freighters.

The next version, the Super 62, was a major redesign. This had only a modest 2.03 m (6 ft 8 in) stretch over earlier models, but introduced a new wing with increased span, more efficient tips, other aerodynamic refinements and increased tankage.

A DC-8 operating from Las Vegas decked out in a Centennial colour scheme in 1976. The DC-8 was the first jet airliner to fly at over Mach 1 when a modified DC-8-40 reached 1073 km/h (667 mph) in a shallow dive on March 24, 1960

The JT3D-3B engines were for the first time cowled in pods having a full-length fan duct giving greater thrust and less drag, hung on completely new curving pylons that reduced interference drag. The main objective in the Super 62 was efficient service at extreme ranges such as from eastern Europe to the US Pacific coast. The first flew on August 29, 1966, and SAS flew the first service on May 22, 1967. The final model was the natural blend of the new wing and engine pods with the long body to give the Super 63, first flown on April 10, 1967 and in service by July 27, the same year. Both the 62 and 63 had F and CF Jet Trader freight and convertible counterparts, the 63F with its outstanding weights and payload of 53 788 kg (118 353 lb) selling to all the chief United States cargo lines.

Had Douglas offered the Super Sixty series in 1961 they would possibly have outsold the 707, which could not so readily be subjected to such a stretching process. Even at the last moment Douglas managed to take the DC-8 production total from 293 to a healthy 556, despite the fact that they are the noisiest and most airfield-demanding of all civil transports (FAA field length of the Super 63 is no less than 3505 m [11 500 ft]).

In 1980 some 404 of the 556 DC-8s were still in service. Their airframe life is excellent, and an increasing number are being booked for remanufacturing and re-engining with the CFM56 turbofan, giving quiet fuel-efficient propulsion and much higher flight performance. The re-engined aircraft will be styled Super 70 series.

DC-8 Series 10

Type: medium-range passenger transport
Maker: Douglas Aircraft
Span: 43.41 m (142 ft 5 in)
Length: 45.87 m (150 ft 6 in)
Height: 12.91 m (42 ft 4 in)
Wing area: 257.6 m²
(2773 sq ft)
Weight: maximum
123 830 kg (273 000 lb); empty
56 578 kg (124 732 lb)
Powerplant: four 6124-kg
(13 500-lb) st Pratt &
Whitney JT3C-6 2-shaft
turbojets
Performance: maximum
cruising speed 933 km/h
(580 mph); range with
maximum payload and no
reserves 6920 km (4300 miles)
Payload: 15 585 kg
(34 360 lb); seats for up to 179
passengers
Crew: 3 to 5
Production: 28

DC-8 Series 20

Specification similar to Series
10 except in following
particulars:
Weight: maximum
125 190 kg (276 000 lb); empty
57 632 kg (127 056 lb)
Powerplant: four 7167-kg
(15 800-lb) Pratt & Whitney
JT4A-3 2-shaft turbojets
Performance: range with
maximum payload and no
reserves 7710 km (4790 miles)
Production: 34, plus 21
converted from Series 10

DC-8 Series 30

Specification similar to Series
10 except in following
particulars:
Weight: maximum
142 880 kg (315 000 lb); empty
60 692 kg (133 803 lb)
Powerplant: four 7945-kg
(17 500-lb) JT4A-11
Performance: range with
maximum payload and no
reserves 9605 km (5970 miles)
Production: 57

DC-8 Series 40

Specification similar to Series
10 except in following
particulars:
Weight: maximum
142 880 kg (315 000 lb); empty
60 068 kg (132 425 lb)
Powerplant: four 7945-kg
(17 500-lb) Rolls-Royce
Conway 509 2-shaft
turbofans, later uprated to
8165-kg (18 000-lb) Conway
509As
Performance: range with
maximum payload and no
reserves 9817 km (6100 miles)
Production: 32

DC-8 Series 50

Specification similar to Series
10 except in following
particulars:
Weight: maximum
147 415 kg (325 000 lb); empty
60 020 kg (132 325 lb)
Powerplant: four 7718-kg
(17 000-lb) Pratt & Whitney
JT3D-1 2-shaft turbofans,
later usually uprated to 8165-
kg (18 000-lb) JT3D-3s
Performance: range with
maximum payload and no
reserves 11 260 km
(7000 miles)
Production: 87, plus 3
converted from Series 30, plus
54 Jet Trader cargo versions

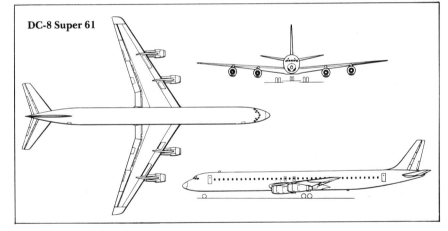

DC-8 Super 61

DC-8 Super 61

Specification similar to Series 10 except in following particulars:
Length: 57.12 m (187 ft 5 in)
Height: 12.92 m (42 ft 5 in)
Wing area: 267.9 m²
(2884 sq ft)
Weight: maximum
147 415 kg (325 000 lb); empty
67 538 kg (148 897 lb)
Powerplant: four 8165-kg
(18 000-lb) JT3D-3s
Performance: range with maximum payload and normal airline reserves
6035 km (3750 miles)

Payload: 30 240 kg
(66 665 lb); seats for up to 259 passengers
Production: 78, plus 10
61CF cargo/passenger versions

DC-8 Super 62

Specification similar to Super 61 except in following particulars:
Span: 45.23 m (148 ft 5 in)
Length: 47.98 m (157 ft 5 in)
Wing area: 271.9 m²
(2927 sq ft)
Weight: maximum
151 950 kg (335 000 lb); empty
64 366 kg (141 903 lb)
Powerplant: four 8618-kg
(19 000-lb) JT3D-7s
Performance: range with maximum payload and normal airline reserves
9640 km (6000 miles)

Payload: 21 470 kg
(47 335 lb); seats for up to 189 passengers
Production: 52 plus 16 F and CF cargo and convertible versions

DC-8 Super 63

Specification similar to Super 62 except in following particulars:
Length: 57.12 m (187 ft 5 in)
Weight: maximum
158 760 kg (350 000 lb) (63 F and CF 161 028 kg
[355 000 lb]); empty 69 739 kg
(153 749 lb)
Performance: range with maximum payload and normal airline reserves
7240 km (4500 miles)
Payload: 30 719 kg
(67 735 lb); seats for up to 259 passengers; (63 F and CF
53 788 kg [118 583 lb] cargo)
Production: 41 plus 66 F and CF cargo and convertible versions

DC-8 Super 73

Specification similar to Super 63CF/F except in following particulars:
Weight: not available
Powerplant: four 9979-kg
(22 000-lb) CFM56 2-shaft turbofans
Performance: dramatically shorter take-off, steeper climb, reduced noise and lower fuel consumption than Super 63; range with maximum payload increased by 1400 km (870 miles); for range of 7600 km (4722 miles) payload with full reserves is increased from 20 400 kg
(45 000 lb) to 25 850 kg
(57 000 lb) or 280 passengers and baggage
Production: 73 conversions of Super 60 series aircraft ordered by 1980

BB-152, VEB

FIRST FLIGHT 1958

THE nucleus of an aircraft industry was set up in 1954 in East Germany under the authority of the state-owned design organization Vereinegung Volkseigener Betriebe Flugzeugbau. Design proceeded on a passenger jet transport of curious configuration. It had a circular-section fuselage, high wing with podded engines, and landing gear reminiscent of the Boeing B-47 with tandem main gears under the fuselage and outrigger wheels under the wingtips retracting into slender fairings as in today's Harrier.

The engine, specially developed for this odd aircraft, was the Pirna Type 014, a simple turbojet with a 12-stage axial compressor first exhibited in public at the 1958 Leipzig Fair. It was thought in the West to have been derived from the Junkers Jumo 012 of 1944–45. Two engines were housed in each underwing pod.

The prototype BB-152 was rolled out of the main VEB aircraft plant at Dresden in late 1958. It looked well-finished, and its smooth metal skin was unpainted apart from DDR colours and the registration DM-ZYA. Fuel was housed in 16 cells in the high wing and two rigid wingtip tanks, with total capacity of 15 000 litres (3410 Imp gal).

The first flight took place on December 4, 1958 but not long afterwards it was announced that the BB-152 had been destroyed in a crash (which was in 1959 said not to have been due to any fault in the aircraft). In spring 1959 the VEB announced that six production BB-152s would be produced in 1960, followed by 18 in 1961. That was the last anyone heard of the programme.

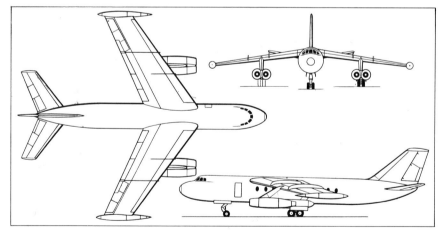

BB-152

Type: short-range passenger transport
Maker: VEB
Span: 27 m (88 ft 7 in)
Length: 31.4 m (103 ft)
Height: 9 m (29 ft 6 in)
Wing area: not available
Weight: production version, take-off 48 000 kg (105 800 lb); equipped empty 28 920 kg (63 760 lb)
Powerplant: four 3150-kg (6945-lb) st Pirna Type 014 turbojets
Performance: maximum speed (estimated) 920 km/h (572 mph); cruising speed 800 km/h (497 mph); range with 48 passengers 2500 km (1550 miles)
Payload: seats for 72 passengers; cargo payload not available
Crew: not available but probably 3
Production: probably one prototype

Top: The prototype BB-152. Nobody in the West ever saw the interior, but it was supposedly furnished to accommodate 72 passengers

CV-880, Convair

FIRST FLIGHT 1959

LIKE so many other fine civil transports the 880 owed its existence to the enthusiasm and almost limitless funds of the multimillionaire Howard Hughes, who was not only a talented pilot and aircraft engineer but also controller of various airlines, including TWA. In 1956 Hughes and TWA could see a market opening up for the first really modern, high-speed jetliner tailored for short/medium sectors common in the US.

Convair Division of General Dynamics had come to the end of the successful Convair-Liner family (the 240, 340 and 440 piston-engined short-haulers) with over 1000 delivered. They were just as eager to get into the jet business, whilst also studying Convair-Liner turboprop conversions as an interim source of business which later yielded the CV-580, 600 and 640. With assurance from Hughes of an order for TWA, the management in San Diego gave the go-ahead in September 1956 to the final refined design in a series of projects which had begun in early 1955 with aircraft similar to the 707 but slightly smaller and considerably lighter, with less fuel capacity. In collaboration with GE the studies were based on the CJ-805 civil version of the advanced J79 turbojet, almost as powerful as the Pratt & Whitney JT3C but less than three-quarters as heavy.

At first the Convair jet was called the Model 22 Skylark. Then it was named Golden Arrow, and as a gimmick all exterior parts were to have an anodized golden finish. Then it was again redesignated Convair 600, for 600 mph. Finally for some

Below: An 880 of Cathay Pacific; despite its excellent features the CV-880 failed to attract as many foreign sales as its competitors

Bottom: A Convair 880 in company livery. The first proposed name was Skylark; this was changed to Golden Arrow, and finally the name settled with CV-880

CV-880

Type: short/medium-range passenger transport
Maker: Convair Division of General Dynamics Corporation, San Diego
Span: 36.58 m (120 ft)
Length: 39.42 m (129 ft 4 in)
Height: 11.07 m (36 ft 4 in)
Wing area: 184.4 m² (1985 sq ft)
Weight: maximum 83 689 kg (184 500 lb); empty 38 238 kg (84 300 lb)
Powerplant: four 5080-kg (11 200-lb) st General Electric CJ-805-3 single-shaft turbojets (880M, 5284-kg [11 650-lb] CJ-805-3Bs)

Performance: economical cruising speed 895 km/h (556 mph); range with maximum payload (880M) 5150 km (3200 miles)
Payload: 9752 kg (21 500 lb); seats for up to 110 passengers
Crew: 3 to 4
Production: 65

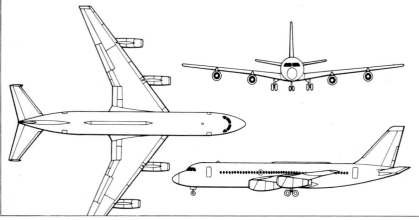

reason this was translated into its equivalent in feet per second, and it was rolled out in late 1958 as the Convair 880. By this time TWA and Delta had placed orders for 40, and during the flight test programme a further 25 were sold.

There were few controversial or risky features in the CV-880, which followed closely the engineering pioneered by the 707. The wing was swept at 35° and contained the fuel in integral tanks. The engines were hung on pylons well ahead and just below the wing, discharging through eight-lobed noise-suppressing nozzles with pointed centre-bodies and fitted with Rolls-Royce-style twin-clamshell reversers deflecting the jets out through lateral grilles. The trim bogie main gears folded inwards to lie in underfloor compartments. The body cross-section was egg-shaped.

FAA certification was obtained on May 1, 1960. By this time it was clear the whole programme had failed to attract sufficient orders to pay for development and tooling costs. The final 17 of the 65 sold were of the slightly stronger Model 31, or 880M type, with an extra centre-section tank to allow operation over longer stage-lengths.

Delta flew the first 880 services in late May 1960, and for the next 15 years got outstanding service. In an attempt to build on this programme they combined to build a bigger and faster derivative, the CV-990. The last CV-880 operator was Hong Kong's Cathay Pacific, whose 880Ms were withdrawn in 1975, and Air Malta, which still had two 880s in use in early 1980.

Above: An Indy Air Convair 880; the first operator of the type was Delta which received its order in January 1960

47

CV-990, Convair

FIRST FLIGHT 1961

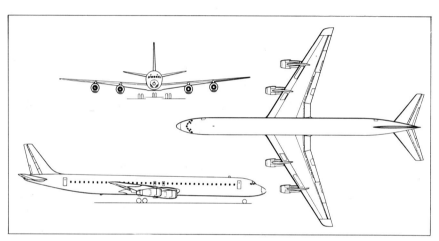

CV-990

Type: medium-range passenger transport
Maker: Convair Division of General Dynamics Corporation
Span: 36.58 m (120 ft)
Length: 42.43 m (139 ft 2½ in)
Height: 12.04 m (39 ft 6 in)
Wing area: 209 m² (2250 sq ft)
Weight: maximum 114 760 kg (253 000 lb); empty 54 840 kg (120 900 lb)
Powerplant: four 7280-kg (16 050-lb) st General Electric CJ-805-23C aft-fan turbofans
Performance: maximum cruising speed 990 km/h (615 mph); economical cruising speed 895 km/h (556 mph); range with maximum payload and reserves 6115 km (3800 miles)
Payload: 11 992 kg (26 440 lb); seats for 149 passengers in service with Spantax
Crew: 4
Production: 37

I N 1958 Convair Division of General Dynamics was keenly aware that it was failing to sell the technically successful Model 880 jetliner in the face of competition from Boeing and Douglas. Instead of accepting the situation and writing off its losses, the division did the natural thing and sought ways to make the 880 more competitive. The best answer appeared to be to fit more powerful and more efficient turbofan engines (then a completely new concept) and enlarge the airframe to seat over 100 passengers. As a further aid to sales an attempt was made to increase the cruising speed so that the new transport could be offered as the fastest in the world.

As before, there was a surprising lack of imagination in deciding what to call the new jetliner. At first it was announced in mid 1958 as the Model 30; then the designation Convair 600 (originally applied to the 880) and resurrected and finally the bold decision was taken to guarantee a cruising speed of 990 km/h (615 mph), reflected in the designation that was finally used, Model 990. Later the name Coronado, the area of Convair's home city of San Diego that had previously been used for the PB2Y wartime flying boat, was officially adopted.

Passenger accommodation was increased by simple stretching of the fuselage, both ahead of and behind the wing, with a few minor alterations to the structure and a large dorsal tunnel fairing for service lines and avionics aerials. The wing was increased in span and otherwise modified to increase area from 209 m² (2250 sq ft), and to

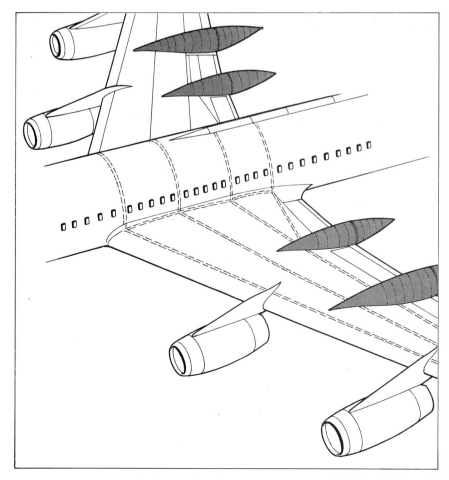

comply with the aerodynamic 'area rule' for minimum transonic drag four large bulges were added above the rear of the wing, projecting far behind the trailing edge. These shapes, variously called Whitcomb fairings (after the discoverer of the area rule), shock bodies or speed bumps, became a distinctive recognition feature and also housed extra fuel, supplementing the increased integral-tank fuel in the new wing. (Two such fairings were added to the wing of the British Victor 2 bomber at the same time.)

General Electric again provided the engines, which though having almost the same designation as on the CV-880 were in fact quite different in capability. Each CJ-805-23C comprised a CJ-805 turbojet with an aft-fan section added at the rear. This consisted of an additional free-running turbine with unique double-deck blades, the outer portions being fan blades working on fresh air in a large-diameter duct around the engine core. After much research it was decided to provide a full-length duct for this extra fan air, so that externally the pods look conventional. Though smoky at high power, the Dash-23C proved to be a reliable engine of much higher thrust and lower fuel consumption than the original plain turbojet. GE later used the same technique in turning the small CJ-610 turbojet into the CF-700 aft-fan for executive jets.

The 990 was underpinned by a launch order from American on July 30, 1958 and subsequently SAS, Swissair, Garuda and Varig placed small orders. During construction the flight-control system was finalized, the surfaces between the shock bodies being all-speed ailerons, with tabbed Fowler flaps inboard of the inner blisters and outboard of the outers as far as the outer engine wakes. Spoilers were added upstream of the flaps, the leading edge outboard of the inner pod pylons was arranged to droop, and the elevators were hinged to an all-moving powered tailplane. First flight took place on January 24, 1961 but it proved impossible at first to come near the guaranteed speeds. Convair faced two years of costly modification and flight-test, unrewarded by sales beyond the totally inadequate 37 already placed.

The first service of the CV-990 took place on March 9, 1962 when Swissair opened its Coronado service to Tokyo. American finally put the aircraft into service, still unable to meet guarantees, on March 18, 1962, on the New York to Chicago route, exacting penalties from Convair, and followed with the first fully modified 990A later that year.

Much harm had been done to the entire programme by this time, however, and leading airlines began to avoid the Convair product, even to the extent of cancelling orders – as in the case of SAS – and refusing to accept delivery – as with Varig.

To General Dynamics the 990 multiplied the failure of the 880 into one of the biggest corporate disasters of all time, with a loss of well over $450 000 000. Yet the fully modified 990A proved popular and capable, and today the Spanish holiday operator Spantax not only has all 14 now flying but intends to continue with them well into the 1980s.

Above: A Spantax Convair 990 at Ringway airport in June 1975. Among other operators were Modern Air Transport and Swissair
Above left: A Swissair CV-990. They named their transports Coronado after the area around San Diego, the home city of the Convair Division of General Dynamics
Left: A detail of the wing of the CV-990; the four blisters on the wing rear edges were added after problems with excessive drag. They gave increased cross-sectional area which helped fill in the total drag envelope of the aircraft. They were also useful as additional fuel tanks

VC10/Super VC10, BAC

FIRST FLIGHT 1962

IN the transition to the jet age the procurement of the British national intercontinental airline, BOAC, could hardly have been more uncertain and ill-conceived. Following the withdrawal of the Comet 1 and decision to transfer the Comet 2 to the RAF instead of allowing these excellent and reliable aircraft to fly with BOAC, the airline suffered an equipment shortage which could have been met by ordering the VC7, the proposed commercial version of the Vickers V.1000 military transport for the RAF. This impressive and carefully engineered long-range aircraft had swept wings and tail and scored over the contemporary early Boeing 707 in having the dramatically new Conway turbofan engine. Instead BOAC emphasized its complete disinterest in the whole project, finally resulting in

cancellation of the whole Vickers programme in November 1955.

Having ensured that Britain had no long-range jetliners, BOAC then began to study them and ordered the Boeing 707 in October 1956. Not content with this, it then insisted on the development of a British aircraft in the same class, the non-existent DH.118, similar to the VC7 and with the same engines. Fortunately this was never built, and Vickers put its own money into studies for jet versions of the turboprop Vanguard. BOAC had meanwhile decided it wanted a jet rather like a 707 but able to use shorter or hot/high airfields. On May 22, 1957, it announced that the VC10, one of the 'Vanjet' studies, best met its needs. In January 1958 it signed for 35, plus an option for 20 more.

Below: The BOAC Super VC10 G-ASGI which first flew in January 1966, received its certificate of airworthiness a month later and was delivered to BOAC on February 12, 1966. One Super VC10 achieved dubious fame when it was blown up at Dawsons Field, Jordan on September 12, 1970 by Palestinian terrorists

VC10

Type: long-range passenger/cargo transport
Maker: Vickers-Armstrongs (Aircraft); BAC
Span: (1100) 42.72 m (140 ft 2 in); (1101–1109) 44.55 m (146 ft 2 in)
Length: 48.36 m (158 ft 8 in)
Height: 12.04 m (39 ft 6 in)
Wing area: (1100–1101) 264.9 m² (2851 sq ft); (1102–1109) 272.8 m² (2936 sq ft)
Weight: maximum (civil) 142 430 kg (314 000 lb); (1109, RAF) 146 510 kg (323 000 lb); empty (typical) 66 670 kg (146 979 lb)
Powerplant: 4 Rolls-Royce

Conway 2-shaft turbofans, (civil) 9240-kg (20 370-lb) Conway 540s; (RAF) 9888-kg (21 800-lb) Conway 301s
Performance: maximum cruising speed 914 km/h (568 mph); economical cruising speed 886 km/h (550 mph); range with maximum payload and no reserves (civil) 8115 km (5040 miles); (RAF) 6275 km (3900 miles)
Payload: (civil, typical) 18 039 kg (39 769 lb); (RAF) 26 030 kg (57 400 lb); seats for up to 151 passengers
Crew: 3 to 5
Production: 32

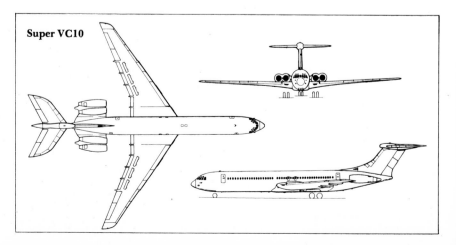

Super VC10

Under Sir George Edwards the Vickers team at Weybridge rapidly developed the Type 1100 (VC10) and flew the prototype on June 29, 1962. A complete new assembly hall was erected to handle the programme, with support from Hurn and other factories. The VC10 had a fuselage similar to that of a 707, but slightly shorter, with four powerful and efficient Conways hung on each side under the T-tail. The extremely efficient wing had slats, Fowler flaps and outboard ailerons, and a basic feature was the use of split control surfaces with each section driven by a separate power unit signalled by duplex autopilots each of which monitored the other. The result was system reliability so high that it was possible to guarantee no catastrophic failure more often than once in each 10 million flights, thus opening the way to automatic landing with autothrottle, autoflare and complete 'hands off' capability in conditions of zero visibility.

Thanks to more powerful Conways and a tremendous performance by Vickers (BAC from February 1960) it was possible to offer a Super VC10 with much greater capacity and transatlantic range. BOAC ordered ten on June 23, 1960 but then slashed the size of the Super, cut back its 35 or 55 original VC10s to only 12, then increased the Supers to 30 and then cut it again to 17. Meanwhile the original VC10 entered service on BOAC West African routes on April 29, 1964, by which time the order for 12 had virtually been completed. BAC also delivered VC10s to British United,

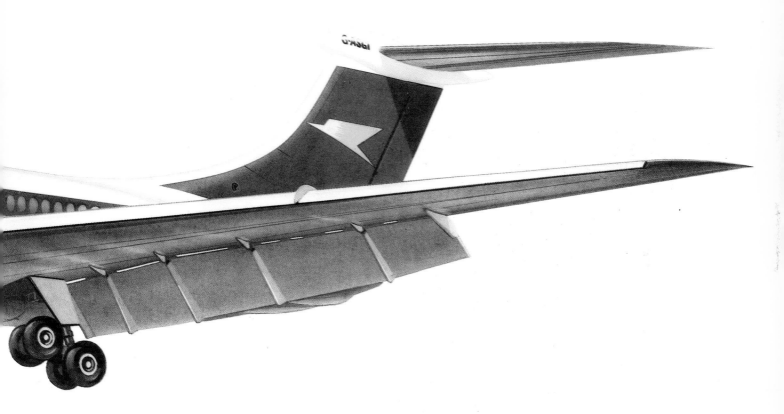

Super VC10

Type: long-range passenger transport (1154, passenger/cargo)
Maker: British Aircraft Corporation
Span: 44.55 m (146 ft 2 in)
Length: 52.32 m (171 ft 8 in)
Height: 12.04 m (39 ft 6 in)
Wing area: 272.4 m² (2932 sq ft)
Weight: maximum 151 950 kg (335 000 lb); empty (1151) 71 940 kg (158 594 lb)
Powerplant: four 9888-kg (21 800-lb) st Rolls-Royce Conway 550 2-shaft turbofans
Performance: maximum cruising speed 935 km/h (581 mph); economical cruising speed 886 km/h (550 mph); range with maximum payload and no reserves 7600 km (4720 miles)
Payload: (1151, passenger) 22 860 kg (50 406 lb); (1154, passenger/cargo) 27 360 kg (60 321 lb); seats for up to 187 passengers
Crew: 3 to 5
Production: 22

Left: Part of the cockpit of a British Airways Super VC10. Both the VC10 and the Super VC10 are popular with crew and passengers. The autothrottle, autoflare and duplex autopilots produce a very reliable aircraft which can be landed in very poor visibility

Laker, Ghana and the RAF, the latter type having the more powerful engines and fin fuel of the Super. The Type 1151 for BOAC (Super) was followed by five Model 1154s for East African. Other airlines showed great interest, but from 1966 BOAC did all it could to harm the British aircraft by criticizing it publicly, calling it 'grossly uneconomic' and demanding a government subsidy for having to operate it.

In fact the VC10 and Super VC10 proved to be superbly engineered and reliable aircraft, extremely popular with crews and the travelling public, and consistently operated at exceptionally high load factors – with very few empty seats. The first Super flew on May 7, 1964 and the type entered BOAC service on April 1, 1965. Like some of the standard VC10s the Super has extended Küchemann-type wingtips and a 4% chord extension on the leading edge inboard to give improved lift. The rear passenger door is aft of the wing, the fin is full of fuel and the rear cargo hold door is relocated on the right side. All four engines have thrust reversers, whereas on the VC10 only the outer engines are so equipped. The engines are of a later type than those of the VC10, and were the most powerful in commercial service until the advent of the Boeing 747 in 1970.

It has never been explained why BOAC, to whose exact requirements both the VC10 and Super VC10 were designed, and which never produced any evidence of technical or commercial shortcoming in either aircraft, should have decided to do all it could to harm the image of the type and

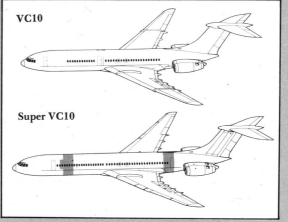

VC10

Super VC10

minimize its export success. Of course the basic BOAC requirement itself was shortsighted, because by the time the VC10 was in service the short runways for which it was designed had all, without exception, been extended at great expense to suit the more severe demands of the American jet transports.

In 1975 BOAC became the Overseas Division of British Airways, and phased out its 12 VC10s, the main second-hand customer being Gulf Air which used them for a further four years. Other standard VC10 aircraft went to British Caledonian, which used them briefly and sold one later to Air Malawi. The surviving 15 Super VC10s of British Airways Overseas Division were still in service in 1980, and there are no immediate plans for their retirement.

Left: The VC10 could carry 151 passengers with aircrew and cabin staff, while the Super VC10 was stretched to take 187 passengers and a similar crew. Engines were more powerful in the Super VC10 and there was an integral fuel tank in the fin. The Super was 13 ft longer than the standard model, two almost equal length sections being added as the colour shows, ahead of and aft of the wing

Top: A British Airways Super
VC10 in flight. The first
Super flew in May 1964
Above: Two of the four RCo
43 Mk 550 Conway turbofans
of Super VC10 G-ASGP
delivered to BOAC in
December 1968
Left: A Super VC10 is
prepared for its next flight.
The baggage and freight
holds are underfloor, fore and
aft of the wing

Trident, Hawker Siddeley

FIRST FLIGHT 1962

IN December 1956 the chairman of BEA announced that for the 1960s the main type to be used would be the efficient Vanguard turboprop, then lately ordered, but that 'a few short-haul jets' might be needed to meet competition. In 1957 BEA issued a specification for a short-haul jet (instead of doing what the French considered a more reasonable thing and buying Caravelles). By the summer of 1957 three main contenders had emerged, the Bristol 200, Avro 740 and de Havilland 121. All were advanced trijets with highly swept wings and tail matched to a cruising speed of 966 km/h (600 mph). At this point Britain had an extremely important and unexpected opportunity to capture the bulk of the enormous world market for a short-haul jet, the US companies being pre-occupied

with the large long-haul 707 and DC-8 and Lockheed having mistakenly built a turboprop. Had one of the three BEA contenders simply been tested against the world market and tailored to suit world demand it could hardly have failed to sell. However, a different story unfolded.

Perhaps the first mistake was government insistence that whoever won the BEA order had to merge with someone else. This ensured long delay, an atmosphere of acrimony and total diversion from the central business of getting the design right. Eventually, on February 12, 1958, the government authorized BEA to open contract negotiations with de Havilland, despite the fact that that company's merger plans had at that time proved either abortive or false (for example, the 'Airco'

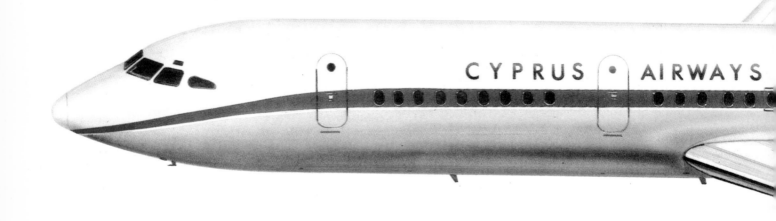

Trident 1

Type: short-range passenger transport
Maker: Hawker Siddeley Aviation
Span: 27.38 m (89 ft 10 in)
Length: 34.97 m (114 ft 9 in)
Height: 8.23 m (27 ft)
Wing area: 126.16 m² (1358 sq ft)
Weight: maximum 52 163 kg (115 000 lb); empty 30 618 kg (67 500 lb)
Powerplant: three 4468-kg (9850-lb) st Rolls-Royce Spey 505 2-shaft turbofans
Performance: typical high-speed cruise 948 km/h (589 mph); range with

maximum payload 1500 km (930 miles)
Payload: 9980 kg (22 000 lb); seats for up to 103 passengers
Crew: 3
Production: 24

Trident 1E

Specification similar to Trident 1 except in following particulars:
Span: 28.96 m (95 ft)
Wing area: 134.33 m² (1446 sq ft)
Weight: maximum 61 462 kg (135 500 lb); empty 32 432 kg (71 500 lb)
Powerplant: three 5170-kg (11 400-lb) st Rolls-Royce Spey 511-5 2-shaft turbofans
Performance: high-speed cruise 974 km/h (605 mph)
Payload: 11 415 kg (25 170 lb); seats for up to 140 passengers
Production: 15

Trident 2E

Type: short-range passenger transport
Maker: Hawker Siddeley Aviation
Span: 29.87 m (98 ft)
Length: 34.97 m (114 ft 9 in)
Height: 8.23 m (27 ft)
Wing area: 135.73 m² (1461 sq ft)
Weight: maximum 65 090 kg (143 500 lb); empty 33 203 kg (73 200 lb)
Powerplant: three 5411-kg (11 930-lb) st Rolls-Royce Spey 512-5W 2-shaft turbofans
Performance: typical high-speed cruise 974 km/h

(605 mph); range with maximum payload (space limited to 9697 kg [21 378 lb]) with full reserves 3910 km (2430 miles)
Payload: 12 156 kg (26 800 lb); seats for up to 149 passengers
Crew: 3
Production: 50

Left: The interior of a Trident 2; Trident development was dogged by interference not only from the government but also from the airlines themselves

Below: A Trident 2E in Cyprus Airways livery; other operators include the Chinese airline CAAC who have ordered 33

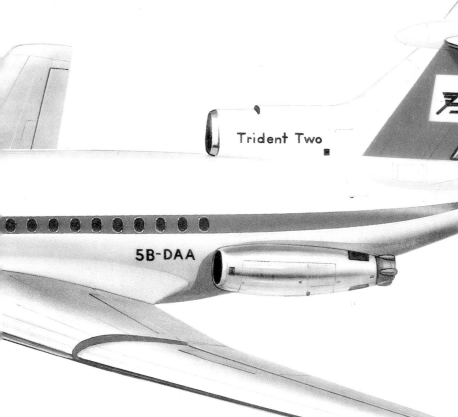

Trident Two

5B-DAA

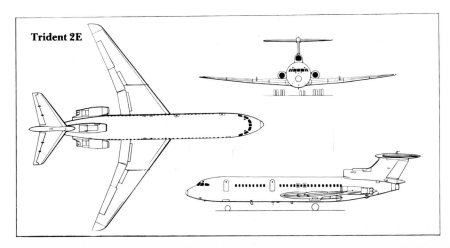

Trident 2E

Trident 3

Type: short-range passenger transport
Maker: Hawker Siddeley Aviation
Span: 29.87 m (98 ft)
Length: 39.98 m (131 ft 2 in)
Height: 8.61 m (28 ft 3 in)
Wing area: 138.7 m² (1493 sq ft)
Weight: maximum 68 040 kg (150 000 lb); empty (152-seat) 37 090 kg (81 778 lb)
Powerplant: three 5425-kg (11 960-lb) st Rolls-Royce Spey 512-5W 2-shaft turbofans, plus one 2381-kg (5250-lb) Rolls-Royce RB.162-86 booster turbojet

Performance: typical high-speed cruise 936 km/h (581 mph); range with maximum payload and full reserves 1761 km (1094 miles)
Payload: 15 296 kg (33 722 lb); seats for up to 180 passengers
Crew: 3
Production: 26

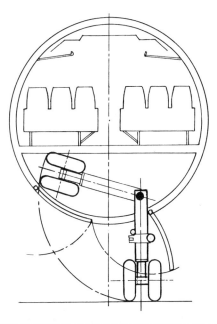

Far left: The interior of the cockpit of a Trident 2; of interest is the sign reading 'Cat 2 Fitted'. This indicates that the aircraft is fitted with Smith's Autoland system which allows landings in Category 2 weather and a 32.8 m (100 ft) decision height

Left: The nosegear of the Trident is unique among commercial aircraft in that it retracts sideways into the fuselage and in order to do this, is displaced 61 cm (2 ft) from the centreline
Below: An engineer checks the nosewheel of a Trident 2 with the landing light clearly visible

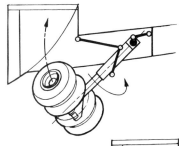

Left: The mainwheels of the Trident during retraction and when stowed in the wings. The two wheels with twin tyres turn through 90° as they are raised after take-off

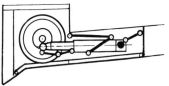

consortium of de Havilland, Fairey and Hunting).

A much more serious mistake was the decision of the BEA board in March 1959 to tear up the DH.121 design and replace it with one scaled down to carry fewer passengers over shorter distances. This threw away the RB.141 engine of 6350 kg (14 000 lb) thrust and at a stroke lost six months in timing while Rolls-Royce came up with a 4445 kg (9800 lb) engine, the RB.163 (later named Spey). De Havilland not only failed to fight the decision but instructed its marketing teams to cease talking to export customers until the BEA specification had been exactly settled.

Later in 1959 the Airco consortium was dissolved and the following year de Havilland joined the Hawker Siddeley Group. Boldly production was put in hand from the start against the BEA launch order for 24. The first Trident 1 flew at Hatfield on January 9, 1962. In all respects it was a very modern aircraft, with three turbofan engines at the rear, with noise-suppressing nozzles and reversers on the outer engines. Wing sweep was 35°, with drooping leading edges and double-slotted trailing-edge flaps. The Smiths autopilot drove the flight controls via a triplexed hydraulic system, one complete pressure system being energized by each engine so that in the event of any failure a 2:1 'majority vote' would ensure correct operation, giving enough reliability for automatic landing in blind conditions. The nose gear was mounted offset to the left and folded across to the right while the main gears had four tyres abreast on one leg, accommodated in neat bays.

Seating up to 103, but normally furnished for 88, the Trident 1 entered BEA service in March 1964. Another 15 aircraft designated Trident 1E were built for other customers, similar in size but with more powerful engines and wings of increased span with slatted leading edges and greater internal fuel capacity. By rearranging the interior and adding an extra emergency exit up to 139 passengers could be accommodated. Hawker Siddeley then planned a grossly stretched Mk 1F but instead the next main version was the 2E, again tailored solely for BEA and aimed at increased range with no change in payload. More powerful engines, the new wing of the 1E and further-increased fuel capacity was matched by structural strengthening and some weight-saving by using titanium instead of steel. BEA ordered 15 in August 1965, and the first flight took place on July 27, 1967. Called Trident Two by BEA, services began on April 18, 1968 with a 97-seat layout. Following trial services with four Mk 1E aircraft bought from Pakistan the Chinese airline CAAC ordered a major fleet consisting of 33 Trident 2Es.

Having insisted on de Havilland making the original design much smaller, BEA subsequently did all they could to make it larger, always handicapped by the small size and power of the Spey engine. After prolonged study with different engines Hawker Siddeley eventually found a way to stretch the fuselage to seat up to 180, without a major change of powerplant, by adding a small fourth engine as a booster for use only during take-off and initial climb. The resulting Trident 3 (Trident Three to BEA) has almost the same wing

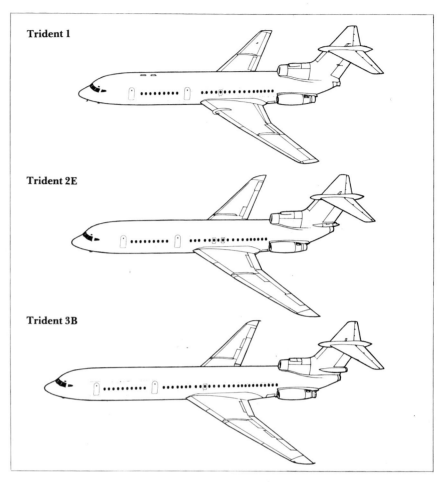

Trident 1

Trident 2E

Trident 3B

as the 2E but with slightly larger area, increased flap span and an increased incidence (angular setting relative to the fuselage), as well as the RB.162-86 boost jet immediately below the rudder and fed by side inlets normally sealed by power-actuated doors.

BEA ordered 26 Trident Threes, the first of which flew on December 11, 1969. Typically furnished for about 150 passengers, these aircraft entered service on April 1, 1971. Hawker Siddeley also developed a considerably more capable version, the 3B, with clearance to even higher weights and with greater fuel capacity, which offers outstanding all-round capability rivalling that of the competitor that stole virtually all the short-haul trijet market, the Boeing 727. By the time the 3B appeared there was virtually no market left, and the only sale was two to CAAC.

In service the Trident proved reasonably popular and trouble-free, though from the start it was handicapped by being smaller than the 727 and, in almost every case, needing a longer runway. Today it has even been outclassed in capability by the 737 and DC-9 twinjets, except in its final Mk 3 and 3B form. A further problem which severely hit BEA in 1977–79 was the discovery of fatigue cracks in wing structures which resulted in prolonged grounding, loss of revenue and remanufacture with a different outer wing imposing lower stresses than the efficient Küchemann streamwise tips of the long-range 2E and 3 as originally built.

In 1980 all operators had disposed of their Tridents except BEA and CAAC.

Above: The early Trident Mk 1 which could carry 88 passengers; the Trident 2E was stretched to carry 97 passengers and fitted with Smith's Autoland system; the Trident 3B has a Rolls-Royce RB.162 to supplement the Spey turbofans for improved performance
Right: A Rolls-Royce Spey engine on a Trident 3

Boeing 727

FIRST FLIGHT 1963

IN February 1956 Boeing began project studies aimed at defining a short/medium-range jet to partner the long-range 707. Just over a year later the British competition between the DH.121, Bristol 200 and Avro 740 showed that Boeing might actually be in a race, especially when PanAm showed genuine interest in the Bristol proposal in early 1958. Boeing remained unflappable and continued to refine the design for the world market until engineering drawings began to be issued in June 1959. Boeing announced the launch of the 727 on December 5, 1960, with orders for 40 each from Eastern and United. Boeing said it predicted a market for 300 but by 1980 it had sold nearly 1800, to make the 727 financially the biggest commercial programme in history.

In 1959 Lord Douglas, chairman of the British airline BEA, suggested to de Havilland that, as the DH.121 and 727 seemed to be so alike, the two companies should get together. Accordingly a large Boeing delegation visited Hatfield and saw everything on the 121; de Havilland then went to Seattle and saw very little of the 727. Had they studied the 727 it might have helped the future Trident, but the British aircraft was so tied to BEA that it had virtually no appeal to other customers.

The 727 at first appeared (quite erroneously) to be a crib of the Trident, especially after the side engines had been relocated further down the fuselage. The main differences were that the 727 was larger and more powerful, had more fuel capacity, slightly more efficient wings with a much better high-lift system (Krüger flaps inboard, slats outboard and triple-slotted flaps on the trailing edge), and auto manual reversion on the ailerons and elevators. Another unusual feature was the hydraulic stairway under the tail, though later this was often sealed shut or deleted in favour of conventional side doors. Main gears had only two tyres, though these are large and could be inflated to a low enough pressure for use from unpaved surfaces in some conditions. Great attention was paid to stopping on bad surfaces, with ground and flight spoilers and lift dumpers, reversers on all three engines and powerful anti-skid wheelbrakes.

The first off the production line, in United colours, flew on February 9, 1963. FAA certification was achieved on December 24, 1963. Eastern flew the first scheduled service on February 1, 1964, well ahead of the British Trident whose design had started in 1958. In fact the 727 was in service in Europe with Lufthansa in the same month the Trident went into regular service with BEA. Production continued to tick over at about 80 to 100 per year, while Boeing introduced a succession of improvements beginning with optional weight increases for the original version which was later designated 727-100. In 1964 Boeing announced the 100C (Cargo) with a large cargo door, strong floor and freight handling systems for switching in less than 2 hours between passenger or cargo or mixed operation. This was soon followed by the 100QC (Quick Change), which cut the time for conversion to 30 min.

In August 1965 Boeing announced the 200, with considerably longer fuselage seating up to 189

Below: A Boeing 727-100 of Ethiopia's national airline. The 727 has been sold to airlines throughout the world and with many features similar to the 707 it presented a relatively easy adaptation for 707 pilots

A Lufthansa 727 taxies before take-off. Lufthansa were the first European airline to operate the type and their order was a useful seal of approval for Boeing's worldwide sales promotion

Right: To achieve satisfactory short-field performance the 727 has a very advanced high-lift system with a triple-slotted flap, slatted leading edge and Krüger flaps
1 Flap rails mounted below wing; 2 Flap carriage; 3 Flap screwjack; 4 Main flap; 5 Fore flap (slot develops as main flap moves rearward); 6 Aft flap (driven down its own curved rails by pulley/cable in main flap; 7 Flap rail fairings; 8 Slatted leading edge; 9 Curved rails for 8; 10 Hydraulic jack for 8

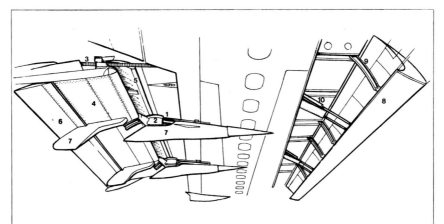

Top: A Dan-Air Boeing 727 with the unique Compass insignia on the tail fin
Right: The massive yet efficient Boeing production line at Seattle with 727-100s at various stages of construction
Left: The complex interior of the cockpit of a Lufthansa 727 which has a useful degree of commonality with the 707

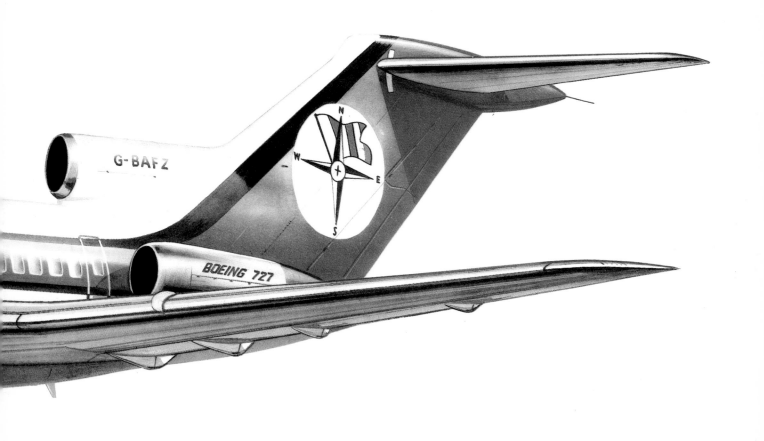

Boeing 727-100

Type: short/medium-range passenger and cargo transport
Maker: Boeing Commercial Airplane Company
Span: 32.92 m (108 ft)
Length: 40.59 m (133 ft 2 in)
Height: 10.36 m (34 ft)
Wing area: 157.9 m² (1700 sq ft)
Weight: maximum (early production) 72 575 kg (160 000 lb); (later) 76 655 kg (169 000 lb); empty (early) 39 734 kg (87 600 lb); (100C) 41 322 kg (91 100 lb)
Powerplant: 3 Pratt & Whitney JT8D 2-shaft turbofans; originally 6350-kg (14 000-lb) st JT8D-1s, later option of 6577-kg (14 500-lb) JT8D-9s
Performance: maximum cruising speed 974 km/h (605 mph); economical cruising speed 917 km/h (570 mph); range with maximum payload and reserves 3058 km (1900 miles)
Payload: varying from 13 154 kg (29 000 lb) for early deliveries to 15 649 kg (34 500 lb) at higher weight and to 19 958 kg (44 000 lb) for all-cargo 100C; seats for up to 131 passengers
Crew: 3
Production: (100) 407; (100C and QC) 164

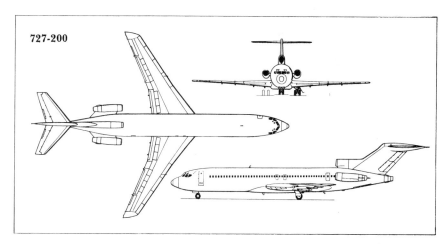

727-200

Boeing 727-200

Type: short/medium-range passenger and cargo transport
Maker: Boeing Commercial Airplane Company
Span: 32.92 m (108 ft)
Length: 46.69 m (153 ft 2 in)
Height: 10.36 m (34 ft)
Wing area: 157.9 m² (1700 sq ft)
Weight: maximum originally 83 820 kg (184 800 lb), (Advanced 200) 86 405 kg (190 500 lb), current production 95 027 kg (209 500 lb); empty originally 44 271 kg (97 600 lb), (Advanced) 44 815 kg (98 800 lb), current

production 46 266 kg (102 000 lb)
Powerplant: standard fitting, three 6577-kg (14 500-lb) st Pratt & Whitney JT8D-9A 2-shaft turbofans; customer option of 7031-kg (15 500-lb) JT8D-15s, 7258-kg (16 000-lb) JT8D-17s or JT8D-17Rs with special emergency rating of 7893 kg (17 400 lb)
Performance: maximum cruising speed 953 km/h (592 mph); economical cruising speed 917 km/h (570 mph); range with payload of 18 144 kg (40 000 lb) and full reserves, originally 2685 km (1670 miles), (Advanced) 2970 km

(1845 miles), current aircraft 3966 km (2464 miles)
Payload: structurally limited to 18 144 kg (40 000 lb); seats for up to 189 passengers
Crew: 3
Production: 1300 by 1980

passengers. Thanks to progressive increases in thrust offered by Pratt & Whitney, Boeing was able to offer not only this version but also, in 1970, the Advanced 727 with a considerable increase in weights and fuel capacities, noise-suppressing engines, a revised passenger interior and improved systems. Features include overhead-duct air-conditioning, large 'carry-all' above floor compartments and – despite use of a simple Sperry single-channel autopilot, not offering the fail-safe philosophy of the British autoland systems – certification in runway visibility of 213 m (700 ft) with only 15 m (50 ft) decision height.

In its first year of operation the 727 suffered a series of often fatal accidents, but it was soon clear these were in almost all cases due to laxity in

letting airspeed bleed off too much on the approach, resulting in a lethal sink rate that could not be arrested by full power. Once pilots learned to fly more precisely 'by the book' this kind of landing was eliminated, and it was soon evident that the 727 was not only as safe as any other aircraft but also an outstandingly versatile, efficient and profitable vehicle. In 1973 Boeing began to study stretched and much heavier 727-300 versions with the refanned JT8D-209 engine but decided not to build this and instead to go ahead in 1978 with the completely redesigned 757. In early 1977 Boeing offered a 200C convertible version of the Advanced which added a small and possibly final push to an amazing sales record reaching nearly 1800 in 1980.

Top left: An Air France Boeing 727-200. 727s suffered a series of accidents in landing before pilots learned how to fly more precisely by the book
Top right: The tail of a 727 showing the air stair similar to the Caravelle
Above: Two Boeing 727-100s in Braniff International colours preparing for another flight

One-Eleven, BAC

FIRST FLIGHT 1963

IN commercial terms the most successful pure jet civil aircraft yet produced by the UK is the British Aerospace One-Eleven. It began life as the design child of a now defunct company, was finalized and brought into production as the progeny of a second company, is now handled by British Aerospace, and is destined finally to be taken over by a Romanian concern.

What is now the One-Eleven stems from the H.107 design study by the Hunting Aircraft Company for a small airliner capable of carrying 48 passengers over a range of 1609 km (1000 miles). Even at this early stage, the design had features that characterize the One-Eleven: a low-set wing of only moderate sweep, a T-tail, and two pod-mounted rear engines in the manner pioneered by the Sud-Aviation Caravelle.

In 1960 the Hunting company was absorbed into the newly formed British Aircraft Corporation, and further development of the basic design was undertaken by the former Hunting and Vickers teams, in Luton and Weybridge respectively. By 1961 it was clear that likely customers would prefer a slightly larger aircraft: the design was thus recast with two Rolls-Royce Spey turbofans in place of the earlier pair of BS.61 or BS.75 turbofans, and seating for 65 five-abreast rather than 48 four-abreast, with typical stage length reduced to 966 km (600 miles). In this revised form the design became the BAC One-Eleven, scheduled for autumn 1964.

With the first batch of 20 aircraft under construction, the promise of the aircraft received its first reward with an order for ten aircraft placed by

British United Airways in May 1961. The first aircraft, to be retained by BAC as a test and demonstration machine, made its maiden flight on August 20, 1963, by which time the basic design had been amended to incorporate seating for up to 79 passengers, and orders had increased to 60. Further confirmation of the One-Eleven's basic potential followed with orders from Braniff and Mohawk in the USA, and finally with the securing of an order for 15 aircraft, with options on a further 15, by American Airlines, one of the 'big four' US domestic companies.

Considerable trouble was experienced during early test flying, the first One-Eleven being destroyed and its crew killed in a crash on October 22, 1963. The cause was ascertained to be a 'deep stall' resulting from the rear-engine and T-tail configuration; fortunately, though, the remedy was found in the relatively simple stick-pusher device to prevent an excessive wing angle of attack. The frankness with which BAC discussed the problem with all interested parties did much to alleviate the possible consequences of the crash and to prevent other designers from encountering the same problem inadvertently.

The first production model was the One-Eleven Series 200, of which 56 were eventually built. This was powered by the 4686-kg (10 330-lb) Spey 506 turbofan, and it received its full certificate of airworthiness on April 6, 1965, allowing BUA to begin scheduled services with the One-Eleven on April 9. The US Federal Aviation Administration's Type Approval was received on April 15, 1965,

Above: A British Airways One-Eleven coming in to land. Intended as a replacement for the Viscount, this aircraft is popular with pilots and passengers alike

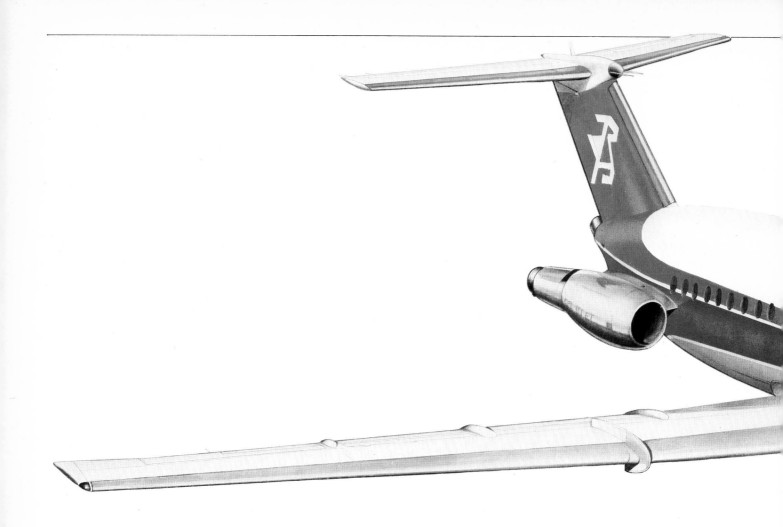

allowing Braniff to begin services on April 25.

The Series 300, of which only nine were built, featured 5171-kg (11 400-lb) Spey 511 engines, extra fuel capacity and maximum weight boosted by 6124 kg (13 500 lb) to 39 463 kg (87 000 lb). Basically similar was the Series 400, designed specifically to meet American requirements, with a large proportion of American equipment. The first of the series, to meet the American Airlines' order, took to the air on July 13, 1965 and was granted its FAA Type Approval on November 22, 1965.

BAC had by this time realized that the basic potential of the One-Eleven could be better used in a 'stretched' version, whose full development began with the receipt of an order for such a Series 500 from British European Airways. The initial Series 400 airframe was modified to serve as the prototype: the fuselage was lengthened by 4.11 m (13 ft 6 in), the wings increased in span by 1.52 m (5 ft), and 5443-kg (12 000-lb) Spey 512-14 turbofans were fitted. The result was a passenger capacity of 97, later increased to the present 119 when higher weights were permitted. This prototype first flew on June 30, 1967, with the initial production machine flying on February 7, 1968. In the definitive form, the Series 500 aircraft are powered by the Spey 512–14DW turbofans with water injection, and production totalled 80.

The final British model of the One-Eleven is the Series 475, a hybrid with the fuselage of the Series 400 mated to the wings and powerplant of the Series 500, to produce an aircraft suitable for 'hot and high' operations. Nine of this model were built.

On May 31, 1979, British Aerospace, which succeeded the British Aircraft Corporation on January 1, 1978, after the nationalization of the British aircraft industry, pulled off a somewhat remarkable aeronautical coup: the transfer of the entire production of One-Elevens to the Grupul Aeronautici Bucuresti, a state-run Romanian industrial consortium. In 1981 British Aerospace are to hand over to the Romanian government two Series 500 and one Series 487 aircraft (the latter being a freight carrier derived from the Series 475) as the start of a programme in which the production of 25 One-Elevens will gradually be switched to Romania by 1985. The 23rd aircraft will be the first wholly Romanian aircraft, of which about 80 are likely to be built at the rate of some six per year.

Top: A BAC One-Eleven Series 500 in the livery of Cyprus Airways, one of the aircraft's most recent customers
Above: A pilot runs a routine check on his instrument panel. There was cause for concern when the first One-Eleven crashed on October 22, 1963, due to a 'deep stall' resulting from the rear engine and the T-tail configuration. The problem was solved, however, by a simple stick-pusher device triggered by any excessive angle of attack and this helped other manufacturers avoid the problem

One-Eleven Series 500

Type: short- and medium-range passenger transport
Maker: British Aerospace Aircraft Group
Span: 28.5 m (93 ft 6 in)
Length: 32.61 m (107 ft)
Height: 7.47 m (24 ft 6 in)
Wing area: 95.78 m² (1031 sq ft)
Weight: maximum 47 401 kg (104 500 lb); empty 24 454 kg (53 911 lb)
Powerplant: two 5693-kg (12 550-lb) st Rolls-Royce RB.163 Spey Mk 512-14DW turbofans
Performance: maximum cruising speed 871 km/h (541 mph) at 6401 m (21 000 ft); range with typical payload and reserves 2744 km (1705 miles)
Payload: 12 288 kg (27 089 lb); seats for up to 119 passengers
Crew: 2
Production: 84

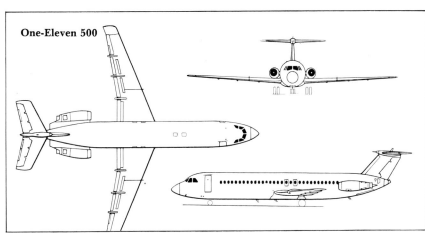

One-Eleven 500

One-Eleven Series 200

Specification similar to Series 500 except in following:
Span: 26.97 m (88 ft 6 in)
Length: 28.5 m (93 ft 6 in)
Wing area: 93.18 m² (1003 sq ft)
Weight: maximum 35 833 kg (79 000 lb); empty 21 049 kg (46 405 lb)
Powerplant: two 4686-kg (10 330-lb) st Rolls-Royce Spey Mk 506 turbofans
Performance: range with typical payload and reserves 1410 km (875 miles)
Payload: 8661 kg (19 095 lb); seats for up to 89 passengers
Production: 56

One-Eleven Series 300

Specification similar to Series 500 except in following:
Span: 26.97 m (88 ft 6 in)
Length: 28.5 m (93 ft 6 in)
Wing area: 93.18 m² (1003 sq ft)
Weight: maximum 40 143 kg (88 500 lb); empty 22 100 kg (48 722 lb)
Powerplant: two 5171-kg (11 400-lb) st Rolls-Royce Spey Mk 511 turbofans
Performance: range with typical payload and reserves 2300 km (1430 miles)
Payload: 10 105 kg (22 278 lb); 89 passengers
Production: 9

One-Eleven Series 400

Specification similar to Series 500 except in following:
Span: 26.97 m (88 ft 6 in)
Length: 28.5 m (93 ft 6 in)
Wing area: 93.18 m² (1003 sq ft)
Weight: maximum 40 143 kg (88 500 lb); empty 22 493 kg (49 587 lb)
Powerplant: two 5171-kg (11 400-lb) st Rolls-Royce Spey Mk 511 turbofans
Performance: range with typical payload and reserves 2300 km (1430 miles)
Payload: 9713 kg (21 413 lb); seats for up to 89 passengers
Production: 70

One-Eleven Series 475

Specification similar to Series 500 except in following particulars:
Length: 28.5 m (93 ft 6 in)
Weight: maximum 44 678 kg (98 500 lb); empty 23 465 kg (51 731 lb)
Powerplant: two 5693-kg (12 550-lb) st Rolls-Royce Spey Mk 512 DW turbofans
Performance: range with typical payload and reserves 3000 km (1865 miles)
Payload: 9647 kg (21 269 lb); seats for up to 89 passengers
Production: 9

One-Eleven 670

1 Radome
2 Weather radar scanner
3 Radar scanner mounting
4 Pressure bulkhead
5 Windscreen panels
6 Windscreen wipers
7 Instrument panel shroud
8 Rudder pedals
9 Nose equipment bay
10 Cockpit floor level
11 Control column
12 Pilot's seat
13 Co-pilot's seat
14 Cockpit roof construction
15 Supernumerary crew seat
16 Cockpit bulkhead
17 Radio rack
18 Right galley
19 Cockpit door
20 Left galley
21 Forward entry door
22 Entry door handle
23 Wing icing inspection light
24 Nosewheel doors
25 Twin nosewheels
26 Retractable airstairs
27 Folding handrail
28 Entry lobby
29 Cabin attendants folding seats
30 Right service door
31 Cabin bulkhead
32 Wardrobe
33 Communications aerials
34 Forward cabin seating
35 Window panel skin doubler plate
36 Freight hold door
37 Forward freight hold
38 Fuselage frame and stringer construction
39 ADF loop aerials
40 Floor beam support structure
41 Air-conditioning distribution ducting
42 Forward/centre fuselage joint frame
43 Front wing spar main frame
44 Ventral air-conditioning plant
45 Left emergency exit
46 Wing centre-section fuel tank
47 Seat rail support beams
48 Right emergency exit window
49 Fuselage skin plating
50 Wing fence
51 Leading-edge de-icing air duct
52 Right wing fuel tanks
53 Right navigation lights
54 Extended wingtip
55 Static dischargers
56 Right aileron
57 Aileron tab
58 Aileron hinge control mechanism
59 Spoilers open position
60 Spoiler jacks
61 Flap screw jacks and gearboxes
62 Flap track fairings
63 Right outboard slotted flaps, open position
64 Aerial cable
65 Cabin window trim panels
66 Rear wing spar main frame
67 Cabin floor panels
68 Centre/rear fuselage joint frame
69 Right three-abreast passenger seats
70 Overhead luggage lockers
71 Passenger overhead service unit
72 Fresh air delivery duct
73 Rail type aerial
74 Right engine nacelle
75 Cabin rear bulkhead
76 Right toilet
77 Rear entry door
78 Aft pressure bulkhead
79 Ejector cowl, closed
80 Eight-lobe exhaust nozzle
81 Fin leading-edge de-icing
82 Fin construction
83 VOR aerial
84 Twin pitot tubes
85 Tailplane bullet fairing
86 Tailplane trimming screw jack
87 Right tailplane
88 Static dischargers
89 Elevator tab
90 Right elevator
91 Communications aerial
92 Elevator control rods
93 Tail navigation light
94 Left aileron tabs
95 Left aileron construction
96 De-icing air outlet louvres
97 Tailplane construction
98 Leading-edge de-icing
99 Rudder upper hinge
100 Rudder construction
101 Hydraulic rudder jacks
102 APU exhaust duct

103 Auxiliary power unit (APU)
104 Fireproof bulkhead
105 Fin mounting sloping frames
106 Engine nacelle pylon
107 Ejector cowl, open position
108 Cowl screw jack
109 Eight-lobe exhaust nozzle
110 Thrust reverser cascades
111 Reverser operating jacks
112 Rear ventral airstairs
113 Detachable engine cowlings
114 Engine bleed air ducting
115 Rolls-Royce Spey 25 Mk 512-14DW turbofan engine
116 Engine accessories
117 Engine mounting frame
118 Fire extinguisher bottles
119 Wash basin
120 Left toilet compartment
121 Engine intake
122 Left two-abreast passenger seats
123 Window panels
124 Rear freight hold
125 Trailing-edge root fillet
126 Hydraulic reservoir
127 Flap operating motor and gearbox
128 Main undercarriage wheel well
129 Undercarriage retraction linkage
130 Main undercarriage pivot mounting
131 Automatic ground spoiler
132 Inboard slotted flap
133 Flap track fairings
134 Flaps down position
135 Flap shroud construction
136 Outboard flight spoilers
137 Flap guide rails
138 Aileron hinge control mechanism
139 Aileron tab
140 Left aileron
141 Static dischargers
142 Extended wingtip construction
143 Left navigation lights
144 Leading-edge construction
145 Front spar
146 Fuel system piping
147 Centre spar
148 Left wing integral fuel tank
149 Rear spar
150 Wing fence/leading-edge fillet
151 Machined wing skin panels
152 Main undercarriage leg strut
153 Automatic wheel brakes
154 Twin mainwheels
155 Leading-edge de-icing air duct
156 Wing attachment joint strap
157 Wing root ventral fairing

Above: A Gulf Air One-Eleven. In 1976 this airline was operating four Series 400 aircraft

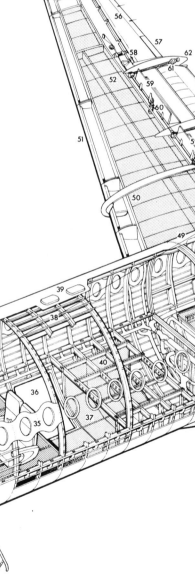

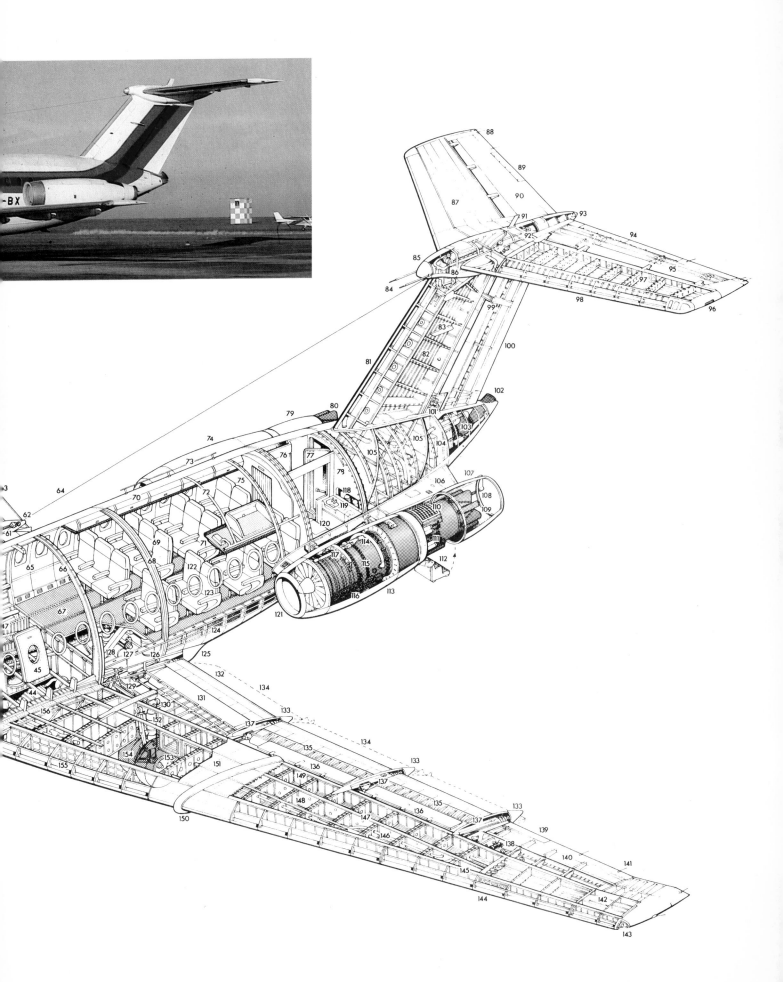

DC-9, McDonnell Douglas

FIRST FLIGHT 1965

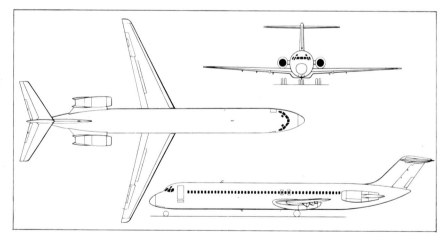

THE McDonnell Douglas DC-9 is the world's best-selling twin-jet airliner, and was the last civil transport designed exclusively by the former Douglas Aircraft Corporation. Designed to meet much the same requirement as the Sud-Aviation Caravelle and BAC One-Eleven, the DC-9 had the considerable advantage of being a later design. This gave it a performance edge over the Caravelle and greater growth potential than the One-Eleven (the latter being limited by its Spey turbofan engines). In addition, the fact that it was earlier than the comparable Boeing 737 allowed the type to enter service and prove itself before the slightly more advanced 737 entered the field.

The DC-9 which emerged in 1965 after a very prolonged gestatory period was in many respects closely akin to the One-Eleven. However, since the early 1950s Douglas had examined a number of different types and configurations under this designation. The original concept had been for a medium-range aircraft to partner the long-range DC-8: with a passenger capacity about two-thirds that of the DC-8, this prospective DC-9 was to have been a four-engined aircraft very similar to the unsuccessful Convair 880. Airline response was lukewarm in the extreme, and during the mid and late 1950s Douglas studied a considerable number of configuration and requirement options in consultation with prospective buyers. By the early 1960s Douglas were close to defining their new aircraft. With the long-range market catered for by the Boeing 707 and the DC-8, and the medium-range bracket filled by the Boeing 727, the new

airliner was to be the main American contender in the short-range field, hitherto dominated by European jet aircraft. Douglas were quick to appreciate that the failings of European short-haul aircraft were several: in the main these were lack of airfield autonomy, comfort, speed and low operating costs compared with the long-range airliners of the period. The definitive DC-9, therefore, had an auxiliary power unit for independence from airfield facilities, built-in airstairs, five-abreast seating, good short-field performance, and the ability to accommodate large freight items. The freight capacity of the original DC-9-10, for example, is 1.6 times that of the Caravelle.

The DC-9 which Douglas announced on April 8, 1963 was in many ways similar to the One-Eleven:

DC-9 Series 50

Type: short- and medium-range passenger transport
Maker: Douglas Aircraft Co
Span: 28.47 m (93 ft 5 in)
Length: 40.72 m (133 ft 7¼ in)
Height: 8.53 m (28 ft)
Wing area: 92.97 m² (1001 sq ft)
Weight: maximum 54 885 kg (121 000 lb); empty 28 069 kg (61 880 lb)
Powerplant: two 7258-kg (16 000-lb) st Pratt & Whitney JT8D-17 turbofans
Performance: maximum cruising speed 929 km/h (577 mph) at 8230 m (27 000 ft); range with 97 passengers, baggage and reserves 3326 km (2067 miles)
Payload: 15 617 kg (34 430 lb); seats for up to 139 passengers
Crew: 2
Production: 972 ordered by 1980

Above: A DC-9-14 operated by the Spanish airline, Spantax. Formed in October 1959 to provide support for oil-prospecting companies, Spantax now provides inclusive tour service to Spain from all parts of Europe
Left: A DC-9-32 in the livery of Air Canada

twin pod-mounted rear turbofans, a high T-tail, and a wing of only moderate sweep. But the company had learned from its somewhat troubled customer response to the DC-8: the DC-9 was planned to be capable of ready adaptation and modification to meet a wide variety of customer requirements, and this was to prove one of the most important factors in the success of the DC-9.

At the time of the Douglas announcement the company had received no firm orders for its new type. In May 1963, however, Delta Air Lines placed an order for 15 DC-9s, with another 15 on option. Work on the first example progressed smoothly, but orders for only 58 aircraft had been received by the time of the first DC-9's initial flight on February 25, 1965. Largely responsible for this disappointing start was the severe airline recession of the period. During 1965 the position improved radically, and by the time that the DC-9 entered service with Delta on December 8, 1965, another 170 DC-9s had been ordered. The success of the DC-9 development programme is attested by the record speed with which the Federal Aviation Administration's Type Approval was secured, the approval being granted on November 23.

The initial production model was the DC-9-10 series, of which 137 were eventually built. High-density passenger accommodation for 90 is possible: with 5443-kg (12000-lb) Pratt & Whitney JT8D-5 turbofans maximum take-off weight is 35244 kg (77700 lb), rising to 41141 kg (90700 lb) with 6350-kg (14000-lb) JT8D-1 or -7 engines. The DC-9-15 was available in two convertible cargo/

passenger layouts, with the higher-powered engines.

Douglas were quick to capitalize on their foresight in designing the DC-9 with considerable 'stretchability' and engines of great growth potential: first to require such an aircraft were Eastern Air Lines, and after a short period with the designation Series 20, the initial stretched model became the definitive Series 30, of which 654 have been ordered. The value of designing the DC-9 round a basically too powerful powerplant, necessitating the use of derated units in the initial Series 10 aircraft, was here revealed. With the relaxation of the FAA's restriction on economically desirable two-man flight crews to aircraft with a maximum take-off weight of less than 36288 kg (80000 lb), Douglas were able to increase the DC-9's capabilities by the relatively simple expedient of 'stretching' the airframe. After an interim fuselage stretch of 2.9 m (9 ft 6 in), Douglas and Eastern settled on a fuselage growth of 4.57 m (15 ft), increasing seating capacity to 115. To keep airfield requirements as low as possible despite increased take-off weight, wing span was also increased by 1.22 m (4 ft) to 28.5 m (93 ft 5 in). The first DC-9-30 flew on August 1, 1966, and the new model entered service in February 1967. Early models were powered by 6350-kg (14000-lb) JT8D-7 engines and had a maximum take-off weight of 44453 kg (98000 lb), while the DC-9-34 has a gross weight of 54885 kg (121000 lb) and is powered by 7258-kg (16000-lb) JT8D-17 turbofans. Two models of the basic mark are available with

Above: The 'friendly smile' of an Air Florida DC-9 photographed at Miami

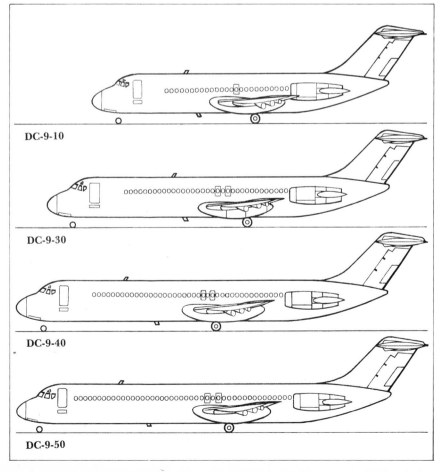

DC-9-10

DC-9-30

DC-9-40

DC-9-50

Left: Side elevations showing the fuselage stretch in the DC-9. As the demand for airliners with increased passenger capacity grew, McDonnell Douglas was forced to lengthen the DC-9 fuselage in order to accommodate more seats

Above: One of the colourful DC-9s operated by Hughes Airwest

convertible passenger/freight or all-freight configurations.

The designation Series 20 was thus taken over by the third basic sub-model, designed specifically for short-field operations. Production was only ten, all for Scandinavian Airlines System. The DC-9-20s have the fuselage of the Series 10, the wings of the Series 30, complete with full-span leading-edge slats, and 6577-kg (14 500-lb) JT8D-11 turbofans; and the model entered service in January 1969.

The next basic model was the Series 40, also produced to meet an SAS requirement for a short-range transport of high capacity. In high-density configuration, the Series 40 can seat up to 125 passengers in a fuselage stretched by another 1.88 m (6 ft 2 in) to 38.27 m (125 ft 7 in). The specialized nature of the model, combined with a range of only 1078 km (670 miles) with a payload of 16 493 kg (36 360 lb), kept orders down to 71.

The penultimate development of the DC-9 is the Series 50 combining the Series 30 wing with yet another stretched fuselage, nearly 30% longer than that of the DC-9-10 and capable of accommodating up to 139 passengers. Like all models of DC-9 it had an extremely high fuel capacity, enabling the aircraft to fly several stages without refuelling. Despite increased weight and drag, the use of the 7257-kg (16 000-lb) JT8D-17 gives the Series 50 aircraft a useful range with maximum payload. Orders total 93, and the model entered service on August 24, 1975 with Swissair, the airline which originated the requirement for the type and also sponsored the later DC-9 Super 80.

Left: A McDonnell Douglas DC-9 Series 50 in flight. Ghana Airways was formed on July 4, 1958 and became entirely state-owned on February 14, 1961, when the government bought the remaining 40% of the shares held by BOAC

Left and right: The Pratt & Whitney JT8D turbofans used on the DC-9. The JT8D-17 develops 7258 kg (16 000 lb) of thrust and in addition to the DC-9, it also powers later models of the Boeing 727 and 737. This type of engine is the commonest on the world's airliners with over 9000 in use

Boeing 737

FIRST FLIGHT 1967

WITH 792 orders to its credit, the Boeing 737 is currently the world's fastest-selling twin-jet airliner, a surprising fact in view of the late start made into the short-haul market by this 'baby' of the Boeing airliner family. Prompted by the relative sales success of the BAC One-Eleven and the Douglas DC-9, Boeing announced its intention of building the 737 on February 19, 1965, at the same time revealing an order for 21 such aircraft placed by Lufthansa. It is interesting to note that when Boeing took the decision in November 1964, the One-Eleven was only five months away from service entry, and the DC-9 would take to the air for the first time in a mere three months.

To save time, design effort and production difficulties, the Boeing design team sensibly opted to use as many components of the 727 – already in production – as possible. The 727 also shares great commonality with the 707, and so the 737 has several features in common with its predecessors: for example, fuselage structure, doors, various panels, ceilings and seats. The engines are basically those of the 727, with the same thrust reversers, starters and forward nacelles, but Boeing decided on a configuration with podded underwing engines rather than the rear-engine layout of the One-Eleven and DC-9. Other differences between the earlier aircraft and the 737 were the latter's fuselage-mounted tailplane and six-abreast seating in the wide fuselage inherited from the 707 and 727. The wide fuselage, despite the portly appearance it gives to the relatively short airframe, has benefits other than structural commonality with the type's predecessors. It allows Boeing-equipped airlines to standardize on internal fittings such as seats, WCs and galleys; it gives considerable internal spaciousness; and it allows the easy accommodation of freight in the holds under the floor forward and aft of the wing. It is worth noting that Boeing's original concept was for an aircraft with a maximum passenger capacity of 85. Lufthansa held out for 100-seat capability, and Boeing finally acceded to produce a design for a 737 capable of carrying 100 passengers over a range of 1127 km (700 miles) at a maximum take-off weight of 38 531 kg (84 950 lb) on the power of two 6350-kg (14 000-lb) Pratt & Whitney JT8D-1 turbofan engines.

Once the decision had been made, Boeing moved with its usual speed: the first 737, a company demonstration model, flew on April 9, 1967; the first 737-100 initial production model for Lufthansa, flew a month later; and the first 737-200 stretched model for United Air Lines, flew on August 8, 1967. Federal Aviation Administration Type Approval of the two production models was secured on December 15 and 21, 1967, respectively. The 737-200 series stemmed from the demand by most potential customers for increased passenger capacity, though the 737-100 ordered by Lufthansa could carry up to 115.

The 737-200 was designed largely round the requirements of United Air Lines, and was announced on April 5, 1965, with the revealing of United's order for 40 of the new model. The fuselage was stretched by 1.83 m (6 ft) to provide a high-density capacity of 130. Power was provided

in early examples by the 6350-kg (14 000-lb) JT8D-1 turbofans, allowing a maximum take-off weight of 43 999 kg (97 000 lb) compared with the 44 362 kg (97 800 lb) of the 737-100 on the same power. With the 7031-kg (15 500-lb) JT8D-15s, however, later production 737-200 models have a maximum take-off weight of 52 390 kg (115 500 lb).

Total sales of the 737-100 were only 30, but though sales of the 737-200 were relatively slow Boeing was convinced that in the later model it had a highly effective short-haul aircraft, if only the airlines could be persuaded of this by the success of early models and Boeing's development of other variants. The first of these was the 737-200C convertible passenger/freight model first flown in September 1968 and in service within four months.

Above: The laser-like effect of a photograph taken at night using an extremely long exposure time. The streaks of light are caused by the lights of service vehicles moving around the Lufthansa 737-100

Far left and left: A Lufthansa 737 taking off. Lufthansa was the first airline to place orders for this 'baby' of the Boeing family

The 737-200C was closely akin to the 727-100C, with a large side-loading freight door to allow the easy loading of standard pallets.

Boeing still felt that customers could be attracted in large numbers if certain failings in the basic model were remedied. These failings centred on lack of fuel economy and range resulting from too high a drag co-efficient, and on poor landing performance as a result of inefficient thrust reversers and inadequate flaps. These failings were redressed by improvements to the wings and flaps, and the provision of new thrust reversers from aircraft number 135 onwards, with modification kits for earlier aircraft should the owner require such.

These modifications were supplemented in 1969 by alterations to the wing leading-edge slats and

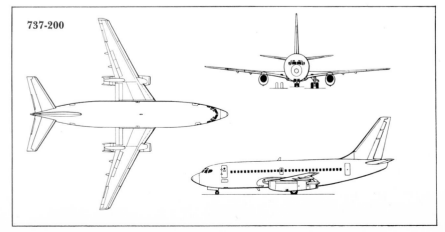

737-200

Above: A Boeing 737-200 in the colours of Gulf Air. Despite the 737's external similarities to other Boeing aircraft and its 60% commonality of parts with the 727, it was in essence a new 1960s design

737-200

Type: short-range passenger transport
Maker: Boeing Commercial Airplane Co
Span: 28.3 m (93 ft)
Length: 30.48 m (100 ft)
Height: 11.4 m (37 ft 4 in)
Wing area: 91.05 m² (980 sq ft)
Weight: maximum 53 070 kg (117 000 lb); empty 27 488 kg (60 600 lb)
Powerplant: two 7258-kg (16 000-lb) st Pratt & Whitney JT8D-17 turbofans
Performance: maximum cruising speed 908 km/h (564 mph) at 7620 m

(25 000 ft); range with maximum payload and reserves 2817 km (1750 miles)
Payload: 15 694 kg (34 600 lb); seats for up to 130 passengers
Crew: 2
Production: 762 (including 200C and 200QC)

737-100

Specification similar to 737-200 except in following particulars:
Length: 28.55 m (93 ft 8 in)
Weight: maximum 42 411 kg (93 500 lb)
Powerplant: two 6350-kg (14 000-lb) st Pratt & Whitney JT8D-7 turbofans
Performance: range with maximum payload and reserves 1850 km (1150 miles)
Payload: seats for up to 115 passengers
Production: 30

Advanced 737-200C

Specification similar to 737-200 except in following particulars:
Weight: empty 27 510 kg (60 650 lb)
Payload: 15 580 kg (34 350 lb)

Advanced 737-200QC

Specification similar to 737-200 except in following particulars:
Weight: empty 27 964 kg (61 650 lb)
Payload: 15 127 kg (33 350 lb)

79

flaps and the widening of the short engine pylons to produce the Advanced 737-200, which first flew on April 15, 1971. It received its type approval on May 3 of the same year, allowing All Nippon Airways to bring the model into service during June 1971. Other improvements on the Advanced 737-200 are optional brakes on the nosewheels, and optional 7031-kg (15 500-lb) JT8D-15 engines.

Pratt & Whitney have also been able to match the growth potential of the Advanced 737-200 with more powerful models of the JT8D turbofan, and by the late 1970s the Advanced 737-200 was available with the 6577-kg (14 500-lb) JT8D-9A, the 7031-kg (15 500-lb) JT8D-15, the 7258-kg (16 000-lb) JT8D-17, or the 7893-kg (17 400-lb) JT8D-17R.

Apart from performance and payload improvements, Boeing astutely realized that another factor which could enhance the 737 family's sales potential was the ability to operate from runways unsuitable for other modern aircraft. Boeing has therefore developed modifications to operate from unpaved runways. These include gravel deflection gear for the main and nose landing gears, fuselage protection against flying gravel and earth, protective features for the flaps and anti-vortex jets under the engine intakes to prevent the ingestion of foreign matter.

The Advanced 737-200 is also available in specialized forms. The two most common are the Advanced 737-200C and the Advanced 737-200QC convertible passenger/freight models. Both these models have strengthened floors and fuselage structures, and an enlarged door for the upper deck, capable of admitting an item measuring 2.15 m (7 ft 0½ in) by 3.4 m (11 ft 2 in). The main difference between the C and QC (Quick Change) models is that the latter has its removable passenger fittings (seats, galleys etc) mounted on pallets for quick removal and installation.

The Advanced 737-200 Executive Jet is basically the same as the Advanced 737-200, but fitted out with a luxurious interior with a wide variety of business equipment options. Passenger capacity is 15, and with extra fuel tankage in the underfloor cargo volume, the Advanced 737-200 Executive Jet has a maximum range of 5560 km (3455 miles).

Despite its official nomenclature as a short-range transport, the 737 in most variants is capable of medium-range operations, and Boeing has also proposed the Advanced 737-200 Long Range in two models. One would be powered by two JT8D-15, -17 or -17R engines and accommodate an extra 3066 litres (674 Imp gal) of fuel in the underfloor freight space, raising fuel capacity to 22 598 litres (4971 Imp gal) and maximum take-off weight to 58 333 kg (128 600 lb): range would be extended by 644 km (400 miles). The other would be basically similar, but have a maximum take-off weight of 56 473 kg (124 500 lb): range would in this case be extended by 467 km (290 miles).

The future of the 737 series seems assured by the fact that major operators are still ordering the type. Both the British Airways and Lufthansa aircraft will feature the advanced avionics and other equipment improvements that will characterize 737 production aircraft in the 1980s.

80

Above: A Boeing 737 belonging to Saudia being loaded up with baggage and cargo. Saudia is a relatively new arrival on the international scene and is the official airline of Saudi Arabia

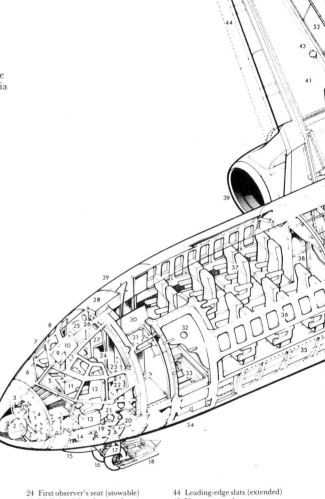

737-200

1 Hinged nose cone
2 Search radar
3 Glide-slope aerial
4 Forward pressure bulkhead
5 Instrument panel shroud
6 Windscreen sections
7 Sliding side windows
8 Eyebrow windows
9 First Officer's seat
10 Overhead panel
11 Centre console
12 Captain's seat
13 Flight kit stowage
14 Circuit breaker panel
15 Nose gear deflector housing
16 Twin nosewheels
17 Nosewheel doors
18 Nose gear gravel deflector
19 Steering cylinders
20 Lock
21 Drag strut
22 Fixed side windows
23 Second observer's seat (optional)

24 First observer's seat (stowable)
25 Wall circuit breaker panel
26 Dome light
27 Flight-deck door
28 Forward galley
29 Service door (right) 76 cm × 165 cm (30 in × 65 in)
30 Coat closet
31 Forward toilet
32 Forward entry door (left), 86 cm × 183 cm (34 in × 72 in)
33 Airstairs stowage (deployed through hatch)
34 Electrical/electronics bay
35 Underfloor forward freight hold
36 Cabin windows
37 Fourteen-seat first-class cabin configuration (96.5-cm [38-in] seat pitch)
38 Inter-class bulkhead
39 Engine air intakes
40 Air-conditioning pre-cooler
41 Integral wing fuel tank (tank No 2)
42 Dry bay
43 Overwing filler

44 Leading-edge slats (extended)
45 Vent surge tank
46 Right navigation light (flashing)
47 Right navigation light (white)
48 Right aileron
49 Aileron balance tab
50 Triple-slotted flaps (extended)
51 Ground spoiler/lift dumper (outer)
52 Wing spoilers (two segments)
53 Ground spoiler/lift dumper (inner)
54 Triple-slotted flap (inner section)
55 Tailpipe shroud
56 Aft wing/nacelle fairing
57 Thrust reverser doors (closed)
58 VHF communications antenna
59 HF communications antenna (optional)
60 Right escape hatch frame surround
61 Forged alloy fuselage main frames (three off)
62 Rolled alloy intermediate frames
63 Floor level (air-conditioning outflow)
64 Centre-section fuel bladder cells (three off)

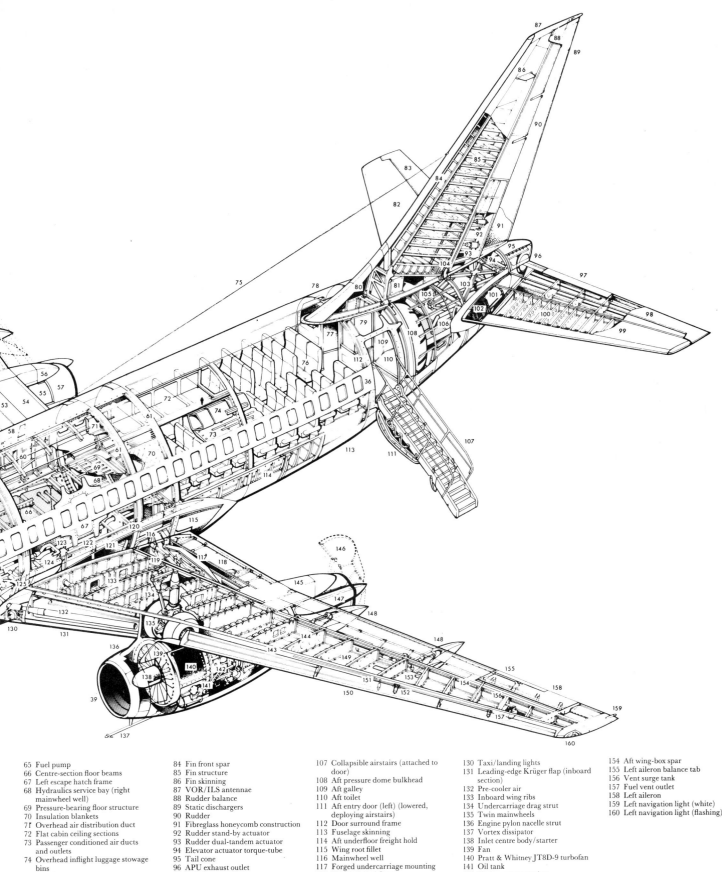

65 Fuel pump
66 Centre-section floor beams
67 Left escape hatch frame
68 Hydraulics service bay (right mainwheel well)
69 Pressure-bearing floor structure
70 Insulation blankets
71 Overhead air distribution duct
72 Flat cabin ceiling sections
73 Passenger conditioned air ducts and outlets
74 Overhead inflight luggage stowage bins
75 Aerial
76 Tourist-class 88-seat cabin configuration (86-cm [34in] seat pitch)
77 Aft bulkhead
78 Aft service door (right) 76 cm × 165 cm (30 in × 65 in)
79 Aft galley
80 Fin forward spar/pressure bulkhead attachment
81 Crash-locator beacon
82 Right tailplane
83 Right elevator

84 Fin front spar
85 Fin structure
86 Fin skinning
87 VOR/ILS antennae
88 Rudder balance
89 Static dischargers
90 Rudder
91 Fibreglass honeycomb construction
92 Rudder stand-by actuator
93 Rudder dual-tandem actuator
94 Elevator actuator torque-tube
95 Tail cone
96 APU exhaust outlet
97 Left elevator tab
98 Left elevator
99 Left horizontal tailplane (variable incidence)
100 Tailplane ribs
101 APU exhaust pipe
102 APU package
103 Forged-beam tailplane centre section
104 Fin rear spar terminal fittings
105 Variable-incidence screw-jack fitment
106 Air conditioning

107 Collapsible airstairs (attached to door)
108 Aft pressure dome bulkhead
109 Aft galley
110 Aft toilet
111 Aft entry door (left) (lowered, deploying airstairs)
112 Door surround frame
113 Fuselage skinning
114 Aft underfloor freight hold
115 Wing root fillet
116 Mainwheel well
117 Forged undercarriage mounting
118 Triple-slotted flaps
119 Undercarriage side strut
120 Fuselage frame attachment
121 Wingroot/fuselage fairing
122 Air-conditioning conduits
123 Coolant air fan
124 Primary heat exchanger
125 Fuselage/front spar attachment
126 Water separator
127 Crew air (left)/passenger cabin air (right) ducts
128 Ram air intake
129 Intake scoop

130 Taxi/landing lights
131 Leading-edge Krüger flap (inboard section)
132 Pre-cooler air
133 Inboard wing ribs
134 Undercarriage drag strut
135 Twin mainwheels
136 Engine pylon nacelle strut
137 Vortex dissipator
138 Inlet centre body/starter
139 Fan
140 Pratt & Whitney JT8D-9 turbofan
141 Oil tank
142 High-pressure section
143 Forward wing box-spar
144 Outer wing ribs
145 Aft wing/nacelle fairing
146 Thrust-reverser doors (extended)
147 Thrust-reverser actuator fairing
148 Flap tracks
149 Wing integral fuel tank (tank No 1)
150 Leading-edge slats
151 Krüger flap anti-icing pipes (telescopic)
152 Flap hydraulic rams
153 Retractable taxi/landing lights

154 Aft wing-box spar
155 Left aileron balance tab
156 Vent surge tank
157 Fuel vent outlet
158 Left aileron
159 Left navigation light (white)
160 Left navigation light (flashing)

81

Tu-134, Tupolev
ESTIMATED FIRST FLIGHT 1963

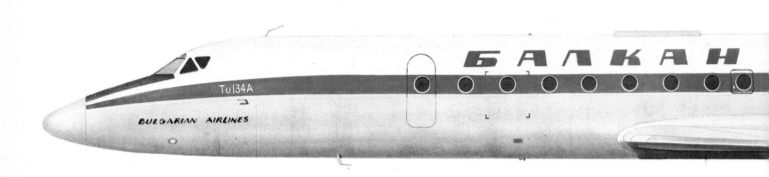

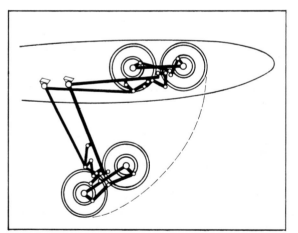

THE Tupolev Tu-134 was the third jet airliner to come from the Tupolev Design Bureau, and is a short-haul transport of medium capacity, comparable in many respects to the BAC One-Eleven and the Douglas DC-9. The origins of the design clearly lie with the Tu-104 and Tu-124, but the Tu-134 was produced to meet an Aeroflot requirement, issued just as the Tu-124 was entering service. The need was for an airliner able to compete not only in operating economics with western airliners, but also in detail finish, passenger comfort and instrumentation and avionics.

Design work began on what was at first known as the Tu-124A in the first half of 1961. Although the same basic design as the Tu-124 was retained, together with many components, the Tu-124A followed western practice in the adoption of a T-tail and rear-mounted engines, with consequent benefits in terms of reduced cabin noise and vibration, a cleaner wing planform and more efficient flaps, and better protection for the engines while being run on the ground. The Tu-124A designation reflected the initial attempt merely to modify the Tu-124 fuselage to the new configuration, but with the development of an entirely new fuselage and the realization that an attempt at modification was counter-productive, the new designation Tu-134 was applied. As noted above, as many Tu-124 components as possible were retained, largely in the high-lift devices and undercarriage.

Despite the revised structure of the Tu-134, and the relocation of the tailplane and engines, the type

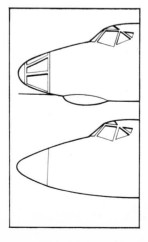

Above: A Tupolev Tu-134A in Bulgarian Airlines markings. The lettering on the side of the aircraft reads 'BALKAN'
Right: Passengers disembarking from an Aeroflot Tu-134

Above: In common with other Tupolev aircraft, the main gear of the Tu-134 retracts backwards and the bogie assembly rotates through 180°, the front wheels ending up at the rear
Left: The two types of nose fitted to the Tu-134. The earlier type, at the top, was equipped with weather radar beneath the cockpit and was fitted with a glazed navigator's station; on the latest models the weather radar is housed in a radome where the glazed cockpit used to be

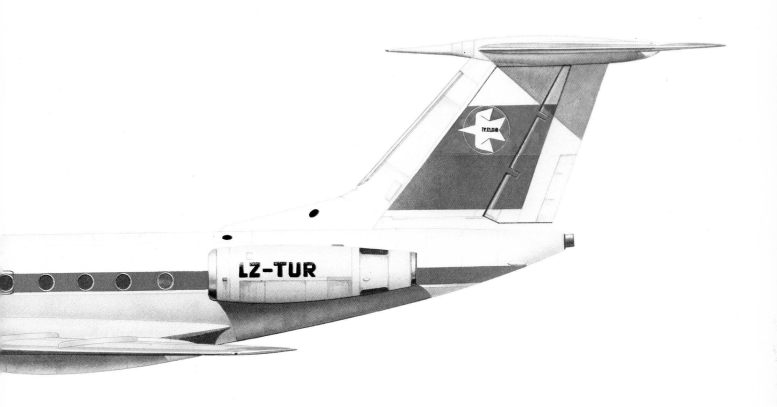

remains in essence an adaptation of the Tu-124, with the wings increased in span by 3.45 m (11 ft 4 in) through the expedient of incorporating a wider centre section and longer wingtips, and with the fuselage lengthened by 1.6 m (5 ft 3 in).

Although the Tu-124A had been announced in 1962, the first prototype did not take to the air until late in the same year, and more than 100 test flights had been made by the time details and photographs of the Tu-134 were revealed to the western press in September 1964. The test phase of the Tu-134 programme involved some six aircraft, and production of definitive airline-standard aircraft began in Kharkov during 1964. There then followed some three years before the machine entered full airline service, Aeroflot operating the type for a number of proving flights over different routes before full services began with the route between Moscow and Sochi on September 9, 1967. The first international service operated by the type was that between Moscow and Stockholm inaugurated on September 12, 1967.

The aircraft which was used on these initial services was the basic Tu-134. At the Paris Air Show of 1969, however, the USSR showed a new version of the aircraft, the Tu-134A. This is powered by two 6800-kg (14 991-lb) Soloviev D-30-2 turbofans fitted with thrust reversers and pneumatic starters, improved wheels and brakes, an inbuilt auxiliary power unit, a bullet fairing projecting forward of the fin/tailplane junction, automatic fuel control and a fuselage stretch of 2.1 m (6 ft 10⅔ in). This raises passenger accommodation, still four-abreast but in wider seats, to a maximum of 80 and increases the space available for baggage by 2 m³ (71 cu ft). The glazed nose of the original Tu-134 and Tu-134A models has now been replaced by a radome for weather radar, and this can be retrofitted to earlier aircraft should the operator so desire. In these earlier aircraft the weather radar was accommodated in a blister unit beneath the cockpit, while the extreme nose of the aircraft was occupied by the navigator. (It is worth noting that in its review of the world's commercial aircraft for 1979, the journal *Flight International* quotes the fuselage stretch of the Tu-134A as being 2.9 m [9 ft 6 in].)

The Tu-134 was designed to complement the Tu-104 and Tu-124 in Aeroflot service, and also to provide the USSR, by matching the performance, operating economics and passenger accommodation of western types, with an airliner of good export potential. In the second of these hopes, however, the USSR has been largely disappointed. For although some 66 export orders have been won, these have all been from Communist bloc countries. Iraqi Airways had one Tu-134, and Egyptair got as far as ordering six of the type, but otherwise Tupolev has failed to secure orders outside the Soviet-dominated bloc.

Production of the Tu-134A continues at Kharkov at the rate of about four aircraft per month, the requirement for the type having been extended, apparently, by difficulties with the Yakovlev Yak-42. This was to have supplemented the Tu-134A but seems to have run into development problems as yet unrevealed to the West.

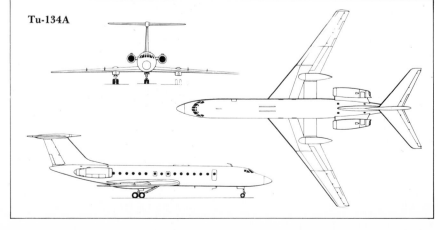

Tu-134A

Tu-134A

Type: short- and medium-range passenger transport
Maker: Tupolev Design Bureau
Span: 29.01 m (95 ft 2 in)
Length: 37.05 m (121 ft 6½ in)
Height: 9.14 m (30 ft)
Wing area: 127.3 m² (1370 sq ft)
Weight: maximum 47 000 kg (103 616 lb); empty 29 000 kg (63 933 lb)
Powerplant: two 6800-kg (14 991-lb) st Soloviev D-30-2 turbofans
Performance: maximum cruising speed 885 km/h (550 mph) at 10 000 m (32 808 ft); range with reserves and maximum payload 2000 km (1243 miles)
Payload: 8200 kg (18 078 lb); seats for up to 80 passengers
Crew: 3
Production: minimum 280 (including Tu-134)

Tu-134

Specification similar to Tu-134A except in following particulars:
Length: 34.95 m (114 ft 8 in)
Weight: maximum 45 000 kg (99 200 lb); empty 27 500 kg (60 627 lb)
Powerplant: two 6800-kg (14 990-lb) st Soloviev D-30 turbofans
Performance: maximum cruising speed 870 km/h (540 mph) at 11 000 m (36 089 ft); range with 3000 kg (6614 lb) payload 3500 km (2175 miles)
Payload: 7700 kg (16 975 lb); seats for up to 72 passengers

Above: A Tu-134A in the livery of the Czechoslovakian state airline CSA. In the background is the massive tail of an Air India Boeing 747

Tu-154, Tupolev

FIRST FLIGHT 1968

THE Tupolev Tu-154 has been aptly described as a scaled-up version of the Tu-134, with three of everything of which the Tu-134 has two: three engines, triple paired wheels on each main undercarriage leg, triple-slotted flaps, triple systems and a three-spar wing structure.

The Tu-154 was announced in the spring of 1966, and was clearly intended to be the main Russian medium- and long-range domestic transport of the 1970s. Continuing the design philosophy which had started with the Tu-104 and been developed with the Tu-124 and Tu-134, the Tu-154 was designed to use a fair proportion of the techniques developed for the Tu-144 supersonic transport. Nevertheless, it was to have a high power-to-weight ratio and sturdy undercarriage to ensure that the aircraft could operate without difficulty from the unpaved runways of airports in the Soviet Union's remoter areas. In common with all its predecessors except the Tu-144, the Tu-154 has wide-track main undercarriage legs which retract backwards into pods projecting behind the wing trailing edge.

The first prototype of the Tu-154 took to the air on October 4, 1968 and was followed by another five development aircraft. It soon became clear that the aircraft in general met its design requirements. Despite being nearly 15% heavier than the Tu-104, the new aircraft could still use existing Tu-104 maintenance and repair facilities. At the same time the evolution of the wing through the Tu-124 and Tu-134, with large-scale use of flaps and slats, meant that the aircraft could operate from short

unpaved runways and carry at least its designed load of 18 000 kg (39 683 lb) over a range of 4000 km (2486 miles). Early test flights confirmed to Aeroflot that it could replace its ageing Antonov An-10, Ilyushin Il-18 and Tupolev Tu-104 aircraft with the new machine.

Part of the Tu-154's success was attributable to the use of a trio of Kuznetsov NK-8-2 turbofans, specially developed for the Tu-154 by a team headed by N D Kuznetsov. These engines are rated at 9500-kg (20 944-lb) st at take-off, and have an adequate power-to-weight ratio and good specific fuel consumption, despite early problems.

Aeroflot received its first Tu-154s in 1970, allowing the airline to begin operational trials and route-proving flights, which almost inevitably preface the

Top: A Tupolev Tu-154B in the livery of the Hungarian airline Malev. The Tu-154B incorporates improvements to the control system and has a greater maximum take-off weight than the Tu-154A
Above: An Aeroflot Tu-154 on the runway at Heathrow

86

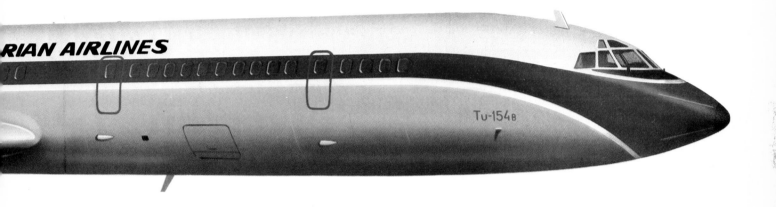

RIAN AIRLINES

Tu-154в

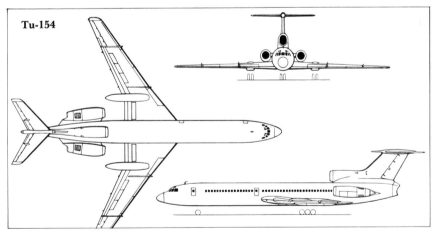

Tu-154

Tu-154

Specification similar to Tu-154B except in following:
Weight: maximum 90 000 kg (198 413 lb); empty 43 500 kg (95 900 lb)
Powerplant: three 9500-kg (20 950-lb) st Kuznetsov NK-8-2 turbofans
Performance: maximum cruising speed 975 km/h (605 mph) at 9500 m (31 150 ft); range with optional tanks and 9000 kg (19 840 lb) payload 6400 km (3977 miles)
Payload: 20 000 kg (44 090 lb); seats for up to 167 passengers

large-scale introduction of any Russian civil transport. Cargo flights between Moscow and the Crimea, Caucasus and Siberia began in May 1971, with the first scheduled passenger services following on November 15, 1971.

Compared with earlier Tupolev designs, the passenger accommodation of the Tu-154 is more modern: whereas the seating of the Tu-134 is four-abreast, that of the Tu-154 is six-abreast, with a maximum capacity of 167.

Early in 1973 it was reported that Tupolev was producing an improved model of the Tu-154, and this Tu-154A first flew later in 1973, entering service with Aeroflot in April 1974. The Tu-154A had replaced the Tu-154 in production at Kuibyshev by 1975. Externally there is little to

Tu-154B

Type: medium- and long-range passenger transport
Maker: Tupolev Design Bureau
Span: 37.55 m (123 ft 2½ in)
Length: 47.9 m (157 ft 1¾ in)
Height: 11.4 m (37 ft 4¾ in)
Wing area: 201.5 m² (2169 sq ft)
Weight: maximum 96 000 kg (211 642 lb); empty 50 775 kg (111 939 lb)
Powerplant: three 10 500-kg (23 148-lb) st Kuznetsov NK-8-2U turbofans
Performance: normal cruising speed approx 900 km/h (559 mph); range

with maximum payload 2750 km (1708 miles)
Payload: 18 000 kg (39 683 lb); seats for up to 169 passengers
Crew: 3 to 4
Production: minimum 240 (including Tu-154 and Tu-154A)

Tu-154A

Specification similar to Tu-154B except in following particulars:
Weight: maximum 94 000 kg (207 235 lb)
Performance: range with 16 000 kg (35 372 lb) payload 3300 km (2050 miles)

differentiate the Tu-154A from the Tu-154: how-ever, the fitting of three 10 500-kg (23 148-lb) NK-8-2U turbofans allows a higher take-off weight of 94 000 kg (207 232 lb) compared with 90 000 kg (198 414 lb), while the provision of an extra 6600 kg (14 550 lb) of fuel reduces the Tu-154A's depend-ence on facilities away from its main bases. The extra fuel, carried in a tank in the centre section between the front and centre spars, cannot be used in flight, but can be transferred to the flight tanks in the wings when the aircraft is on the ground. Maximum seating is for 168 passengers in high-density configuration. However, a more usual arrangement is for 152 passengers in summer or 144 in winter, to provide wardrobe space for the heavy winter clothes of the passengers.

Left: The interior of a Tu-154
Below: A Hungarian Tu-154 coming in to land at Heathrow, showing its six-wheel main gears suitable for use on Class 2 airfields of gravel or packed dirt

Another improved version, the Tu-154B, appeared in 1977. This is again externally identical with the Tu-154A, and is fitted with the same NK-8-2U turbofans. The improvements are largely in the control system, which now allows limited automatic landings, the type of radar carried, the increase in maximum passenger capacity to 169, the incorporation of the centre-section fuel tank into the main fuel system, and an increase in maximum take-off weight.

It seems that the provision of the centre-section fuel tank in the Tu-154A was associated with difficulties in the aircraft's longitudinal control, thus requiring the provision of considerable ballast. From the fact that the tank has now been incorporated in the Tu-154B's main fuel system, it is clear that the problem has been solved. Another control feature found on the Tu-154B but not on the two previous models is the use of spoilers for low-speed control, enabling the span of the ailerons to be reduced in favour of longer-span spoilers.

It has recently been reported from East German sources that the Tu-154B has been cleared for operations with up to 180 passengers and at a maximum take-off weight of 100 000 kg (220 460 lb). Future versions of this important type are likely to centre on the use of the 12 990-kg (28 638-lb) NK-86 turbofan to improve payload/range. Other developments may include an all-freight model, further improvements in landing characteristics, especially in poor weather, and avionics to obviate the need for a navigator.

Il-62, Ilyushin

FIRST FLIGHT 1963

THE Ilyushin Il-62 occupies an important niche in Soviet aviation history as that country's first true long-range four-engined jet transport, and also the first Soviet rear-engined civil aircraft to get into production. Much play was made in 1962, with the revealing of the first details of the Il-62 in the Russian press, of the similarities between the Russian aircraft and the slightly earlier British VC10 developed by Vickers and produced by the British Aircraft Corporation. In this instance, though, it seems clear that similar airline requirements had given rise to a close similarity of design philosophy: four engines mounted in pods in pairs at the rear of the fuselage to leave the wing aerodynamically clean for maximum efficiency; large wing area to ensure minimum runway requirements; 32.5 to 35% of wing sweep for high-speed cruising; and a T-tail to leave the rear fuselage clear for the engines.

Revealed on September 24, 1962, when the prototype was inspected by Nikita Khrushchev, the Il-62 first flew in January 1963, the delay probably being occasioned by the unavailability of the Kuznetsov NK-8, which had been designed for use in the Il-62.

With the adoption of a drooped saw-tooth extension of the outer two-thirds of the leading edges, the low-speed problem was apparently solved, and the test programme, involving two prototypes and three pre-production aircraft, then moved ahead satisfactorily. Production of the Il-62 for Aeroflot began at Kazan in 1965, and during 1966 the airline operated a small number of aircraft on proving flights, the most notable being the 6150 km (3822 miles) between Moscow and Khabarovsk in eastern Siberia in 8 hours at an average speed of almost 770 km/h (478 mph).

The first scheduled services flown by the Il-62 were those between Moscow and Khabarovsk, and between Moscow and Novosibirsk, started on March 10, 1967. The first international service was that between Moscow and Montreal, inaugurated on September 15, 1967 for Expo '67. Maximum capacity of this initial model is 186 economy-class passengers, plus up to 48 m³ (1695 cu ft) of baggage, the latter being loaded in only 15 min thanks to the use of special pre-packed containers. Maximum payload is 23 000 kg (50 706 lb).

Early operations confirmed that the operating economics of the Il-62 were poor, largely as a result of the indifferent performance of the NK-8-4 turbofans. In 1970, therefore, the USSR announced a new model, the Il-62M200 or Il-62M. This first appeared in 1971, and is dimensionally identical with its predecessor. The main differences between the two types lie in the Il-62M's new powerplant and extra fuel capacity. The engine now used is the 11 500-kg (25 353-lb) Soloviev D-30KU turbofan. The outer pair of engines is fitted with clamshell-type thrust reversers in place of the cascade type used in the Il-62, with consequent improvements in the Il-62M's landing performance. The Il-62M also features an extra fuel tank, located in the fin and capable of holding 5000 litres (1100 Imp gal), which helps to give the Il-62M a maximum payload range 1300 km (808 miles) greater than

Right: An Ilyushin Il-62 in the colours of the East German airline, Interflug
Below: An Aeroflot Il-62M at Heathrow. As well as Aeroflot and Interflug, Il-62s are operated by most of the Eastern-bloc airlines

CCCP-86623

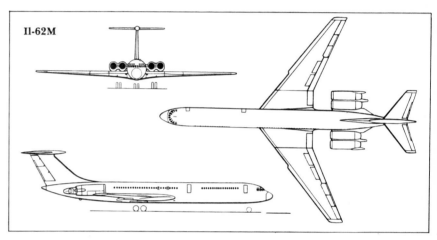

Il-62M

the Il-62. Some suggestion of the problems facing the NK-8-4 turbofan may be gauged from the fact that in 1972 two Il-62s crashed with a total loss of 332 lives, both crashes probably being attributable to engine failures.

The latest version of this important Russian transport is the Il-62MK, announced in 1978. This is basically the Il-62M with a strengthened airframe for high-frequency operations, derated D-30KU engines, a passenger capacity of up to 195, compared with the Il-62M's 186, maximum take-off weight increased by 2000 kg (4409 lb) from 165 000 kg (363 759 lb), maximum payload also increased by 2000 kg (4409 lb), and range with a 10 000-kg (22 046-lb) payload reduced by only 400 km (249 miles).

Il-62MK

Type: long-range passenger transport
Maker: Ilyushin Design Bureau
Span: 43.2 m (141 ft 9 in)
Length: 53.12 m (174 ft 3½ in)
Height: 12.35 m (40 ft 6¼ in)
Wing area: 279.6 m² (3010 sq ft)
Weight: maximum 167 000 kg (368 168 lb); empty not available
Powerplant: four 11 500-kg (25 353-lb) st Soloviev D-30KU turbofans
Performance: normal cruising speed up to 900 km/h (559 mph); range with maximum fuel and a payload of 10 000 kg (22 046 lb), 9600 km (5965 miles)
Payload: 25 000 kg (55 115 lb); seats for up to 195 passengers
Crew: 5 to 7
Production: minimum 135 ordered by 1980

Il-62

Specification similar to Il-62MK except in following particulars:
Weight: maximum 162 000 kg (357 150 lb); empty 66 400 kg (146 390 lb)
Powerplant: four 10 500-kg (23 150-lb) st Kuznetsov NK-8-4 turbofans
Performance: range with maximum payload 6700 km (4160 miles)
Payload: 23 000 kg (50 700 lb); seats for up to 186 passengers

Il-62M

Specification similar to Il-62MK except in following particulars:
Weight: maximum 165 000 kg (363 760 lb)
Performance: range with maximum payload 8000 km (4970 miles)
Payload: 23 000 kg (50 700 lb); seats for up to 186 passengers

F28 Fellowship, Fokker

FIRST FLIGHT 1967

ALTHOUGH it is nominally a Dutch aircraft, the Fokker F28 Fellowship is in fact an international aircraft, designed in collaboration with other European companies. Initially funded by the Dutch Aircraft Development Board with a loan guaranteed by the Dutch government, the F28 was built in collaboration with Short Brothers (19%) and two German companies, VFW-Fokker and Messerschmitt-Bölkow-Blohm (35%).

The F28 was designed as a jet-engined supplement to the already successful F27 Friendship turboprop short- and medium-range transport, and was announced by the still independent Fokker company in April 1962. (It was in 1969 that Fokker merged with VFW to form Zentralgesellschaft VFW-Fokker GmbH.) The new

aircraft was at first proposed with a capacity of 50 passengers over a range of 1600 km (994 miles) on the power of two rear-mounted podded Rolls-Royce RB.183 Spey Junior turbofans, after the use of two Bristol Siddeley BS.75s had been considered. The design of the new aircraft followed the trend of the time: slightly swept wings, podded engines mounted on the sides of the rear fuselage, and a T-tail. With commendable foresight, Fokker realized that sales of the F28 would be in a steady trickle of small orders over a long period, rather than large orders over a short period followed by a few supplementary orders over the next few years. This conditioned Fokker's production approach: major components were sub-contracted (MBB building the fuselage from the wing trailing edge to

Below: An F28 Fellowship in the markings of the Swedish airline, Linjeflyg. In 1976, Linjeflyg received the first of its ten Mk 4000s, with five more on option

the rear bulkhead, VFW-Fokker the rear fuselage and tail, and Shorts the outer wings) for final assembly at Schiphol-Oost. Such a programme had very beneficial results in keeping to a minimum the factory space required for the F28.

Production of the first three prototypes began in July 1964 and by this time the basic capacity of the first production model had been raised to 60. Progress with the prototypes was unhurried, and it was not until November 1965 that the first F28 was ordered by Lufttransport-Unternehmen (LTU). The three prototypes flew on May 9, August 3 and October 20, 1967, powered by the Spey 550 turbofan. By 1968 the third aircraft had been brought up to full production standard, and the first aircraft for the LTU order took to the air on

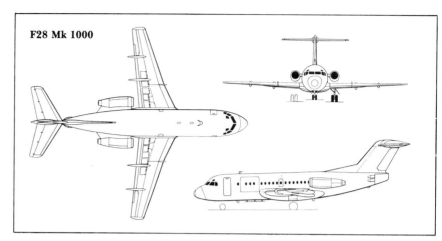

F28 Mk 1000

F28 Mk 6000

Type: short-range transport
Maker: Fokker-VFW BV
Span: 25.07 m (82 ft 3 in)
Length: 29.61 m (97 ft 1¾ in)
Height: 8.47 m (27 ft 9½ in)
Wing area: 79 m² (850 sq ft)
Weight: maximum 33 110 kg (72 994 lb); empty 17 660 kg (38 933 lb)
Powerplant: two 4481-kg (9900-lb) st Rolls-Royce RB.183-2 Spey Mk 555-15H turbofans
Performance: maximum cruising speed 843 km/h (524 mph) at 7000 m (22 966 ft); range with 85 passengers 1705 km (1059 miles)
Payload: 9556 kg (21 067 lb); seats for up to 85 passengers
Crew: 2 to 3
Production: 146 ordered by 1980

F28 Mk 2000

Specification similar to Mk 6000 except in following particulars:
Span: 23.58 m (77 ft 4¼ in)
Wing area: 76.4 m² (822 sq ft)
Weight: maximum 29 485 kg (65 000 lb); empty 16 690 kg (36 795 lb)
Powerplant: two 4468-kg (9850-lb) st Rolls-Royce RB.183-2 Spey Mk 555-15 turbofans
Performance: range in long-range configuration 1296 km (806 miles)
Payload; 8030 kg (17 705 lb)
Production: 10 ordered by 1980

F28 Mk 1000

Specification similar to Mk 6000 except in following particulars:
Span: 23.58 m (77 ft 4¼ in)
Length: 27.4 m (89 ft 10¾ in)
Wing area: 76.4 m² (822 sq ft)
Weight: maximum 29 485 kg (65 000 lb); empty 16 084 kg (35 464 lb)
Powerplant: two 4468-kg (9850-lb) st Rolls-Royce RB.183-2 Spey Mk 555-15 turbofans
Performance: range in long-range configuration 2093 km (1300 miles)
Payload: 8636 kg (19 036 lb); seats for up to 65 passengers
Production: 97 ordered by 1980

F28 Mk 3000

Specification similar to the Mk 6000 except in following particulars:
Length: 24.55 m (86 ft 6½ in)
Weight: maximum 32 200 kg (71 000 lb); empty 16 415 kg (36 190 lb)
Performance: range in long-range configuration 2593 km (1611 miles)
Payload: 8985 kg (19 810 lb); seats for up to 65 passengers
Production: 15

F28 Mk 4000

Specification similar to Mk 6000 except in following particulars:
Weight: maximum 32 200 kg (71 000 lb); empty 17 117 kg (37 736 lb)
Performance: range in long-range configuration 1852 km (1151 miles)
Payload: 8965 kg (19 764 lb)
Production: 24

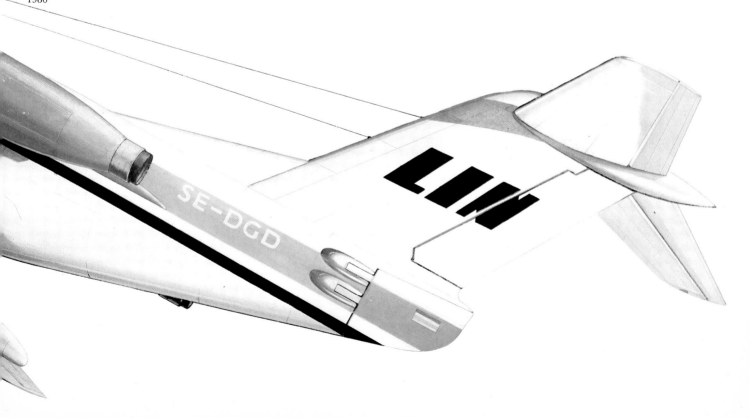

F28 Mk 4000

1 Radome
2 Weather radar scanner
3 Front pressure bulkhead
4 Radar equipment mounting
5 Windscreen wipers
6 Windscreen frame
7 Instrument panel shroud
8 Back of instrument panel
9 Rudder pedals
10 Ram air intake
11 Cockpit roof control panel
12 Overhead window
13 Co-pilot's seat
14 Pilot's seat
15 Control column
16 Pilot's side console
17 Air conditioning plant
18 Nosewheel doors
19 Nose undercarriage leg
20 Twin nosewheels
21 Cockpit roof construction
22 Radio and electronics rack
23 Radio rack cooling duct
24 Galley
25 Stewardess' seat
26 Curtained doorway to passenger cabin
27 Handrail
28 Entrance vestibule
29 Entry stairway
30 VHF aerial
31 Main passenger door
32 Upper VHF aerial
33 Air-conditioning duct
34 Forward cabin passenger seating
35 Seat rails
36 Freight and baggage hold door
37 ADF loop aerials
38 Fuselage frame and stringer construction
39 Soundproofing panels
40 Underfloor freight and baggage hold
41 Window panels
42 Cabin floor construction
43 Hot air duct
44 Wing centre section front spar
45 HF aerial fixing
46 Leading-edge fence
47 Right wing integral fuel tank
48 Fuel filler
49 Right navigation light
50 Static discharge wicks
51 Right aileron
52 Aileron tab
53 Flap mechanism fairings
54 Right outer flaps
55 Outboard spoilers (open)
56 Right inboard flaps
57 Inboard spoilers (open)
58 Centre section main fuselage frames
59 Air distribution duct
60 Wing centre section construction
61 Emergency escape windows
62 Mainwheel well pressurized cover
63 Left mainwheel well
64 Cabin window trim panels
65 Rear cabin seating
66 Passenger overhead service panels
67 Overhead luggage bins
68 Cabin rear bulkhead
69 Right engine cowling
70 Toilet
71 Wash basin
72 Air intake to APU
73 Fin root fairing
74 Fuselage sloping frames
75 De-icing air duct
76 HF aerials
77 Fin leading edge de-icing
78 Fin construction
79 Tailplane hydraulic jacks
80 Tailplane de-icing air duct
81 Anti-collision light
82 Right tailplane
83 Right elevator
84 Tailplane pivot fairing
85 Elevator hinge controls
86 Tailcone fairing
87 Tail navigation light
88 Left elevator
89 Tailplane construction
90 Leading edge de-icing
91 Tailplane pivot
92 Rudder
93 Rudder hydraulic jack
94 Left airbrake (open)
95 Airbrake jack housing
96 Rear fuselage construction
97 Hydraulic accumulators
98 Exhaust silencer nozzle
99 Engine pylon fairing
100 Bleed air ducting
101 Rolls Royce Mk 555-15 Spey engine
102 Engine mountings
103 Engine cowlings
104 Auxiliary power unit (APU)
105 Engine mounting beam
106 Air intake
107 Five-abreast passenger seating
108 Underfloor air duct
109 Trailing edge wing root fairing
110 Inboard flap track fairing
111 Left inboard spoilers
112 Left flaps
113 Flap mechanism fairings
114 Left outboard spoilers
115 Flap construction
116 Aileron tab
117 Left aileron
118 Static discharge wicks
119 Left wingtip
120 Left navigation light
121 Outer wing rib construction
122 Leading edge de-icing air ducts
123 Leading edge construction
124 Lattice ribs
125 Wing integral fuel tanks
126 Twin mainwheels
127 Main undercarriage leg
128 Leading edge fence
129 Undercarriage retraction jack fixing
130 Wing panel bolted joint
131 Corrugated inner wing skin
132 Wing spar attachment frame
133 Leading edge de-icing air duct

Above: An Air Alpes F28. Intended as a successor to the highly successful F27 Friendship, it likewise incorporates many British parts including wing (Shorts), engines (Rolls-Royce) and landing gear (Dowty)

able feature of this engine, apart from its low weight and low specific fuel consumption, is its low rate of performance fall-off with altitude, enabling the Yak-40 to operate from short airfields at high altitudes. To make the Yak-40 independent of airfield services there is an AI-9 auxiliary power unit, mounted in the fin behind the intake for the central engine, and a ventral airstep door leading into the passenger accommodation. This is normally provided with seating for 27 passengers three-abreast, or for 32 passengers four-abreast.

The domestic Russian demand for the Yak-40 was so great that production of the type was inaugurated at a factory in Saratov, with production rates rising steadily to eight aircraft per month in 1973. By the spring of 1973, moreover, Yak-40s had carried more than 8 000 000 passengers, and flown more than 200 000 000 km (124 277 630 miles). The Yak-40 had also become the most important Russian transport aircraft of the decade on stages up to 1500 km (932 miles) in length, the more so in remoter and more mountainous areas.

In common with most other aircraft, the Yak-40 has undergone modification and improvement as a result of service use. The most important of these has been the addition of a clamshell thrust-reverser on the central engine; another visible alteration has been the removal of the bullet fairing projecting forward of the fin/tailplane junction.

In 1970 and 1971 there were reports of a stretched model of the Yak-40, designated Yak-40M and intended to carry up to 40 passengers. There has been no further news of this variant,

Above: An Aeroflot Yak-40 coming in to land. It is equipped with weather radar and other instruments which enable it to make ILS (instrument landing system) approaches in Category 2 weather conditions
Left: A General Air Yak-40. Note the ventral airstair at the rear of the aircraft

however, and it is assumed that there was insufficient need for the type. For export Yakovlev has developed the Yak-40V, powered by three 1750-kg (3858-lb) AI-25T turbofans, with a fuel capacity of 4000 kg (8818 lb) instead of the Yak-40's 3000 kg (6614 lb). The extra power available allows the Yak-40V to be operated in 27-seat configuration at a maximum take-off weight of 16 000 kg (35 273 lb), or in 32-seat configuration at 16 500 kg (36 376 lb). Export sales of the Yak-40 have been poor, though there is still a possibility that since Russian production has ended, the production line may be sold to ICX Aviation in the USA, who might manufacture the type as the X-Avia with three Garrett-AiResearch TFE731-3 turbofans, each rated at 1678 kg (3700 lb) st.

Yak-42, Yakovlev

FIRST FLIGHT 1974

THE Yakovlev Yak-42 has certain similarities with the Yak-40, but is an altogether more ambitious aircraft of far superior capabilities. Although it retains the same basic configuration as the Yak-40 (T-tail, triple rear-mounted engines and a low-set wing), the Yak-42 is designed to meet other basic requirements such as far higher payload, superior performance and less stringent airfield needs. The Yak-42 is therefore a considerably larger aircraft than its predecessor, fitted with more powerful high-bypass turbofans, and a swept wing of lower aspect ratio than that of the Yakovlev Yak-40.

Whereas the wing of the Yak-40 had been designed specifically for low cruising speeds and minimum runway lengths (thus featuring maximum area, high aspect ratio, straight planform and large plain flaps), that of the Yak-42 is more ambitious, but still planned to bestow good airfield performance on the Yak-42, which is intended for operations in remote areas and all climatic conditions. In its capacity as a short- and medium-range airliner, the Yak-42 is intended to replace types such as the Ilyushin Il-18 and Tupolev Tu-134 on the main airline routes, and the Antonov An-24 on local routes.

Design of the Yak-42 began in the early 1970s, and a mock-up of the type was shown to western visitors in 1973. Three different prototypes were built; the first flew on March 7, 1974, was fitted with a wing of only 11° sweep, and was laid out internally with accommodation for 100 local-service passengers. The second prototype was

provided with a wing of 23° sweep and accommodation for up to 120 passengers; the third prototype was basically similar to the second, but with improved de-icing provision and better fairings for the mainwheel legs.

Like its predecessor, the Yak-40, the Yak-42's mainwheels retract inwards into wells in the lower side of the fuselage, and are not covered by doors when retracted.

The two angles of wing sweep were exhaustively tested in terms of airfield performance and overall performance, and the 23° sweep was standardized for production aircraft, which are to be produced in two basic variants.

For local operations Aeroflot plans to use the 100-seat version pioneered internally by the first prototype.

The main method of entry and exit is a ventral airstair door under the tail, and another airstair door in the left side of the forward fuselage; seating is six-abreast and there are stowage areas for carry-on baggage and coats in front of and behind the passenger accommodation. For trunk routes there is the 120-seater type whose interior was presaged by that of the second and third prototypes, which had three additional six-abreast rows of seats.

In this 120-seat version of the Yak-40 airliner the passengers' baggage is loaded into containers, six and three of which can be stowed in the forward freight hold and rear freight hold respectively. The Yak-42 is equipped with a chain-drive handling system built into the aircraft's floor.

Like the Yak-40, the Yak-42 was designed to use

Top: A Yak-42 in Aeroflot livery. In 1977 Aeroflot ordered 200 of these aircraft, anticipating a total production run of around 2000. Since then, however, very little has been heard in the West of the development of the Yak-42 and prototypes have flown with different angles of wing sweep! Above: An Aeroflot Yak-42 at Le Bourget. In the foreground is a Yak-50, winner of the 1976 world aerobatic championships

a specially developed engine, the Lotarev D-36 produced under the supervision of Vladimir A Lotarev, successor to the late Aleksandr G Ivchenko. The D-36 is the first engine to bear Lotarev's name, and is an ambitious engine designed to meet difficult performance, noise and emission parameters. The development of the D-36, rated at 6485 kg (14 297 lb) st, appeared to be entirely normal and in 1977 Aeroflot ordered the first 200 of an anticipated production run of 2000 Yak-42s.

Since that time, however, Aeroflot planning documents available in the West have made no mention of the Yak-42, leading to speculation that severe problems have been met in bringing the D-36 up to the specified airline requirements. Thrust reversers are fitted to the two outer engines, and an auxiliary power unit is fitted as standard to make the Yak-42 independent of airfield services. Right from the start of the Yak-42's design, it was planned to cruise on all three engines, and this in all probability reflects operating experience with the Yak-40. The Yak-42 is also intended to operate in temperatures ranging from a low of −50°C to a high of +50°C.

An alternative explanation for the Yak-42's heavily delayed entry into regular service is that Aeroflot's efforts were concerned exclusively with getting the wide-body Ilyushin Il-86 into service in time for the controversial 1980 Olympic Games in Moscow, and so all other aircraft manufacturing programmes have been shelved or accorded only the lowest priority.

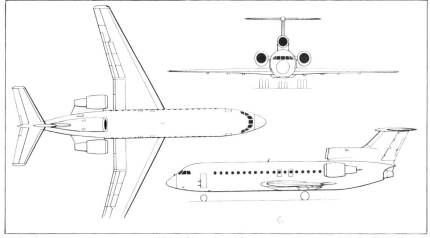

Yak-42

Type: short- and medium-range transport
Maker: Yakovlev Design Bureau
Span: 34.2 m (112 ft 2½ in)
Length: 36.38 m (119 ft 4¼ in)
Height: 9.8 m (32 ft 1¾ in)
Wing area: 150 m² (1615 sq ft)
Weight: maximum 52 000 kg (114 639 lb); empty 28 960 kg (63 845 lb)
Powerplant: three 6485-kg (14 297-lb) st Lotarev D-36 turbofans
Performance: normal cruising speed 820 km/h (510 mph) at 8000 m (26 246 ft); range with maximum payload and reserves 1000 km (621 miles)
Payload: 14 500 kg (31 967 lb); seats for up to 120 passengers
Crew: 2
Production: approx 2000

Top: An Aeroflot Yak-42 being inspected by visiting members of the public. The two outer Lotarev D-36 turbofans are fitted with thrust reversers, and an auxiliary power unit is standard

Mercure, Dassault Breguet

FIRST FLIGHT 1971

THE programme to develop and launch the Dassault Mercure medium-range high-capacity airliner was one of the boldest private ventures initiated by a European manufacturer since World War II. It is typical of the forceful policies of Dassault, the company which developed private ventures such as the Mirage III fighter and Mystère/Falcon series of business jets, that it should have turned to an entirely new kind of aircraft in the mid 1960s.

With no previous experience of large jet-engined transports to aid it, the company assessed the civil market very carefully before deciding in 1968 to produce a 150-seat airliner able to operate more effectively and economically over ranges not exceeding 1500 km (932 miles). Dassault calculated the market for such an aircraft to be about 1500 in the nine years up to 1981. The apparent validity of Dassault's assessment is testified by the willingness of the French government to lend the manufacturer 56% of the launch capital (to be repaid from initial sales). Of the other 44% of the capital, Dassault contributed 14%, and the remaining 30% was found by SABCA in Belgium, Canadair in Canada, Aeritalia in Italy, CASA in Spain, and F + W in Switzerland, all on a cost-and risk-sharing basis.

Tailored as it was to a very specific requirement, the Mercure was in all important aspects of conventional design, with a low-set wing, tailplane mounted on the sides of the rear fuselage, and two podded Pratt & Whitney JT8D turbofans under the wings. Confident that the aircraft would meet the user requirements and secure substantial orders, Dassault spent large sums building new factories for the Mercure programme.

The first prototype, powered by a pair of 6804-kg (15000-lb) JT8D-11 engines, made its initial flight on May 28, 1971. Early flight trials with these engines showed serious deficiencies in performance, but much was expected of the later installation of the type's designed powerplant, a pair of 7031-kg (15500-lb) JT8D-15 turbofans. In this new guise the first prototype again took to the air on September 7, 1971, but once again flight performance and low-speed handling proved to be worse than anticipated. New leading-edge slats were tested on the second prototype, which made its first flight on September 7, 1972, and these remedied the low-speed handling characteristics.

With the capital involved in the region of 1 million French francs, Dassault had said that no production would be undertaken unless at least 50 firm orders were secured. In the event, however, the company started production with only ten firm orders, from the French internal operator Air Inter, placed on January 29, 1972. The first of these aircraft flew on July 17, 1973 and after the type had received its French certificate of airworthiness on February 12, 1974, Air Inter's first two Mercures were delivered on May 16, and June 11, 1974 respectively. Air Inter operated its first Mercure service on June 4, 1974 and it proved popular in service. Yet, despite the widespread international manufacturing programme, no other customer came forward.

Right and below right: The Mercure in its Air Inter livery. Air Inter is obliged to operate the type with the help of a government subsidy because of the lack of orders from other airlines
Below: An Air Inter Mercure taking off at Le Bourget, showing the landing gear being retracted

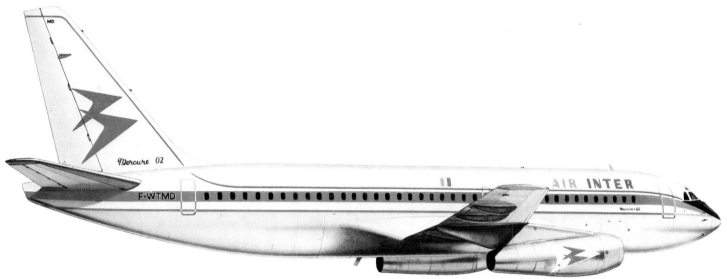

Air Inter thus remained the only operator of the type, despite strenuous efforts by Avions Marcel Dassault/Breguet Aviation (as the company had become in December 1971) to promote the Mercure and a projected improved variant, the Mercure 200 developed in collaboration with McDonnell Douglas. Intended as a possible successor to the Mercure and the DC-9, the design (at first called Super Mercure, then Mercure 200) was to accommodate up to 186 passengers in a fuselage lengthened by 6 m (19 ft 8 in) and be powered by two 9979-kg (22 000-lb) SNECMA/General Electric CFM56 high bypass ratio turbofans. Much enhanced performance would be obtained, including a range of 3750 km (2330 miles) with 160 passengers, but nothing has come of the project.

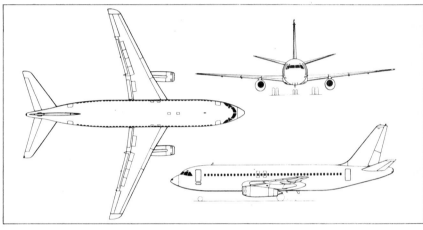

Mercure

Type: short-range transport
Maker: Avions Marcel Dassault/Breguet Aviation
Span: 30.55 m (100 ft 3 in)
Length: 34.84 m (114 ft 3½ in)
Height: 11.35 m (37 ft 3¼ in)
Wing area: 116 m²
(1249 sq ft)
Weight: maximum 56 500 kg
(124 560 lb); empty 31 800 kg
(70 107 lb)
Powerplant: two 7031-kg
(15 500-lb) st Pratt &
Whitney JT8D-15 turbofans
Performance: maximum
cruising speed 925 km/h
(575 mph) at 6100 m
(20 013 ft); range with 150
passengers and reserves
2085 km (1296 miles)
Payload: 16 200 kg
(35 715 lb); seats for up to 162
passengers
Crew: 2
Production: 10

An-72, Antonov

FIRST FLIGHT 1977

ALTHOUGH it is likely that the Antonov An-72 will be used by both the Russian civil and military authorities, it appears that this interesting new aircraft was developed to meet an Aeroflot requirement for a STOL (short take-off and landing) successor to the same design bureau's An-24 short-range transport.

Bearing a strong conceptual likeness to the Boeing YC-14 (contender in the now-postponed US Advanced Medium STOL Transport [AMST] programme) the An-72 has the primary distinguishing feature of its engine location. The two high bypass ratio turbofans are mounted on the inner sections of the wing leading edges. Such a location has the useful effect of preventing stones and the like from entering the intakes, but was designed to promote the 'Coanda effect'. In such an arrangement, the efflux from the engines, exhausting at about 40% of the chord over the upper surface of the high-set wing, is ideally placed to flow over, and so to attach itself to the full-span double- and triple-slotted trailing-edge flaps. The flaps extend along most of the trailing edges inboard of the ailerons, and the net effect of the engine efflux attaching itself to these flaps is for the efflux to be directed strongly downwards, thus generating a great deal of lift.

The net effect of the system is to allow the aircraft to fly safely at much lower speeds than 'conventional' aircraft, and so operate from smaller airfields than would otherwise have been possible. The location of the tailplane on top of the fin and rudder assembly keeps it well clear of the jet efflux

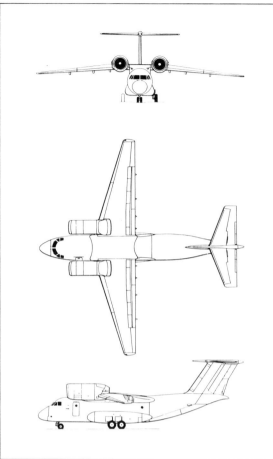

An-72
Type: light STOL transport
Maker: Antonov Design Bureau
Span: 25.83 m (84 ft 9 in)
Length: 26.58 m (87 ft 2¼ in)
Height: 8.23 m (27 ft 0¼ in)
Wing area: not available
Weight: maximum approx 34 565 kg (76 202 lb); empty not available
Powerplant: two 6485-kg (14 297-lb) st Lotarev D-36 turbofans
Performance: cruising speed up to 720 km/h (447 mph); range with maximum payload approx 1000 km (621 miles)
Payload: 7500 kg (16 535 lb); seats for up to 52 passengers
Crew: 3
Production: 2 prototypes by 1980

Left and above: The Antonov An-72 was designed to meet an Aeroflot requirement for a STOL (short take-off and landing) replacement for the propeller-driven An-24. It now seems probable, however, that the An-72 will be used by both civil and military authorities

and the control problems that would otherwise have been inevitable.

Another feature essential for operations from ill-prepared runways and fields is incorporated on the An-72, in the form of a rugged tricycle undercarriage. Each main unit consists of two large wheels with low-pressure tyres, while the twin nosewheels are smaller. The mainwheels on each side are located not on a twin-wheel bogie, but on two independent trailing legs to improve the aircraft's ability to operate from bumpy surfaces and unprepared runways.

Apart from its Lotarev D-36 engines, the An-72 has a number of other features in common with the Yakovlev Yak-42 medium-range airliner, such as its radar and navigation system. And in common with other Russian transport aircraft, the An-72 is fitted with an overhead crane on a fore and aft beam to facilitate loading. Passenger carrying is a secondary consideration. Present accommodation in the two prototypes does allow for 40 seats, mounted either along the sides of the freight compartment or on pallets, while production aircraft will probably have seating for up to 52 passengers.

Nominal payload is 5000 kg (11 023 lb), but the An-72 seems well able to handle a payload of up to 7500 kg (16 535 lb).

At maximum take-off weight the An-72 needs a 1250-m (4101-ft) runway, while a reduction in take-off weight to 30 000 kg (67 240 lb) reduces the runway length required to 1200 m (3935 ft). The future of the An-72 is at present being evaluated in the light of a continuing test programme with the two prototypes.

If the type is judged adequate, there seems every likelihood that the type will be placed in widespread production.

It remains possible, however, that the An-72 is an interim type, and that the type programme is intended to provide experimental data for the USSR to develop a STOL transport as advanced as the YC-14 and the competing McDonnell Douglas YC-15, with electronically controlled flaps and spoilers, and a more sophisticated efflux-control system. It is also not clear, as yet, whether or not the Antonov An-72 uses a supercritical wing section such as the one that is embodied on the Boeing YC-14 aircraft.

Below: The original prototype of the An-72. The tail end is significantly different from that of the second prototype, this one having been found unsatisfactory
Bottom: An Aeroflot An-72. The Russian lettering under the wing says 'experimental'. The nose in the foreground is that of an Ilyushin Il-76

Il-76, Ilyushin
FIRST FLIGHT 1971

ALTHOUGH there is relatively little known about it in the West, the Ilyushin Il-76 is one of the most important aircraft types to appear in recent years. The origins of the Il-76 lie in a Soviet air force requirement for a strategic freight aircraft with a secondary flight-refuelling capability, but the Il-76 has since made a considerable impact in the development of resources-rich areas of the USSR inaccessible to other means of heavy transport.

Designed as a high-performance heavy freighter with a pressurized hold, the first Il-76 prototype for the Soviet air force made its maiden flight on March 25, 1971. It was immediately clear that in the new type, destined for both military and civil use, the Russians had an extremely useful aircraft, the positioning of the wing above the fuselage ensuring a large and unobstructed freight compartment. Designed to be able to carry a load of 40 000 kg (88 184 lb) over a range of 5000 km (3107 miles) at a speed of at least 833 km/h (518 mph), the Il-76 has achieved the first two requirements comfortably, and failed to meet the third by only 33 km/h (20 mph).

The prototype was shown in public at the Paris Air Show, with civil markings and the Aeroflot insignia, in 1971. The Soviets subsequently reported an Aeroflot order for 100, mainly for operation in Siberia and the underdeveloped regions of the USSR, where it could use short, unprepared landing strips. The aircraft was designed to be operated by a flight crew of four.

The establishment of no less than 24 world records for altitude with payload, and for speed with payload, in July 1975 set the seal on the remarkable performance of the Il-76. Among the most important of the type's records are the lifting of a 70 121-kg (154 588-lb) payload to 2000 m (6562 ft), and an average speed of 857.66 km/h (533 mph) with nine payloads between 30 000 kg (66 138 lb) and 70 000 kg (154 321 lb) over a closed circuit of 1000 km (621 miles). Apart from its excellent performance, the Il-76 also has first-class airfield performance. Take-off distances of only 850 m (2789 ft) have been quoted, although it is uncertain if this reflects take-off at the maximum weight of 157 000 kg (346 120 lb) or at a weight which has been reduced by the carriage of fuel for a short-haul flight.

The keys to the Il-76's performance are the engines and wings. The four turbofan engines are Soloviev D-30KPs, each rated at 12 000 kg (26 455 lb) st. In its earlier D-30K form this engine is used on the Ilyushin Il-62M and the re-engined Tupolev Tu-154A, but for use in the Il-76 the special D-30KP has a higher bypass ratio. The wings, which have a considerable anhedral angle, have two-part double-slotted trailing-edge flaps between the fuselage and the ailerons, with spoilers in front of the flaps, and leading-edge slats covering nearly the whole of the wing's span. The combination of engines and high-lift devices on a large wing ensure the notable short-field performance of the type. A clamshell thrust-reverser is fitted to each engine to ensure that landing distances are kept to an absolute minimum.

Above and left: The Ilyushin Il-76T was delivered to Aeroflot in 1976. This versatile aircraft serves in large numbers in the Soviet V-TA military transport force and has also been supplied to the Iraqi Air Force. With its multi-wheel undercarriage it has an outstanding short take-off performance, and with variable-pressure tyres can operate from unprepared airstrips

The undercarriage of the Il-76 is typical of the type now common for operations from prepared and unprepared runways: its configuration is basically of the tricycle type, but with the mainwheel bogies retracting into blisters on the fuselage sides. The nosewheel unit, consisting of one pair of wheels on each side of the central oleo leg, retracts into the fuselage just aft of the blister housing the ground-mapping radar. The mainwheel units each consist of four pairs of wheels in two transverse rows. All the tyres are of the low-pressure type for soft-field use. The left undercarriage blister also houses the auxiliary power unit which is essential for the Il-76 to be completely independent of airfield facilities.

Freight is loaded into the capacious fuselage up a ramp under the tail after the opening of large clamshell doors. Loading is facilitated by the provision of two overhead cranes on ceiling-mounted rails running the entire length of the pressurized freight compartment. Each crane has a capacity of about 2275 kg (5015 lb).

The latest version of the Il-76 is the Il-76T, which is the model in service with Aeroflot. This has larger rear clamshell doors and increased fuel capacity (about 20%), carried in the outer wings. The extra fuel and increased take-off weight allows the Il-76T to operate in the payload-limited rather than fuel-limited role, with a range some 1700 km (1056 miles) greater than that of the Il-76. Production is continuing, and it appears that the USSR will try to export the type to western operators in the near future.

Il-76

Above: The Il-76T with its 'bomb aimer's nose' which allows the navigator to make visual fixes on the terrain while in flight. The Il-76T has a pressurized hold for freight or vehicles

Il-76T

Type: medium- and long-range freighter
Maker: Ilyushin Design Bureau
Span: 50.5 m (165 ft 8 in)
Length: 46.59 m (152 ft 10¼ in)
Height: 14.76 m (48 ft 5 in)
Wing area: 300 m² (3229 sq ft)
Weight: maximum 170 000 kg (374 780 lb); empty not available
Powerplant: four 12 000-kg (26 455-lb) st Soloviev D30KP turbofans
Performance: cruising speed up to 800 km/h (497 mph); range with maximum payload 5000 km (3107 miles)
Payload: 40 000 kg (88 183 lb)
Crew: 3
Production: not available

Concorde, Aérospatiale/British Aerospace

FIRST FLIGHT 1969

ALTHOUGH the Tupolev Tu-144 has the historical distinction of being the first supersonic transport (SST) to fly and to enter service, the Concorde SST produced jointly by Aérospatiale and British Aerospace (legatees of the British Aircraft Corporation and Sud-Aviation) has the honour of being the world's first SST to carry fare-paying passengers on scheduled services. One of the most significant international programmes launched in the 1960s and 1970s, the Concorde resulted from a number of design studies evolved by British and French aircraft manufacturers during the 1950s. The novelty of the whole programme, necessitating vast expenditure on hitherto unexplored aspects of civil aviation, convinced the British and French governments, who would ultimately have to bear the financial burden for the development of an SST, that they should pool their efforts and split the costs.

The development of the Concorde as an Anglo-French project was facilitated by the fact that the two most advanced designs evolved by the separate national teams had produced aircraft of marked similarity: the Sud-Aviation Super Caravelle and the Bristol 223. Both these designs were for delta-winged aircraft with slim fuselages and four engines located in pairs under the rear portions of the wings. Externally, the French and British aircraft differed principally in that the former had a leading edge of ogival planform, compared with the latter's straight leading edge; the Super Caravelle had straight-edged vertical tail surfaces compared with the Bristol 223's basically curved unit; the

Super Caravelle had a fixed nose section compared with the 223's hinged nose capable of 'drooping' to provide the pilot with adequate visibility for take-off and landing; finally the Super Caravelle had its engine nacelles of curved section compared with the 223's rectangular ducts.

Both teams had studied the feasibility of using exotic materials to allow a cruising speed of Mach 3, but an examination of the difficulties and cost of using materials such as stainless steel persuaded the two teams to accept a cruising speed of about Mach 2, at which no problems were encountered by structures of special high-temperature aluminium alloy.

The Bristol 223 had been finalized as a result of lengthy processes under the overall aegis of the Supersonic Transport Aircraft Committee established in 1956, and in its definitive form was to be capable of carrying 110 passengers on the North Atlantic route between London and New York at a cruising speed of Mach 2. The Super Caravelle had been designed for short inter-city ranges, and the unveiling of the project at the 1961 Paris air show came as something of a surprise to the aviation world. The anticipated costs of the two programmes, and the similarities of the two projected aircraft, were thus strong spurs to the British and French governments to pool their efforts and resources. The 1962 government agreement came some 16 months after the British Aircraft Corporation (formed in 1960 by a merger of Bristol, English Electric and Vickers) and Sud-Aviation first started to investigate the possibility of joining

Top: A Singapore Airlines Concorde at the moment of take-off, showing the vapour in the strong vortex over the wing which contributes to the lift
Above: A front view of Concorde, clearly showing the half-raised visor which protects the windscreen from overheating at high speed. It is also aerodynamically essential during supersonic flight

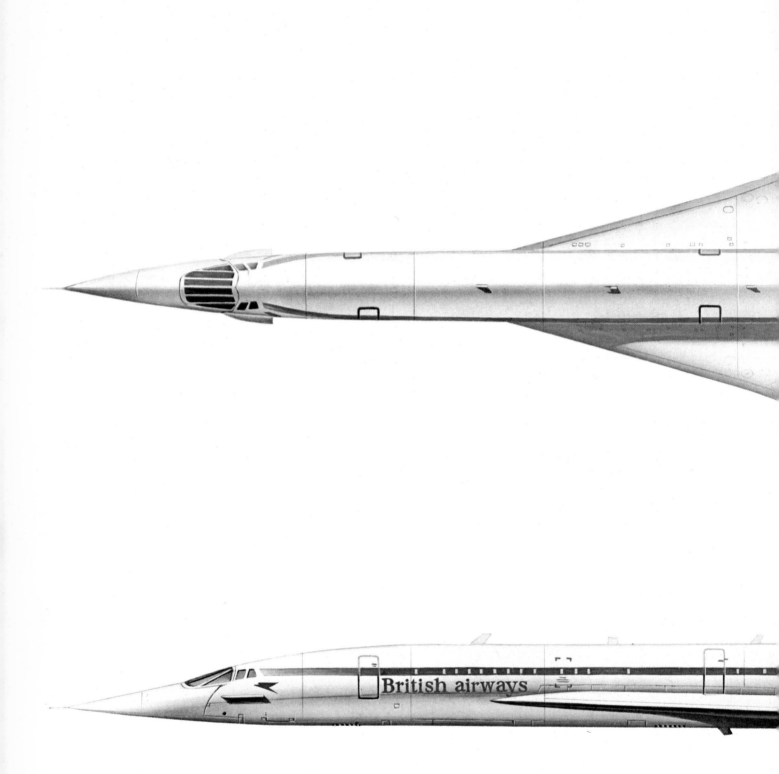

forces during a meeting in Paris on June 8, 1961. The effect of the governmental agreement was to formalize the arrangement whereby BAC and Sud-Aviation (absorbed into the Société Nationale Industrielle Aérospatiale in 1970) were to be equal partners in the development and production of the airframe, with Bristol Siddeley (later absorbed into Rolls-Royce) and SNECMA (Société Nationale d'Etude et de Construction de Moteurs d'Aviation) as equal partners in the design and production of the engines.

In 1963, following talks with long-haul airlines, the aircraft was significantly enlarged to operate over much greater ranges. For a time Sud-Aviation marketed a short-haul version which was later dropped from the programme.

The characteristic delta wing of the new aircraft, with its complex cambering and ogival leading edge, was achieved only after very careful experimentation (using the Fairey Delta 2 re-winged with an ogival delta as the BAC 221 for supersonic work, and the Handley Page 115 for low-speed trials with a narrow-delta planform), combined with exhaustive computer-aided examination of the theoretical aspects of such a wing. The results have been excellent.

Combined with the wing is a fuselage of a considerable fineness ratio to keep supersonic drag to a minimum. Up to 144 passengers can be accommodated in four-abreast seating, but the Concorde is normally fitted out with accommodation for 128 passengers seated three-abreast. The

Above: A British Airways Concorde. British Airways and Air France are the main users of Concorde but under various agreements Concordes are also used by SIA (Singapore) and Braniff (USA)

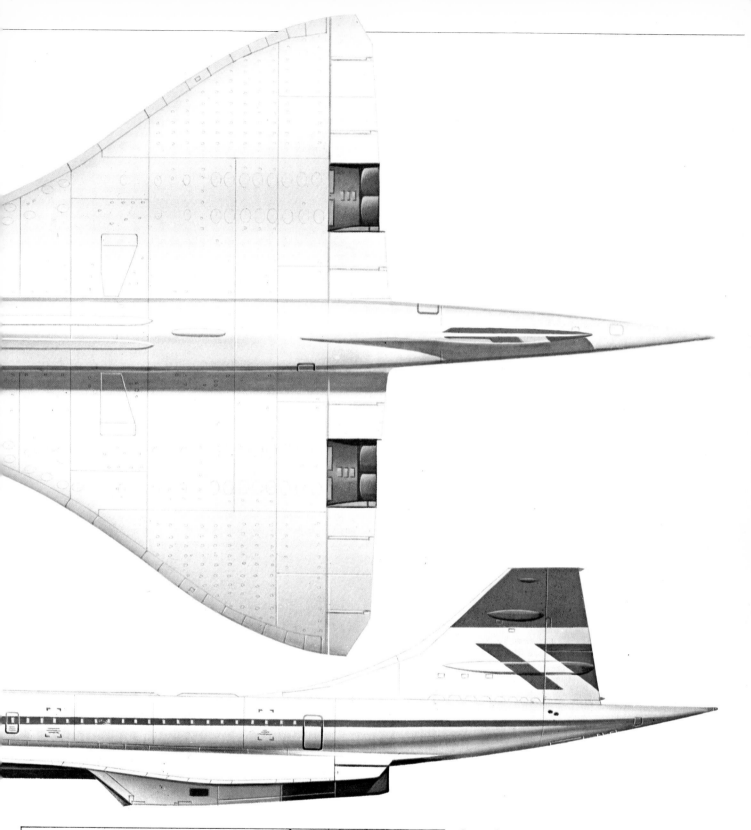

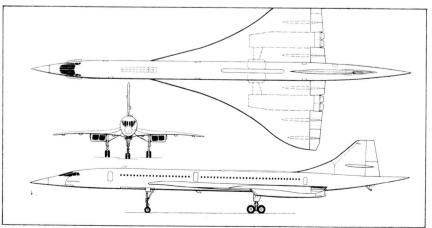

Concorde

Type: long-range supersonic transport
Maker: Société Nationale Industrielle Aérospatiale and British Aerospace Aircraft Group
Span: 25.55 m (83 ft 10 in)
Length: 62.1 m (203 ft 9 in)
Height: 11.4 m (37 ft 5 in)
Wing area: 358 m² (3856 sq ft)
Weight: maximum 185 065 kg (407 994 lb); empty 78 700 kg (173 502 lb)
Powerplant: four 17 259-kg (38 050-lb) st Rolls-Royce/SNECMA Olympus 593 Mk 610 afterburning turbojets
Performance: maximum cruising speed 2179 km/h (1354 mph) or Mach 2.04 at 15 635 m (51 300 ft); range with maximum payload and reserves at Mach 2.02 6228 km (3870 miles)
Payload: 12 700 kg (28 000 lb); seats for up to 144 passengers
Crew: 3
Production: 16

The vulture-like poise of
Concorde rotating for take off.
Each of its four Rolls-
Royce/SNECMA Olympus
593 turbojets generates
17 259 kg (38 050 lb) of static
thrust with its afterburner in
operation

aerodynamic reasons for so narrow a fuselage were inescapable, but the main criticism of the type from the passenger point of view has been the relatively cramped interior, with seats slightly narrower than those normally used in airliners. As the Concorde cruises at up to 18 288 m (60 000 ft), about half as high again as subsonic airliners, cabin pressurization is a relatively high 0.75 kg/cm^2 (10.7 lb/sq in), which made the designers' task that little bit more difficult. Another interesting facet of the fuselage design is the hinged nose, which is drooped to $-5°$ for take-off and to $-15°$ for landing. In the raised position, the nose is faired into the fuselage contours by a retractable visor.

The main fuel tankage comprises five tanks in each wing and four tanks in the fuselage, but there is also a subsidiary group of tanks designed principally to trim the aircraft longitudinally. One of the difficulties associated with the delta wing is that at transonic speeds the aerodynamic centre of pressure moves aft, necessitating the retrimming of the aircraft. For this purpose, therefore, the fuselage of the Concorde is provided with three additional tanks: two tanks forward of the centre of gravity, and a 12 729-litre (2800-Imp gal) tank under the fin. As the aircraft accelerates up to and through Mach 1, fuel is pumped from the forward tanks to the rear tank to maintain the correct centre of gravity; the process is reversed as the aircraft decelerates from the cruising phase of its flight. Without this relatively simple expedient, aerodynamic means would have to be employed, with a

Right: An engineer checking the installations for the radio and electronics equipment
Far right: Two Concordes under construction at Filton, near Bristol

Concorde

1 Variable geometry drooping nose
2 Weather radar
3 Spring pot
4 Visor jack
5 'A'-frame
6 Visor uplock
7 Visor guide rails and carriage
8 Droop nose jacks
9 Droop nose guide rails
10 Droop nose hinge
11 Rudder pedals
12 Captain's seat
13 Instrument panel shroud
14 Forward pressure bulkhead
15 Retracting visor
16 Multi-layer windscreen
17 Windscreen fluid rain clearance and wipers
18 Second pilot's seat
19 Roof panel
20 Flight-deck air duct
21 Third crew member's seat
22 Control relay jacks
23 First supernumerary's seat

24 Second supernumerary's folding seat (optional)
25 Radio and electronics racks (Channel 2)
26 Radio and electronics racks (Channel 1)
27 Plug-type forward passenger door
28 Slide/life-raft pack stowage
29 Cabin staff tip-up seat
30 Forward galley units (left and right)
31 Toilets (2)
32 Coats (crew and passengers)
33 Twelve 26-man life-rafts
34 VHF1 antenna
35 Overhead racks (with doors)
36 Cabin furnishing (heat and sound insulated)
37 Four-abreast one-class passenger accommodation
38 Seat rails
39 Metal-faced floor panels
40 Nosewheel well
41 Nosewheel main doors
42 Nosewheel leg
43 Shock absorber

44 Twin nosewheels
45 Torque links
46 Steering mechanism
47 Telescopic strut
48 Lateral bracing struts
49 Nosewheel actuating jacks
50 Underfloor air-conditioning ducts
51 Nosewheel door actuator
52 Nosewheel secondary (aft) doors
53 Fuselage frame (single flange)
54 Machined window panel
55 Underfloor forward baggage compartment (6.72 m^3 [237 cu ft])
56 Fuel lines
57 Lattice ribs
58 No 9 (left forward) trim tank
59 Single-web spar
60 No 10 (left forward) trim tank
61 Middle passenger doors (left and right)
62 Cabin staff tip-up seat
63 Toilets
64 Emergency radio stowage
65 Provision for VHF3
66 Overhead baggage racks
67 Cabin aft section

68 Fuselage frame
69 Tank vent gallery
70 No 1 forward collector tank
71 Lattice ribs
72 Engine-feed pumps
73 Accumulator
74 No 5 fuel tank
75 Trim transfer gallery
76 Leading-edge machined ribs
77 Removable leading-edge sections
78 Expansion joints between sections
79 Contents unit
80 Inlet control valve
81 Transfer pumps
82 Flight-deck air duct
83 No 8 fuselage tank
84 Vapour seal above tank
85 Pre-stretched integrally machined wing skin panels
86 Pressure-floor curved membranes
87 No 8 wing tank
88 No 4 forward collector tank
89 No 10 right forward trim tank
90 No 9 right forward trim tank
91 Quick-lock removable inspection panels

92 Spraymat leading-edge de-icing panels
93 Leading-edge anti-icing strip
94 Spar-box machined girder side pieces
95 No 7 fuel tank
96 No 7a fuel tank
97 Static dischargers
98 Elevon
99 Inter-elevon flexible joint
100 Combined secondary nozzles/reverser buckets
101 Nozzle-mounting spigots
102 Cabin air delivery/distribution
103 Inspection panels
104 Cold-air unit
105 Fuel-cooled heat exchanger
106 Fuel/hydraulic oil heat exchanger
107 Fire-suppression bottles
108 Main spar frame
109 Accumulator
110 No 3 aft collector tank
111 Control linkage
112 'Z'-section spot-welded stringers
113 Riser to distribution duct
114 Anti-surge bulkheads

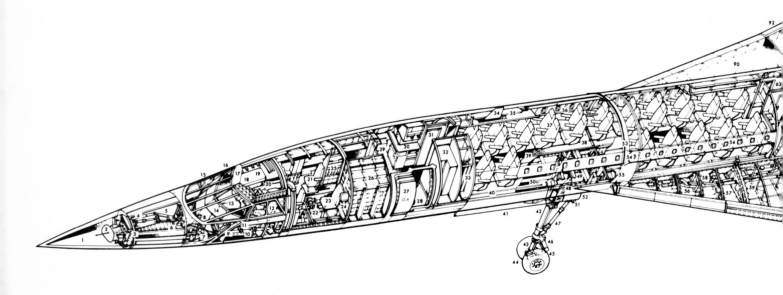

115 No 6 (underfloor) fuel tank
116 Machined pressurized keel box
117 Fuselage frame
118 Double-flange frame/floor join
119 Machined pressure-floor support beams
120 Left undercarriage well
121 Mainwheel door
122 Fuselage/wing attachments
123 Main spar frame
124 Mainwheel retraction link
125 Mainwheel actuating jack
126 Cross beam
127 Forked link
128 Drag strut
129 Mainwheel leg
130 Shock absorber
131 Pitch dampers
132 Four-wheel main undercarriage
133 Bogie beam
134 Torque links
135 Intake boundary layer splitter
136 Honeycomb intake nose section
137 Spraymat intake lip de-icing
138 Ramp motor and gearbox
139 Forward ramp

140 Aft ramp
141 Inlet flap
142 Spill door actuator
143 Intake duct
144 Tank vent gallery
145 Engine front support links
146 Engine-mounting transverse equalizers
147 Oil tank
148 Primary heat exchanger
149 Secondary heat exchanger
150 Heat-exchanger exhaust air
151 Rolls-Royce SNECMA Olympus 593 Mk 610 turbojet
152 Outer wing fixing (340 high-tensile steel bolts)
153 Engine main mounting

154 Power control unit mounting
155 No 5a fuel tank
156 Tank vent
157 Transfer pump
158 Left outer elevon control unit fairing
159 Static dischargers
160 Honeycomb elevon structure
161 Flexible joint
162 Left middle elevon control hinge/fairing
163 Power control unit twin output
164 Control rod linkage
165 Nacelle aft support link
166 Reverser-bucket actuating screw jack
167 Retractable silencer lobes ('spades')
168 Primary (inner) variable nozzle
169 Pneumatic nozzle actuators
170 Nozzle-mounting spigots
171 Left inner elevon control hinge/fairing
172 Control rod linkage

173 Manual stand-by power control
174 Accumulator
175 Vent and pressurization system
176 Forged wing/fuselage main frames
177 Ground-supply air-conditioning connection
178 Control mixing unit
179 Control rod (elevon) linkage
180 Aft galley unit
181 Rear emergency doors (left and right)
182 Wingroot fillet
183 Air-conditioning manual discharge valve
184 Automatic discharge/relief valve
185 First-aid oxygen cylinders
186 Rear baggage compartment (door to right)
187 Rear pressure bulkhead
188 Fin support frames
189 No 11 aft trim tank
190 Machined centre posts
191 Shock absorber
192 Retractable tail bumper
193 Tail bumper door

194 Nitrogen Dewar
195 Monergol tank (see 197)
196 Fuel jettison
197 Monergol-powered emergency power unit (pre-production aircraft only)
198 Tail cone
199 Rear navigation light
200 Rudder lower section
201 Servo control unit fairing (manual stand-by)
202 Fixed rudder stub
203 Multi-bolt fin-spar attachment
204 Fin construction
205 Fin spar
206 Air-conditioning ducting
207 HF antenna
208 Finroot fairing
209 Leading-edge structure
210 Servo unit threshold bellcrank
211 Servo control unit fairing
212 VOR antenna
213 Rudder upper section
214 Static dischargers

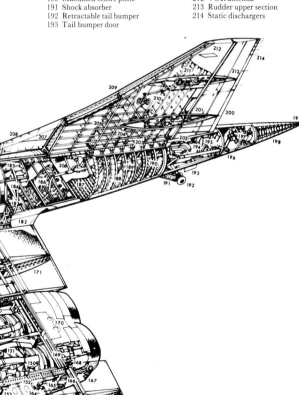

A Rolls-Royce/SNECMA Olympus 593, developed in the UK and France to power Concorde. Rolls-Royce manufactured the engine and SNECMA produced the afterburner, convergent/divergent exhaust nozzle and reverser

consequent increase in drag and also in fuel consumption.

The problem of the engines with which to power the Concorde was a thorny one: to give the aircraft the designed performance it was essential that the chosen powerplant should have high thrust for good take-off, acceleration and cruising perform-ance, combined with low specific fuel consumption to ensure good range. At the time of the Concorde's design the turbojet appeared to meet these requirements better than a turbofan, largely as a result of the turbojet's high performance and low frontal area. But such an engine with a very high pressure ratio would have too high a turbine entry temperature despite its low weight; and an engine with a relatively high bypass ratio would have good specific fuel consumption but only at the expense of a relatively low specific thrust, high installed weight and large frontal area. The designers finally opted for a turbojet with a medium pressure ratio, fed through highly complex and fully automatic variable-geometry intakes. The best choice thus seemed to be the Bristol Olympus afterburning turbojet, already under development for the unfortunately cancelled BAC TSR.2 strike and reconnaissance aircraft. A special model, the Olympus 593, was developed by the British (60%) and French (40%). Test flown under the fuselage of a Vulcan bomber, the Olympus 593 had minor problems with fuel consumption, noise emission and smoke generation, but has now been developed into an effective engine. All four engines, located in paired underwing ducts, are fitted with clamshell thrust-reversers.

Production was to be undertaken jointly, with aircraft coming off twin final assembly lines, one in Toulouse and the other at Filton near Bristol. Sud/Aérospatiale was responsible for the rear cabin section, wings, control surfaces, control systems, hydraulic systems, air-conditioning system, radio system and navigation system. BAC's area of responsibility was the three forward fuselage sections, rear fuselage, vertical tail surfaces, engine nacelles and associated ducting, fuel system, electrical system, engine installation, insulation and fire-warning and extinguishing systems.

By 1965 the design had advanced sufficiently for construction of two prototypes to begin: Concorde 001 at Toulouse, and Concorde 002 at Filton. The building of these two aircraft began in April, and both machines first flew in 1969, 001 on March 2 and 002 on April 9. Throughout the test programme 001 was slightly ahead of 002, first reaching Mach 1 on October 1, 1969 and Mach 2 on November 4, 1970. Slightly smaller than production Concordes, 001 and 002 had a maximum take-off weight of some 147 874 kg (326 000 lb).

These two aircraft were later joined by the two pre-production models, Concordes 01 and 02 (later 101 and 102, built at Filton and Toulouse respectively). These first flew on December 17, 1971 and January 10, 1973, and were more typical of the production standard Concorde. The fuselage was lengthened by 2.6 m (8 ft 6½ in) to 58.84 m (193 ft ½ in), increasing the pressurized fuselage length by 5.9 m (19 ft 3½ in). Changes also included improved wing geometry, revised visor, and ulti-

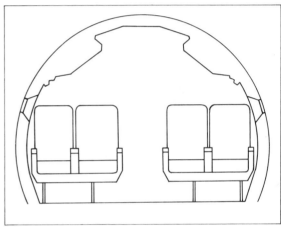

mately production standard Olympus 593 Mk 602 engines, each rated at 17 259 kg (38 050 lb) st with 17% afterburning. Maximum take-off weight was 174 635 kg (385 000 lb).

The first two production aircraft, Concordes 201 and 202 from Toulouse and Filton respectively, made their first flights on December 6, 1973 and February 13, 1974, have a maximum take-off weight of 181 440 kg (400 000 lb) and are powered by Olympus 593 Mk 610 turbojets, each rated at 17 259 kg (38 050 lb) st with 17% afterburning. These aircraft were used by the manufacturers largely for development trials. The next two production aircraft, Concordes 203 and 204, were also used for trials, mostly range and payload.

The prime users of the new airliner, British Airways and Air France, finally put the type into service on May 24, 1976, the British Concorde 206 flying the London to Bahrain route, and the French 205 the Paris to Rio de Janeiro route via Dakar. Since then the route network has been greatly extended and Braniff and Singapore Airlines also fly sectors.

The introduction of the aircraft into airline service was accompanied by widespread environmentalist protests and political argument especially in the United States, and the lateness of the whole programme has militated against an effective service life and further sales. Production aircraft totalled 16, the last making its first flight on April 20, 1979. The whole project has overrun its costs by an enormous margin, but slight profits in the future are possible.

Top: The flight-deck of Concorde, showing the engineer's panel on the right
Above left: The cabin Machmeter, indicating a speed of Mach 2
Above: A cross-section of Concorde's passenger cabin. The fuselage is only 262.6 cm (103.4 in) wide, allowing for only four 45.7-cm (18-in) seats with an aisle of 43.2 cm (17 in). A wide-bodied SST would be too long to fit airports

Tu-144, Tupolev

FIRST FLIGHT 1968

THE Tupolev Tu-144 was the first supersonic airliner in the world to fly and enter service, and is by any standards a milestone in the history of transport. It is indicative of the speed and determination with which the Russians can move, however, that the origins of the design appear to be later than several American supersonic transport (SST) designs, with full-scale development beginning after that of the Anglo-French Concorde SST. It seems fairly clear that the original design of the Tu-144 owed much to the concerted espionage effort launched by the Russians from 1961 onwards to discover as much as possible of British and French progress with the varied and challenging problems of SST design.

First revealed in public as a model at the 1965 Paris air show, the Tu-144 right from the start displayed a number of remarkable similarities with the Concorde, including a cambered delta wing with an ogival leading edge, a slim fuselage, and 'drooping' nose to ensure good pilot vision at high angles of attack. Indeed, the aircraft was so like Concorde that the western popular press dubbed it the 'Soviet Concorde' or the 'Concordskii'. Like the British and French, the Russians conducted a considerable quantity of flight-test work with smaller aircraft incorporating Tu-144 features: the most notable was a Mikoyan-Gurevich MiG-21 fighter with a scaled-down Tu-144 wing replacing its delta wing and the conventional horizontal tailplane.

Unlike the Concorde team, the Russian desig-

A Tupolev Tu-144 on display at Le Bourget. Apparent in this photograph is the Tu-144 similarity with Concorde. In the right background is an Il-76

ners under the supervision of Alexei Andreevich Tupolev, son of the bureau's founder, opted to power their aircraft with afterburning turbofans. These are Kuznetsov NK-144s, specially developed from the NK-8 and initially capable of providing a dry thrust of 13 000 kg (28 660 lb), afterburning raising this figure to 17 500 kg (38 581 lb). All four engines were located in a single large duct under the rear fuselage.

Though slightly cruder in execution than its western counterpart, the Tu-144 is slightly larger than Concorde, and designed to cruise at higher speeds (Mach 2.2 or 2.3).

For the test phase of the programme three prototypes were built at the Zhukovsky factory outside Moscow: two were flying prototypes, and the third was for structural testing. The first flying prototype was finished in the second half of 1968, and first flew on December 31 of that year, beating the first Concorde into the air by some two months. Mach 1 was exceeded on June 5, 1969, at an altitude of 11 000 m (36 089 ft), and on May 26, 1970, the Tu-144 exceeded Mach 2 at 16 300 m (53 477 ft). All of these were firsts for a civil aircraft. The Tu-144 was shown to the public for the first time on May 21, 1970, at Sheremetyevo Airport outside Moscow and it was claimed at this time that the Tu-144 had entered series production at Voronezh.

All was not well with the test programme, however. The first prototype had by May 1972 amassed some 200 hours in the air, 100 of them at

supersonic speeds, during about 150 test flights. Considering that the aircraft had been available for nearly three and a half years, this is hardly an impressive total and indicative of severe problems. As a matter of fact, the second and third Tu-144s had each completed only a few flights by May 1972.

· The result was a virtual redesign of the type. In this revised form, first seen in Russia at the beginning of 1973 and in the West at the Paris air show of May 1973, the Tu-144 had been enlarged somewhat. The ogival wings had been replaced by new wings of compound delta planform, the engines had been relocated in two pairs in long underwing ducts, the undercarriage had been revised and retractable 'moustache' foreplanes had been added just aft of the flight-deck to improve low-speed lift and handling characteristics. These improvements notwithstanding, the aircraft exhibited at Paris in 1973 (the second production aircraft) crashed during a display, probably as a result of pilot error as indicated by the fact that the Tu-144 shown at the 1975 Paris show differed only in detail from the 1973 aircraft. Naturally enough, these and other production aircraft make use of the fully developed NK-144 turbofan, rated at 15 000 kg (33 069 lb) dry thrust, afterburning providing a maximum thrust of 20 000 kg (44 092 lb). Although each pair of engines is housed in a single duct, a vertical plate in the intake separates the airflow to each engine. To ensure the right airflow to the engines, each intake has a fully automatic movable ramp. For cruising, about 35% afterburning is generally used.

Standard accommodation is for 140 passengers in three cabins: at the front there is accommodation for 11 first-class passengers seated three-abreast; next comes the forward tourist-class accommodation, with 30 passengers seated five-abreast; and finally there is another tourist-class compartment with seating for 99 in 15 five-abreast and six four-abreast rows.

The first four production Tu-144s were made available to Aeroflot for route-proving trials during the first six months of 1974: the main route flown was that between Moscow and Vladivostok, with an intermediate stop at Tyumen. The first scheduled flight operated by the Tu-144 was between Moscow and Alma Ata on December 26, 1975. The Tu-144 carried mail and covered the 3500-km (2175-mile) route in 1 hour 59 min, at an average speed of about 1765 km/h (1097 mph). Further mail and freight flights were flown during 1976 and 1977, despite a spate of problems associated with the need to use a fair degree of afterburning, leading to heavy fuel consumption, and compressor stalls. Passenger-carrying flights were started in November 1977, but following at least one crash the Tu-144 was withdrawn from airline service on June 1, 1978. The fact that the Russians have tried unsuccessfully to secure from Lucas an electronic fuel-control system seems to indicate engine problems. Aérospatiale has been helping the Russians with the problem, but it is possible that the Tu-144 may be revised radically to make use of new Kolesov engines of advanced variable-geometry design.

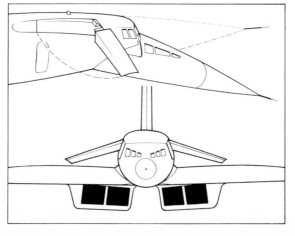

Above and above right: The prototype Tu-144 had wings with a definite ogival form, investigated and tested with a rebuilt MiG-21 fighter
Left: The drooping nose and the canard noseplanes which are deployed for landing and take-off but fold flush into the fuselage for cruising
Right: A close up of the canards; when open they have an overall span of 6.1 m (20 ft). They have anhedral when open and incorporate fixed double leading-edge slats plus double-slotted trailing-edge flaps

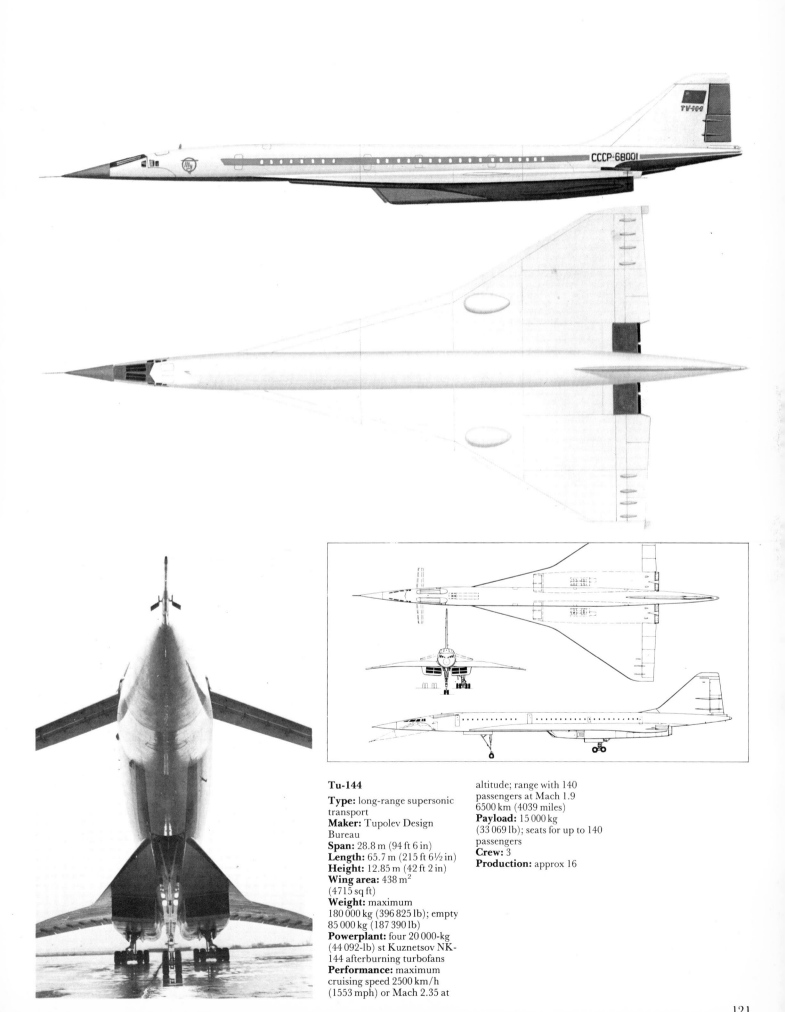

Tu-144

Type: long-range supersonic transport
Maker: Tupolev Design Bureau
Span: 28.8 m (94 ft 6 in)
Length: 65.7 m (215 ft 6½ in)
Height: 12.85 m (42 ft 2 in)
Wing area: 438 m²
(4715 sq ft)
Weight: maximum
180 000 kg (396 825 lb); empty
85 000 kg (187 390 lb)
Powerplant: four 20 000-kg
(44 092-lb) st Kuznetsov NK-
144 afterburning turbofans
Performance: maximum
cruising speed 2500 km/h
(1553 mph) or Mach 2.35 at

altitude; range with 140
passengers at Mach 1.9
6500 km (4039 miles)
Payload: 15 000 kg
(33 069 lb); seats for up to 140
passengers
Crew: 3
Production: approx 16

121

DC-9 Super 80, McDonnell Douglas

FIRST FLIGHT 1979

THE Super 80 series of McDonnell Douglas's best-selling DC-9 family has been evolved in response to customer requirements for increased capacity over the same short- and medium-range routes as earlier DC-9s. At the same time McDonnell Douglas has taken the opportunity to improve the basic aircraft by the incorporation of newer technology in the airframe and engines which improves the Super 80's operating economics.

The origins of the new model lay in a 1975 test carried out by McDonnell Douglas: a standard DC-9 was flown with a pair of 'refanned' Pratt & Whitney JT8D turbofans: these engines, whose first production model is the JT8D-209, were developed by combining the high-pressure core of the JT8D-9 with a new low-pressure fan of greater diameter, and a new low-pressure compressor, these last two features being derived from the NASA JT8D Refan Program technology. The effect of the transmogrification is to raise basic thrust to 8732 kg (19 250 lb), at the same time reducing noise and specific fuel consumption, the latter by about 10% at the engines' maximum cruise ratings.

The success of the experiment led McDonnell Douglas to propose a number of DC-9 variants. Among these were the DC-9 Series 50RS with a fuselage stretch of 2.41 m (7 ft 11 in) and a pair of JT8D-209s; the DC-9 Series 50-17R with the same fuselage stretch and a pair of JT8D-17Rs; the DC-9 Series 60 with a fuselage stretch of 5.28 m (17 ft 4 in) and a pair of the considerably more powerful SNECMA/General Electric CFM56 or Pratt & Whitney JT10D turbofans; and the DC-9SC based on the Series 50RS but with a wing of supercritical design to improve cruising performance.

The experience gained with these projects led finally to the proposed DC-9 Series 55 of 1977: this was to have a fuselage stretched by 3.86 m (12 ft 8 in) and be powered by two JT8D-209s of an earlier type. Consultation with prospective buyers determined McDonnell Douglas on a further fuselage stretch, and thus was born the revised DC-9 Series 55, later designated Super 80. Maximum passenger capacity is raised to 172 compared with the DC-9 Series 50's 139, with a parallel increase in hold volume to 35.2 m³ (1243 cu ft) from 29.3 m³ (1034 cu ft). The wings, whose extra span comes from root plugs and a 0.61-m (2-ft) kinked extension at each wingtip, have some 28% more area than those of the DC-9 Series 50 aircraft.

McDonnell Douglas formally announced the Super 80 series in October 1977, by which time orders for 27 production Super 81s had been placed, Swissair leading with 15 aircraft. But although the first Super 80 was expected to fly in July 1979, there were some considerable delays, and the first flight was some three and a half months late. This was partly attributable to manpower problems and late delivery of items of equipment and other materials, but also to the need of the McDonnell Douglas designers and engineers to strengthen the wing centre section in view of the higher operating weights of the type, and also to relocate many of the control runs in the wings.

The only other DC-9 Super 80 model currently

available is the Super 82, powered by two JT8D-217 turbofans each rated at 9458 kg (20 850 lb) st and permitting maximum take-off weights in the order of 66 679 kg (147 000 lb). Full certification of the DC-9 Super 81 was expected in July 1980, with the Super 82 some months later. It is anticipated that the main use of the Super 81 will be for operations in temperate climates, while the Super 82 will be most useful with its higher-rated engines for operations in 'hot and high' conditions. By early 1980 McDonnell Douglas had not received an order from a significant US domestic operator. They have also announced the Super 80S: this will be yet further stretched with engines such as the Pratt & Whitney STF-517, Rolls-Royce RB.432 or SNECMA/General Electric CFM56.

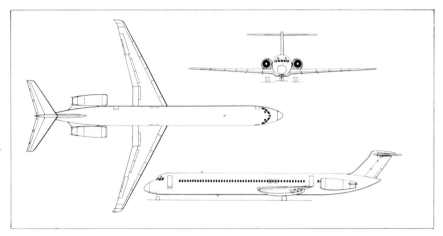

Right: A McDonnell Douglas DC-9 Super 80 in flight. The Super 80 was developed to meet a customer requirement for a short/medium-range aircraft with a greater capacity than offered by earlier DC-9 versions

DC-9 Super 80

Type: short- and medium-range transport
Maker: Douglas Aircraft Co
Span: 32.87 m (107 ft 10 in)
Length: 45.06 m (147 ft 10 in)
Height: 9.04 m (29 ft 8 in)
Wing area: 118.8 m² (1279 sq ft)
Weight: maximum 63 504 kg (140 000 lb); empty 35 683 kg (78 666 lb)
Powerplant: two 9458-kg (20 850-lb) st Pratt & Whitney JT8D-209 turbofans

Performance (estimated): maximum cruising speed 929 km/h (577 mph) at 8230 m (27 000 ft); range with maximum payload and reserves 2575 km (1600 miles)
Payload: 18 236 kg (40 203 lb); seats for up to 172 passengers

Crew: 2

Production: 65 ordered by 1980

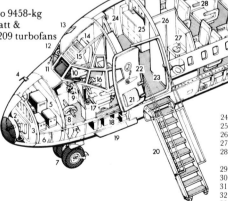

DC-9 Super 80

1 Radome
2 Weather radar scanner
3 Front pressure bulkhead
4 Pitot tube
5 Radio and electronics bay
6 Nosewheel well
7 Twin nosewheels
8 Rudder pedals
9 Instrument panel
10 Instrument panel shroud
11 Windscreen wipers
12 Windscreen panels
13 Cockpit eyebrow windows
14 1st officer's seat
15 Overhead switch panel
16 Captain's seat
17 Nosewheel steering control
18 Underfloor electrical and electronics bay
19 Nose strake
20 Retractable airstairs
21 Door mounted escape chute
22 Forward passenger door, open
23 Entry lobby
24 Right service door
25 Forward galley
26 Toilet compartment
27 Wash hand basin
28 Four-abreast 1st-class seating compartment, 12 passengers
29 D/F loop aerials
30 VHF aerial
31 Curtained cabin divider
32 Cabin window panel
33 Pressurization valves
34 Fuselage lower lobe frame construction
35 Wardrobe
36 Five-abreast tourist class seating, 125 passengers
37 Overhead stowage bins
38 Cabin roof frames
39 Air conditioning ducting
40 Cabin roof trim panels
41 Floor beam construction
42 Forward freight hold
43 Forward freight hold rear door 24.04 m³ (849 cu ft) capacity
44 Left overhead stowage bin rack

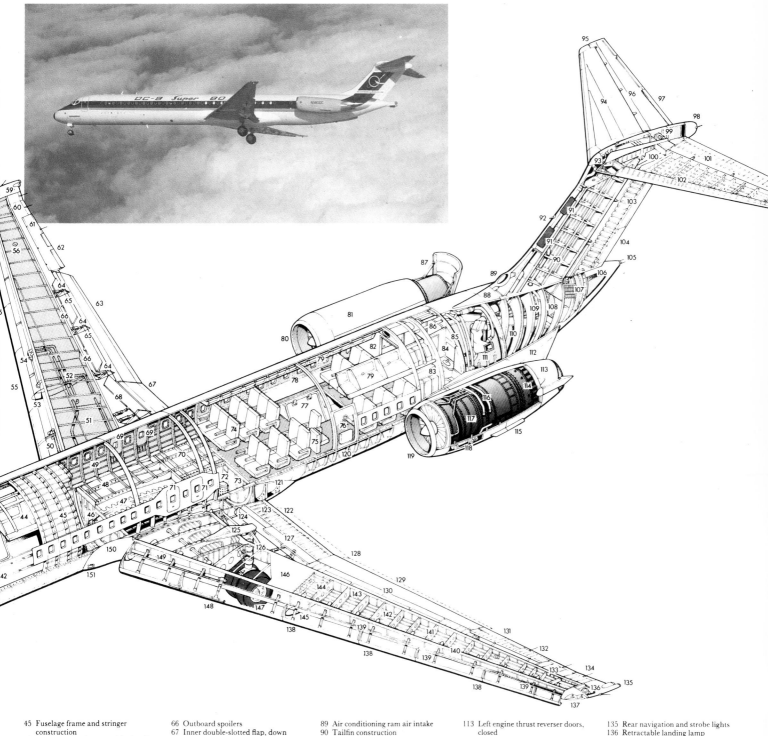

45 Fuselage frame and stringer
   construction
46 Leading-edge slat central hydraulic
   jack control
47 Wing panel centreline joint
48 Floor beam construction
49 Centre fuselage construction
50 Cable drive to leading-edge slats
51 Right wing integral fuel tank, total
   system capacity 21 876 litres
   (4812 Imp gal)
52 Fuel system piping
53 Ventral wing fence/vortilon
54 Pressure refuelling connections
55 Leading-edge slat segments, open
56 Overwing fuel filler cap
57 Right navigation lights
58 Extended wingtip
59 Rear navigation and strobe lights
60 Static dischargers
61 Right aileron
62 Aileron tabs
63 Right outer double-slotted flap,
64 Flap hydraulic jacks
65 Flap hinge brackets

66 Outboard spoilers
67 Inner double-slotted flap, down
   position
68 Inboard spoiler
69 Right emergency exit windows
70 Pressure floor above wheel bay
71 Left emergency exit windows
72 Hydraulic reservoir
73 Main undercarriage wheel well
74 Rear cabin tourist class seats
75 Cabin attendants folding seat
76 Rear service door/emergency exit
77 Rear underfloor freight hold door
78 Cabin wall trim panels
79 Overhead stowage bins
80 Right engine intake
81 Detachable engine cowlings
82 Cabin rear bulkhead
83 Rear galleys, left and right
84 Toilet compartments, left and right
85 Rear pressure bulkhead
86 Rear entry door
87 Engine thrust reverser, open
   position
88 Fin root fillet

89 Air conditioning ram air intake
90 Tailfin construction
91 VOR aerials
92 Rudder feel system pressure senso
93 Tailplane trim jack
94 Right tailplane
95 Elevator horn balance
96 Right elevator
97 Elevator tabs
98 Tailplane bullet fairing
99 Elevator hinge controls
100 Tailplane pivot mounting
101 Left elevator
102 Tailplane construction
103 Rudder construction
104 Rudder tab
105 Static dischargers
106 Tailcone, jettisonable for
    emergency exit
107 Air conditioning louvres
108 Sloping fin attachment frames
109 Tailplane de-icing air duct
110 Rear entry airstairs tunnel
111 Air conditioning plant
112 Engine pylon

113 Left engine thrust reverser doors,
    closed
114 Radial lobe engine silencer
115 Nacelle strake
116 Bleed air piping
117 Pratt & Whitney JT8D-209
    turbofan engine
118 Engine accessory gearbox
119 Left engine intake
120 Rear underfloor freight hold,
    12.6 m³ (445 cu ft) capacity
121 Wing root trailing-edge fillet
122 Left inner double-slotted flap
123 Flap rib construction
124 Flap vane
125 Main undercarriage mounting
126 Main undercarriage leg strut
127 Inboard spoiler
128 Flap down position
129 Outer double-slotted flap
130 Outboard spoilers
131 Aileron tabs
132 Left aileron
133 Fixed portion of trailing edge
134 Static dischargers

135 Rear navigation and strobe lights
136 Retractable landing lamp
137 Left navigation lights
138 Leading-edge slat segments, open
139 Slat guide rails
140 Front spar
141 Wing rib construction
142 Left wing integral fuel tank
143 Rear spar
144 Wing stringers
145 Ventral wing fence/vortilon
146 Wing skin plating
147 Twin mainwheels
148 Slat de-icing air duct
149 Air supply duct
150 Wing root fillet
151 Taxiing lamp

123

BAe 146, British Aerospace

FIRST FLIGHT 1981

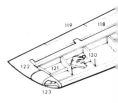

IN common with all too many British aviation projects, the gestation of the British Aerospace 146 has been lengthy, largely as a result of having been put on ice for nearly four years. The origins of the design lie with a Hawker Siddeley proposal, revealed in August 1973, for a short-range transport powered by four quiet turbofans. Funding for the project was to be provided largely by the British government, but national economic crisis followed soon after the Hawker Siddeley announcement, and this made it foolish at that time to invest the money.

During April 1977 Hawker Siddeley was absorbed into Britain's new nationalized aviation industry, British Aerospace. This at last provided just sufficient finance for the completion of the design, plus the production of assembly jigs and test rigs while extensive wind-tunnel testing confirmed the basic soundness of the design.

In July 1978 the British Aerospace 146, as the type had now become, was again launched with the promise of substantial government aid. The requirement to which the 146 has been designed is a difficult one: it calls for a relatively small aircraft able to offer the same degree of passenger comfort as is available in far larger wide-bodied airliners, combined with low aircraft-mile and seat-mile costs, first-class airfield performance and, most importantly, low operating noise. Such an airliner, for which a large market is supposed to exist, does not meet the needs of larger operators, however, and so the sales effort of British Aerospace is directed towards smaller, and often more cautious, operators. Some 130 possible buyers have been approached, but although considerable interest has been shown, in practical terms it needs a larger operator to make the initial order and so get full-scale production under way.

Despite a major engineering strike and shortages of various components and materials, British Aerospace expected the first 146-100 to fly by February 1981, to receive its certificate of airworthiness by the end of 1981, and to reach its first customers during 1982, with production targets being reached during that year. Paradoxically, the very lateness of the programme has been of some benefit, for the major teething troubles of the Avco Lycoming ALF502 turbofan's gearbox and fuel consumption problems will probably be cured during the Canadair Challenger business jet's troublesome

development programme, whereas the problems would otherwise have plagued the flight tests of the 146. Among the risk-sharing partners in the 146 programme are Avco Aerostructures (USA) for the wing, Saab-Scania (Sweden) for tailplanes and control surfaces and Short Brothers for engine pods.

The first model will be the 146-100, which is intended largely for operations from semi-prepared runways on airfields with only minimal services. This is fully in keeping with the expressed role of the 146 and to a great extent dictates the configuration of the aircraft, which resembles rough-field freighters more than other airliners. The wing is high-set and of a Hawker Siddeley high-lift airfoil; in keeping with the likely customer capabilities, the high-lift devices fitted are minimal, consisting only of broad-span single-section Fowler flaps. The soft-field main landing gears each have twin wheels on one axle, and low-pressure tyres are optional. The mainwheels retract into fairings on the sides of the fuselage. To help make the aircraft independent of ground services, an auxiliary power unit can be fitted.

The 146-200 will be essentially similar, but based on a fuselage some 2.4 m (7 ft 10½ in) longer than the 100's 26.16 m (85 ft 10 in), capable of carrying up to 106 passengers six-abreast. The 146-200 will be capable of operations from paved runways only. The maximum take-off weight of the 146-200 will be some 6192 kg (13 650 lb) greater than the 33 498 kg (73 850 lb) of the 146-100, and the performance of the British Aerospace 146-200 will consequently be lower.

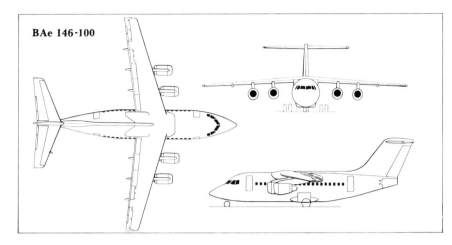

BAe 146-100

BAe 146-200

Type: short-range transport
Maker: British Aerospace Aircraft Group
Span: 26.34 m (86 ft 5 in)
Length: 28.56 m (93 ft 8½ in)
Height: 8.61 m (28 ft 3 in)
Wing area: 77.3 m² (832 sq ft)
Weight (estimated): maximum 39 690 kg (87 500 lb); empty 21 065 kg (46 440 lb)
Powerplant: four 3039-kg (6700-lb) st Avco Lycoming ALF502R-3 turbofans
Performance (estimated): maximum cruising speed 761 km/h (473 mph) at 6706 m (22 000 ft); range with

maximum payload and no reserves 2857 km (1775 miles)
Payload: 10 006 kg (22 060 lb); seats for up to 106 passengers
Crew: 2
Production: first orders in 1980

BAe 146

1 Elevator mass balance
2 Twin tabs
3 Elevators, manually operated
4 Fixed tailplane
5 Elevator control linkage
6 Tab linkage
7 Tailplane box
8 Anti-icing ducts to tailplane leading edge
9 Detachable fin leading-edge section
10 Two-spar fin structure
11 Fin stringers/rib construction
12 Rudder hydraulic jacks
13 Rudder construction
14 Rear navigation lights
15 Petal-type airbrakes
16 Airbrakes (extended — max 60° deflection)
17 Airbrake hydraulic jack
18 Cross-connecting strut (pantograph linkage)
19 Fin/fuselage attachment points
20 APU (optional)
21 APU exhaust
22 Air-conditioning packs
23 Rear service door (plug type, outward-opening)
24 Twin seats
25 Rear pressure dome
26 Ram air intake
27 Engine air bleed ducts

28 Rear passenger door (plug type, outward-opening)
29 Rear toilet
30 Door hinge/mechanism
31 Doorway (airstairs optional)
32 Airstairs stowage
33 Cabin floor
34 Bulkhead
35 Wingroot fairing
36 Landing gear rear bulkhead frame
37 Fuselage construction
38 Wing skinning, jointed on aircraft centreline
39 Lift spoilers — three identical surfaces each wing
40 Roll spoiler — one each wing
41 Aileron trim and servo tabs
42 Left aileron (honeycomb construction)
43 Left navigation light
44 Vent inlet
45 Fuel lines
46 Left landing light
47 Engine pylons
48 Left engine nacelles
49 Wingroot fairing
50 Wing/fuselage attachment
51 Hat-racks and passenger baggage
52 Hydraulics equipment bay
53 Five-abreast passenger accommodation
54 Cabin floor — sandwich panel with non-metallic core

55 Bulkhead, rear of cargo hold
56 Main forward cargo hold
57 Floor structure
58 Fuselage construction — closed section type stringers bonded to skin
59 Cabin entry door
60 Forward cabin bulkhead
61 Forward passenger door (plug type, outward-opening)
62 Overhead control runs
63 Flight-deck door
64 Forward toilet
65 Air-conditioning outlets
66 Overhead panel
67 Captain's seat
68 Glare shield
69 Flat windscreen sections
70 Windscreen wipers (electrical)
71 Front pressure bulkhead
72 Oxygen bottle
73 Weather radar
74 Radome
75 Twin nosewheels — hydraulically steered

76 Nosewheel leg flap
77 Rudder pedals
78 Centre instrument console
79 Stringerless front fuselage construction
80 Underfloor electrics bay
81 Side console
82 First Officer's seat
83 Direct-vision panel
84 Vestibule
85 Forward service door
86 Door opening lever
87 Locking mechanism lever
88 Attendant's folding seat, and cabin galley area
89 Cabin windows
90 Cargo door, plug type
91 Floor support structure
92 Main landing gear retraction jack
93 Side strut
94 Twin mainwheels
95 Main landing gear
96 Shock absorber strut
97 Front landing gear pivot bearing
98 Front wing spar — single piece machined
99 Flap interconnecting drive shaft
100 Rear cargo door (plug type)
101 Flap tracks
102 Landing gear door
103 Right landing light
104 Leading-edge construction
105 Pylon structure box
106 Intake
107 Avco Lycoming ALF 502-H turbofan
108 Sliding gas generator cowling
109 Wing anti-icing duct (outboard of pylons only)
110 Tabbed Fowler flaps, one piece each wing
111 Flap track fairings
112 Flap carriage
113 Wing stiffeners
114 Undersurface inspection panels
115 Right roll spoiler
116 Fuel lines
117 Wing rib stations
118 Right aileron
119 Aileron trim and servo tabs
120 Vent inlet
121 Vent surge box
122 Aileron mass balance
123 Right navigation light

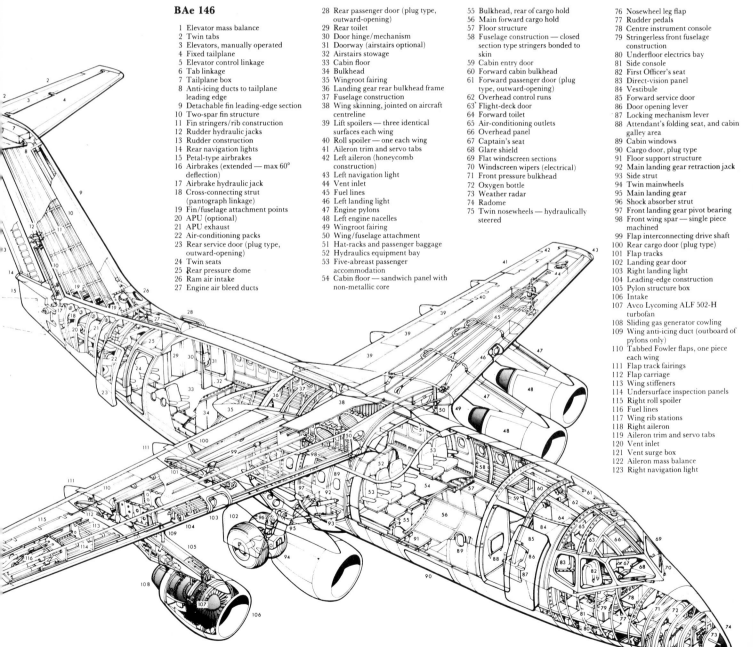

Boeing 757

ESTIMATED FIRST FLIGHT 1982

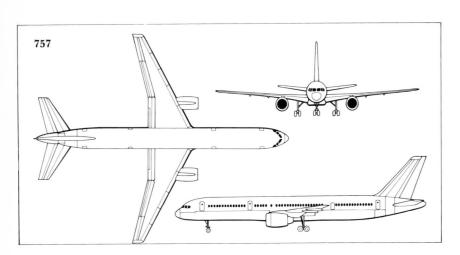

757

757-200

Type: short- and medium-range transport
Maker: Boeing Commercial Airplane Co
Span: 37.95 m (124 ft 6 in)
Length: 47.32 m (155 ft 3 in)
Height: 13.56 m (44 ft 6 in)
Wing area: 181.25 m² (1951 sq ft)
Weight: maximum 100 245 kg (221 000 lb); empty (RB.211) 59 272 kg (130 670 lb) (CF6) 58 999 kg (130 070 lb)
Powerplant: two 16 919-kg (37 300-lb) st Rolls-Royce

RB.211-535C turbofans, or two 16 479-kg (36 330-lb) st General Electric CF6-32C1 turbofans
Performance (estimated): maximum cruising speed 916 km/h (569 mph) at 8839 m (29 000 ft); range with 29 030 kg (64 000 lb) payload and no reserves 2221 km (1380 miles)
Payload: 29 030 kg (64 000 lb); seats for up to 233 passengers
Crew: 2
Production: 40 ordered by 1980

THE Boeing 757 is something of an oddity among the generation of large airliners currently being developed. Whereas all its contemporaries are wide-bodied aircraft, the Boeing 757 has a narrow fuselage, with capacity for up to 233 passengers positioned in a single-aisle six-abreast seating formation.

Launched in March 1979 with the receipt of substantial orders from British Airways (19) and Eastern Airlines (21), the 757 programme is the culmination of a Boeing analysis of the optimum way of developing an aircraft capable of flying short- and medium-range routes at minimum seat-mile cost and where frequency requirements combine with traffic forecasts to indicate that a larger aircraft would not be cost effective. Although the

original 757 concept relied heavily on features derived from the Boeing 727, continuing development moved the concept gradually away from this base. As it now stands, the 757 has much in common with the other major Boeing civil project, the 767 wide-bodied airliner. For example, during 1979 it was decided to replace the forward fuselage and T-tail of the 757, inherited from the 727, with similar items from the 767. The nose section can be faired quite simply into the narrower fuselage of the Boeing 757, and provides more space than that of the 727 model, while the tail surfaces are merely shorter variants of those which are fitted to the Boeing 767.

These changes made at a fairly late stage of the design process, have inevitably been costly, but

126

Boeing is convinced that increased commonality with the 767 will in the long term reduce production costs. Boeing is carrying all the launch costs of the new airliner, though some 53% of the aircraft is to be built by sub-contractors. These include Avco Aerostructures (parts of the wing centre section), CASA (some moving wing sections), Fairchild-Republic (centre cabin section), Rockwell (forward fuselage) and Short Brothers (parts of the moving wing sections).

One of the key factors in Boeing's design is the use of second generation turbofans with a high bypass ratio. One such engine is carried in a pylon-mounted pod under each wing, an alternative powerplant of two Rolls-Royce RB.211-535Cs or a pair of General Electric CF6-32C1s being avail-able. The RB.211 is rated at 16 919 kg (37 300 lb) st and the CF6 at 16 479 kg (36 330 lb) st. Cruising performance with the two types of engine will be fairly comparable, though the use of the CF6 provides the aircraft with a maximum-fuel range 97 km (60 miles) greater than that of RB.211-powered aircraft, at the expense of a take-off run lengthened by some 177 m (580 ft) to 2060 m (6760 ft) at sea level.

It is anticipated that production 757s will be available from 1983, the RB.211-powered model first, followed a few months later by the CF6-powered variant. In 1984, moreover, a stretched model will become available: this will have a maximum take-off weight in the order of 104 328 kg (230 000 lb).

Above: A Boeing 757 in the livery of British Airways, the first airline to order this unusual aircraft. It is unusual because, in this age of wide-bodied aircraft, the 757 has a narrow fuselage. The airline claims passengers on fairly short flights will be just as happy as in more capacious competitors

F29, Fokker

ESTIMATED FIRST FLIGHT 1983

Above: The Fokker-VFW F29, which is scheduled for initial deliveries in 1985. The manufacturer hopes to involve other companies in the construction of the F29 and the Dutch government are supplying half the money to launch the programme

UNDER consideration as a successor to the F28 Fellowship, the Fokker-VFW F29 programme owes its inception largely to the appointment of a new company chairman, Frans Swarttouw. This change in the company's leadership was reflected swiftly by the establishment of a group to study future airline requirements in the light of the latest airliner production techniques.

The group's first recommendation was that a fuselage based on that of the F28, with five-abreast seating, would meet a general demand for a small twin-jet for operations over short- and medium-range routes. But after further discussions with 28 possible purchasers, the Fokker study group revised its concept and opted for a larger fuselage, capable of carrying up to 160 passengers in six-abreast seating.

The F29 would, however, be similar in concept to the F28, with two rear-mounted engines and a T-tail, optimized for short-range routes and operations from unsophisticated airfields.

The company has received considerable encouragement from several prospective buyers, the most notable being those with an interest in transport aircraft with a field performance at least comparable with current STOL (short take-off and landing) types. The proposed F29 is intended to meet such a requirement, aided by a supercritical wing (derived from that intended for the F28 successors) and widespread use of composite materials to keep down weight but ensure high structural integrity.

The Dutch government has agreed to cover half the cost of launching the F29, which will probably

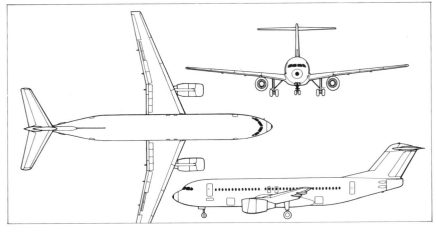

be ready for initial deliveries in 1985, and Fokker-VFW is currently looking for partners in the project. Both Boeing and Lockheed have been approached, apparently without success, and Fokker-VFW's efforts are now devoted to interesting the growing Japanese aircraft industry in participation as a partner. Detailed discussions have been taking place with the Japanese Ministry of International Trade and Industry, and this might also involve Japanese partnership in development and production of the F29's most likely engine, the Rolls-Royce RB.432, basically a scaled-up version of the RB.401. In August 1979 Rolls-Royce signed, through the auspices of the MITI, an agreement to develop the engine with Ishikawajima-Harima, Kawasaki and Mitsubishi.

F29

Type: short- and medium-range transport
Maker: Fokker-VFW BV
Span: not available
Length: not available
Height: not available
Wing area: not available
Weight: not available
Powerplant: probably two 9526-kg (21 000-lb) st Rolls-Royce RB.432 turbofans
Performance: not available
Payload: probably seats for up to 160 passengers
Crew: probably 2
Production: under development in 1980

L-1011 TriStar, Lockheed

FIRST FLIGHT 1970

Left: A Delta Air Lines TriStar L-1011-193C at Miami. Having started as a crop-dusting concern in 1924, by 1980 Delta was the world's fifth-largest airline in terms of passenger miles and was operating 29 TriStars
Below: The wide body of the all-economy class L-1011
Bottom: The TriStar instrument panel with illumination turned on and tape engine instruments in the centre

IT was requirements from American Airlines which gave birth to the McDonnell Douglas DC-10 series, and home-market sponsorship also launched the Lockheed L-1011, the second of the American wide-bodied aircraft.

The beginnings were made in January 1966 when the future requirements for medium-range airliners which had been published by potential operators were studied carefully by Lockheed. The chief requirement was the demand that the new type should be capable of taking off with a full load from existing runways, some of them relatively short, such as New York La Guardia, while still being able to carry a full payload between Los Angeles and Chicago. This influenced the decision to drop the first ideas to design a twin-engined aircraft and substitute instead a three-engined layout. In the search for a suitable turbofan the promised Rolls-Royce RB.211 seemed to offer what was required and this extremely modern three-shaft turbofan was submitted in the basic design.

Work was begun in the summer of 1968, first metal being cut during March of the following year, although it was not until November 16, 1970 that the L-1011 made its first flight. During the next year, two more aircraft were flown, in February and May.

By the beginning of 1972 trials had been completed, including those carried out in February when it was found necessary to test the unloading of 400 passengers in an emergency. Six doors were used for this, situated three each side of the fuselage with the forward pair staggered between

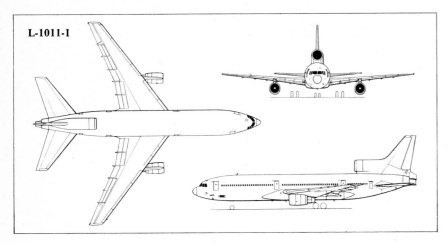

L-1011-1

Type: short/medium-haul transport
Maker: Lockheed Aircraft Corporation
Span: 47.34 m (155 ft 4 in)
Length: 54.17 m (177 ft 8½ in)
Height: 16.87 m (55 ft 4 in)
Wing area: 320 m² (3456 sq ft)
Weight: maximum 195 050 kg (430 000 lb); empty 109 045 kg (240 000 lb)
Powerplant: three 19 050-kg (42 000-lb) st Rolls-Royce RB.211-22B three-shaft turbofans
Performance: maximum cruising speed 964 km/h (599 mph) at 9145 m (30 000 ft); range with payload 5319 km (3305 miles)
Payload: 38 373 kg (84 600 lb); seats for up to 400 passengers
Crew: 3
Production: 148

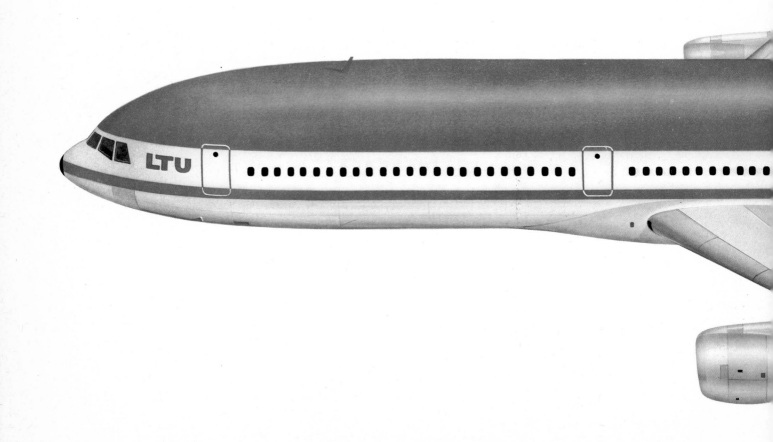

L-1011-200

Specification similar to
L-1011-1 except in following
particulars:
Type: medium-haul
transport
Weight: maximum
216 363 kg (477 000 lb); empty
111 495 kg (245 800 lb)
Powerplant: three 21 772-kg
(48 000-lb) st Rolls-Royce
RB.211-524 turbofans
Performance: maximum
speed 982 km/h (610 mph) at
9145 m (30 000 ft); range with
payload 6820 km (4238 miles)
Payload: 33 020 kg
(72 800 lb)
Production: 8

L-1011-500

Specification similar to
L-1011-1 except in following:
Type: long-range transport
Length: 50.05 m (164 ft
2½ in)
Weight: maximum
224 980 kg (496 000 lb); empty
109 298 kg (240 963 lb)
Powerplant: three 22 680-kg
(50 000-lb) st RB.211-524B
turbofans
Performance: maximum
speed 973 km/h (605 mph);
range 9653 km (5998 miles)
Payload: 44 015 kg
(97 037 lb); seats for 300
passengers
Production: 7 by 1980

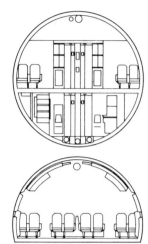

Left above: The galley of the
TriStar with the refrigeration
and oven units on the lower
level connected by a lift to the
passenger level
Left below: As in many
airliners the main doors of the
TriStar pull in and slide
upwards
Below: A Lockheed L-1011-
193L TriStar of the German
airline LTU (Luftransport
Unternehmen). LTU was
founded in 1955 and
concentrates on inclusive-tour
and general charter work

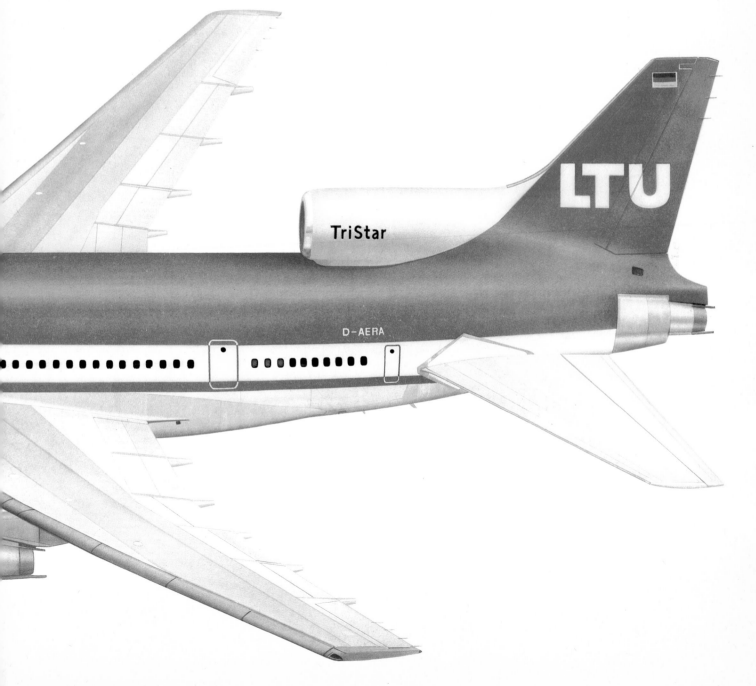

the sides aft of the flight-deck. Only eight weeks later the first machine was delivered to Eastern Air Lines, closely followed by one for Trans World Airlines, and these were used for a programme of flight-crew instruction before the new machines were committed to scheduled operations, which, for Eastern Air Lines began on April 26, 1972.

The design features of the TriStar appeared to break little new ground, but in fact the systems engineering was exceptionally advanced and has continued to progress with the introduction of new developments not completely matched by other manufacturers.

From the start crew comments were favourable. The controls were fully powered from a set of four independent hydraulic systems.

One feature which did excite comment was the provision of self-contained stairways, hydraulically operated so that passengers could be disembarked at airports with no facilities. This was a far-sighted provision because today even wide-bodied jets on charter operations occasionally call at unusual destinations.

The production of the new airliner had given employment to around 15 000 workers by the end of 1972, only three months after an L-1011 had been shown to buyers at the Farnborough Air Display in September 1972. This particular machine was finished in the livery of the then British European Airways (BEA), and for the first time in Britain it was possible to appreciate the size of the engines, particularly the pair mounted beneath the wings on short pylons. The undercarriage comprised a set of four-wheel bogies at each side with comparatively small twin nosewheels. The main bogies of the gear retracted into the wing centre section.

Of the firm orders for 117 TriStars received in 1972–73, the largest number came from Eastern Airlines which required 37. Nearly all of the operators had options on further models totalling 82, the largest number being required by the Japanese All-Nippon Airways. By the following summer total orders had risen to 135 with options on a further 65.

By this time variants were available in the series. On May 29, 1973 a further pair of models was announced which were intended to appeal to the extended-range market. They were designated L-1011-2LR, L-1011-100 and -200. The 100 introduced the 22B version of the RB.211 turbofan. It had an improved take-off rating, matched to greater fuel capacity for a lengthened operational range.

The long-distance 200 was intended as a replacement for the ageing jets in operation around the world which had entered service at the beginning of the jet age. The engines were the same as those of the other new version so that there was no increase in the total weight, but some considerable redesigning of the interior had taken place. The chief feature was the reduction in length of the passenger cabin in order to allow the galley, formerly accommodated beneath the main deck, to be brought to the same level as the main deck. This left the entire area under the floor for increased baggage, and the greater range was met by an

TriStar 500

1 Radome
2 VOR localizer aerial
3 Radar scanner dish
4 ILS glideslope aerial
5 Front pressure bulkhead
6 Curved windscreen panels
7 Windscreen wipers
8 Instrument panel shroud
9 Rudder pedals
10 Cockpit floor level
11 Ventral access door
12 Forward underfloor radio and electronics bay
13 Pitot tubes
14 Observer's seat
15 Captain's seat
16 First officer's seat
17 Overhead panel
18 Flight engineer's station
19 Cockpit roof escape hatch
20 Air-conditioning ducting
21 Forward galley units
22 Right service door
23 Forward toilet compartments
24 Curtained cabin divider
25 Wardrobe
26 Forward passenger door
27 Cabin attendant's folding seat
28 Nose undercarriage wheel bay
29 Ram air intake
30 Heat exchanger
31 Nose undercarriage leg strut
32 Twin nosewheels
33 Steering jacks
34 Nosewheel doors
35 Air-conditioning plant, left and right
36 Cabin window panel
37 Six-abreast first-class seating, 24 seats
38 Forward underfloor freight hold
39 Forward freight door
40 VHF aerial
41 Curtained cabin divider
42 Overhead stowage bins
43 Nine-abreast tourist-class seating, 222 seats
44 Baggage/freight containers, 12 LD-3 containers forwardW
45 Fuselage frame and stringer construction
46 Wing root fillet
47 Taxiing lamp
48 Bleed air system ducting
49 Escape chute and life raft stowage
50 Mid-centre entry door
51 Centre section galley units
52 Fuselage centre-section construction
53 Wing centre-section carry-through structure
54 Dry bay
55 Centre-section fuel tanks
56 Floor beam construction
57 Fuselage/front spar attachment main frame
58 Anti-collision lights
59 Right inboard fuel tank bay
60 Thrust reverser cascade, open
61 Right engine nacelle
62 Nacelle pylon
63 Fixed portion of leading edge
64 Fuel surge box and boost pump reservoir
65 Fuel system piping

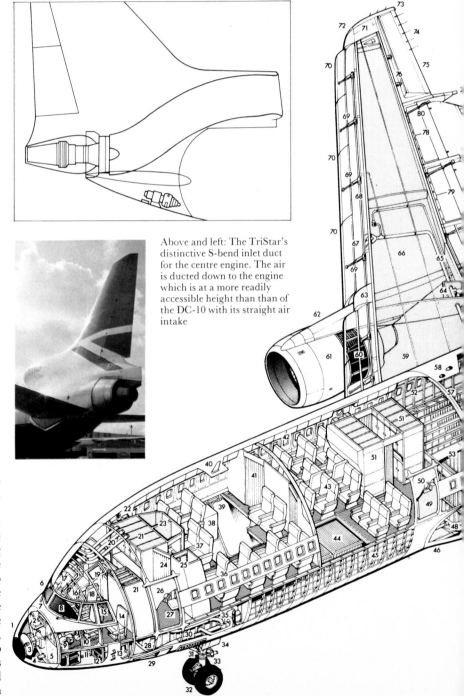

Above and left: The TriStar's distinctive S-bend inlet duct for the centre engine. The air is ducted down to the engine which is at a more readily accessible height than than of the DC-10 with its straight air intake

66 Outboard fuel tank bay
67 Pressure refuelling connections
68 Screw jack drive shaft
69 Slat screw jacks
70 Leading-edge slat segments, open
71 Extended wingtip fairing
72 Right navigation light
73 Wingtip strobe light
74 Static dischargers
75 Right 'active control' aileron
76 Aileron hydraulic jacks
77 Fuel jettison pipe
78 Outboard spoilers
79 Outboard spoilers/speedbrakes
80 Flap screw jacks
81 Flap track fairings
82 Outboard double-slotted flap,
   down
83 Inboard aileron
84 Inboard double-slotted flap, down
85 Flap vane
86 Inboard spoilers/speedbrakes
87 Fuselage/rear spar attachment
   main frame
88 Cabin trim panels
89 Pressure floor over wheel bay
90 Hydraulic reservoirs
91 Centre section service bay
92 Main undercarriage retracted
   position
93 Hydraulic flap drive motors
94 Cabin floor panels
95 Seat attachment rails
96 Overhead air conditioning ducting
97 Fuselage frame and stringer
   construction
98 Cabin ceiling panelling
99 Overhead stowage bins
100 Rear cabin seating
101 Cabin roof lighting panels
102 Noise attenuating intake fairing
103 Centre engine intake
104 Intake duct support structure
105 Aft galley units
106 Rear toilet compartments (5)
107 Rear pressure dome
108 Tailplane centre section
109 Variable incidence tailplane
    hydraulic jacks
110 Intake S-duct
111 Intake de-icing air supply
112 Sloping fin spar bulkhead
113 Right tailplane

114 Right elevator
115 HF aerial
116 Tailfin construction
117 Fin leading edge
118 VOR aerial
119 Rudder mass balance
120 Static dischargers
121 Rudder construction
122 Rudder hydraulic jacks
123 Engine bleed air system
124 Centre engine pylon mounting
125 Tail fairing
126 Detachable engine cowlings
127 Centre engine installation
128 Geared elevator hinge control
129 Left elevator
130 Elevator balance weights
131 Tailplane tip fairing
132 Tailplane construction
133 Moving tailplane sealing fairing
134 Pratt & Whitney of Canada 720-
    shp auxiliary power unit
135 Rear cabin door
136 Aft electronics bay
137 Underfloor cargo compartment
138 Wing root trailing-edge fillet

139 Aft underfloor freight
    compartment, 7 LD-3 containers
140 Left inboard double-slotted flap
141 Flap down position
142 Flap track fairings
143 Inboard spoilers/speedbrakes
144 Inboard aileron
145 Aileron hydraulic jacks
146 Outboard spoilers/speedbrakes
147 Outboard double-slotted flap
148 Flap down position
149 Flap track fairings
150 Outboard spoilers
151 Fuel jettison pipe
152 Left 'active control' aileron
153 Static dischargers
154 Left wingtip strobe lights
155 Extended wingtip fairing
156 Left navigation light
157 Rear spar
158 Fuel tank bay access panels
159 Front spar
160 Outboard leading-edge slat
    segments, open
161 Slat guide rails
162 Screw jacks

163 Wing rib construction
164 Pressure refuelling connections
165 Wing integral fuel tank bays
166 Slat de-icing air duct
167 Stringer construction
168 Wing skin plating
169 Undercarriage pivot fixing
170 Main undercarriage leg strut
171 Undercarriage side struts
172 Inboard integral fuel tank bay
173 Bleed air ducting
174 Screw jack drive shaft
175 Slat screw jacks
176 Inboard leading-edge slat
    segments, open

177 Four-wheel main undercarriage
    bogie
178 Left engine pylon
179 Detachable engine cowlings
180 Left engine intake
181 Rolls-Royce RB.211-524B turbofan
    engine
182 Oil cooler
183 Engine accessory gearbox
184 Thrust reverser cascades, closed
185 Fan air exhaust duct
186 Hot stream exhaust nozzle

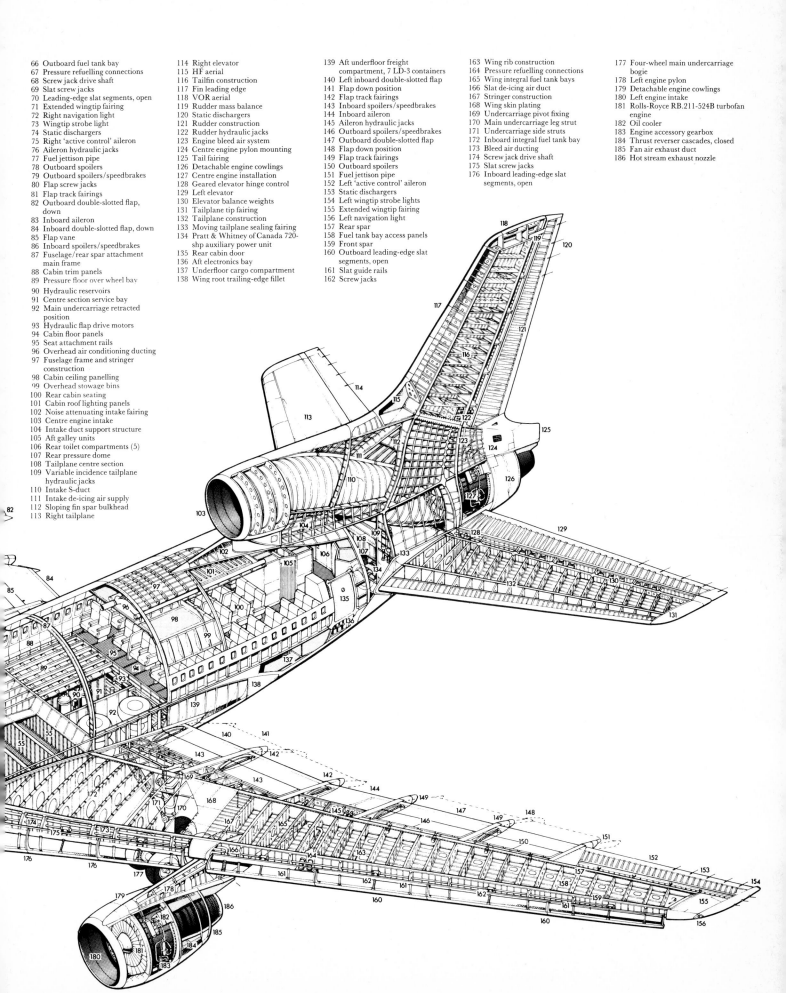

133

Right: Trailing-edge controls and leading-edge flaps and slats on the Lockheed Tri-Star: 1 trailing-edge flaps in the cruise position; 2 deployed for landing; 3 the leading-edge Krüger flaps retracted; 4 deployed – the flaps extend from the pylons to the wing root; 5 the leading-edge slat which extends from the pylon to the tip; 6 the slat rolls out on tracks to deploy
Far right: 7 Outboard aileron; 8 flight spoilers; 9 inboard aileron; 10 ground spoilers; 11 ball screw jacks; 12 flap tracks and fairings; 13 torque rod to leading-edge flaps; 14 asymmetric sense and control unit; 15 torque rod to slats; 16 leading-edge Krüger flap drive motor and gearbox; 17 leading-edge slat drive motor and gearbox

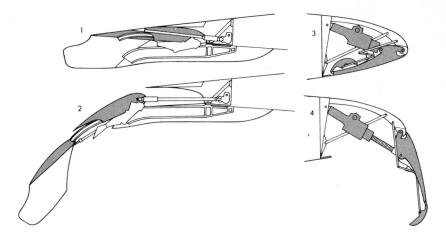

extra tank in the centre section. The first customers for these longer-range models were Saudia and Cathay Pacific.

However, in February 1971 the Rolls-Royce company went bankrupt, and it was not until government funds had been made available to save the company and production and supply of the RB.211 could be guaranteed, that it was considered safe to proceed with the development programme.

During the early 1970s the repercussions of the Rolls-Royce crash severely hit Lockheed, which had to go to unprecedented lengths to secure loans and other support from banks and the United States government, causing prolonged debate in Congress. In turn, this, and the delayed launch of the higher-thrust versions of the RB.211 seriously delayed the L-1011 programme by holding up the extended-range versions, so that for nearly five years the DC-10 had this market to itself.

In operation the RB.211 engines proved better than had been predicted. Under a wide variety of flight conditions they had given a markedly reduced vibration reading, while the low level of smoke emission had also been in their favour. In the United States, where environmentalists were expressing strong misgivings not only about the degree of visible atmospheric pollution by American jet engines but also their noise levels, the British turbofan was well received since it eliminated visible smoke and established decibel levels that were outstandingly low. Indeed it was not long

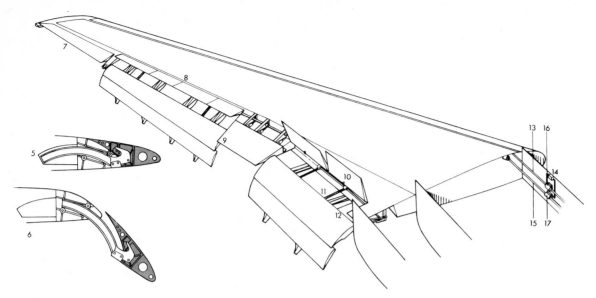

before the TriStar was given the nickname 'Whisperliner' – the name even appeared after a time on the aircraft operated by Eastern Air Lines.

The TriStar wing, sub-contracted partly to Avco at Nashville, has a special Lockheed section with a reduction of dihedral at the trailing edge between the inboard portion of the centre section and the roots of the outer panels. The whole of the main box forms integral fuel tankage. There is some technical novelty in the two-spar box construction of the ailerons, which have honeycomb trailing portions and a mechanical linkage with the flight spoilers.

Aluminium honeycomb also forms the main part of the trailing edge of the Fowler flaps. The leading edges of the outer wings are fitted with four slats, with a break in the area of the pylons, and three further sections inboard. For high-lift when landing and taking off these slats are hydraulically rolled out and down along curved tracks.

The fuselage is not the usual elliptical section but is circular for most of its length, with a diameter approaching 6 m (19 ft 8 in), the skin joints being bonded. The tail, major parts of which are of glass-reinforced composites, (in future graphite epoxy may be substituted) has a variable-incidence tailplane with variable gearing to the elevators. All surfaces are powered.

The main floor incorporates eight seat tracks so that twin-aisle seating can be provided in a variety of arrangements from six- to ten-abreast. In most configurations large galleys are provided under the

Far left: The first take-off of the PanAm L-1011-500 *Clipper Eagle*, giving an excellent view of its landing gear and three Rolls-Royce RB.211-525B engines
Left: Final inspection of RB.211 plumbing around the fan case

A British Airways TriStar L-1011-500 with its Rolls-Royce engines. The RB.211 was so clean and quiet that Eastern gave it the class name of 'Whisperliner,' which endeared it to the powerful US environmentalists

floor, with lifts to shuttle stewardesses and large trolleys to and from the passenger levels. The APU (auxiliary power unit) is exceptionally capable, the prime mover being the Canadian Pratt & Whitney PT6T power section.

The close of 1979 saw the culmination of tests of the L-1011-500 variant and deliveries to Pan American were promised for 1980. This is the model with technologically advanced 'active ailerons', automatically powered to relieve wing bending loads caused by rough air and allow the span to be extended, thus allowing range to be substantially increased. Meanwhile four have been accepted by British Airways and two by Delta. The earlier machines of this delivery will be upgraded by the fitting of a redesigned low-pressure and intermediate-pressure turbine (the 05 module) in the RB.211-524B4 in 1981. Also a DC-8F replacement, the 500F freighter, is being developed.

The Lockheed organization is also occupied with the problem of fuel economy. Some of the investigations into this field are conducted in conjunction with PanAm, and the 500 model has been significant already in underlining the good economics of the type. At the same time it is accepted in some quarters that the company machine, used as a flying test laboratory, will be fitted with an active flying tail. This is a measure designed to follow the investigations into the active control system as applied to the standard tail unit, and a means whereby the centre of gravity may be moved over a wide range yet countered by a smaller horizontal tail.

The existing empennage is $119\,\mathrm{m}^2$ ($1280\,\mathrm{sq\,ft}$) in area. This would be replaced by one of only $83\,\mathrm{m}^2$ ($898\,\mathrm{sq\,ft}$) with resultant economies not only in weight but also fuel consumption. Other research programmes into the use of fuel include means of reducing expenditure by increasing the cg range (ie the distance within which an aircraft can safely have its centre of gravity) and the carriage of extra tanks at the rear. This project is covered by the TriStar 500VLR designation.

It seems likely that any new long-range model will be powered by the projected RB.211-524G giving $24\,494\,\mathrm{kg}$ ($54\,000\,\mathrm{lb}$) st, with a passenger capacity of about 350 and also an increased wing area. The most promising way of achieving this appears to be the incorporation of an enlarged centre section.

Plans for the future also include the proposed 600 and 600A variants which would form an entirely new group of airliners quite distinct from the established TriStar form, as they would be twins. In 1980 the decision to go ahead on these, first proposed in 1976, had not been taken.

There remains one more variant of the TriStar worthy of mention. This is the 250 model, a long-range version dimensionally identical to the L-1011-1 with RB.524B engines offering $21\,773\,\mathrm{kg}$ ($48\,000\,\mathrm{lb}$) st, and with an increased maximum weight of $224\,986\,\mathrm{kg}$ ($496\,000\,\mathrm{lb}$).

In general, however, the future looks especially healthy for Lockheed. The order total stands at 232 in addition to 75 options. Of these orders the company hoped to deliver 23 during 1980 and to increase this figure to 30 for 1981.

Top left: TriStar fuselage mating with titanium bands at the assembly plant at Palmdale. At this stage the nose, centre and tail sections are joined together. Note the variety of airlines who have ordered TriStars
Above left: TriStar flight-deck assembly. The nose, including cockpit, is pre-wired and instruments are installed before the fuselage mating stage
Above: Cutting out the window holes in the TriStar skin using a heavy steel jig
Left: The largest autoclave in the world, at plant B-1 Burbank, California, where fuselage skins are bonded together into sections in a partial vacuum at 94°C
Below left: A crew of painters on special lifts apply polyurethane paint to a TriStar

Boeing 747

TO TRY to meet competition from the Douglas DC-8 series the Boeing company embarked on a programme of successively more capable versions of their already-proven 707 model, culminating in the 707-320C. However by the mid 1960s it became evident that an entirely new concept was called for. This reached practical form on April 13, 1966 by the announcement from Seattle that Pan American World Airways had signed a contract worth $520 million for 25 of a new type of aircraft. It was capable of seating 350 and 490 passengers in a single-deck cabin 6.1 m (20 ft) wide, an increase of 2.13 m (7 ft) over the largest commercial aircraft then in existence. For such a massive machine the term 'Jumbo Jet' was quickly coined.

A concept of such magnitude which boasted a tail height above the ground in excess of that of three ordinary houses might have suffered operating restrictions from its weight alone. For the powerplant, Boeing chose the Pratt & Whitney development, the JT9D. The first was capable of providing 18 597 kg (41 000 lb) thrust, sufficient for the 747 to use any airfield adequate for a 707.

Clearly allied to the earlier Boeing design trends, the new machine was nevertheless an entirely fresh concept incorporating in its initial form a proposal for a twin-deck cabin of which the length exceeded that of the earlier machine by as much as 24.4 m (80 ft). However the 747 materialized as a single-decker, but even so had a capacity almost three times that of the largest 707-320B. This was done by the arrangement of the seating in three blocks divided by twin aisles, although this was only one

138

of a number of arrangements proposed. In addition a small lounge was provided, capable of taking 16 people on the same level as the flight-deck with access via a circular stairway from the main passenger cabin.

Several varieties of passenger accommodation were anticipated, plus a freighter and a convertible passenger/cargo version.

Many of the features of the Boeing 747 had been originally devised for the US Air Force's entry in the CX-HLS contest. Unlike that design for a military freighter the 747 was given the most acutely swept wing of any commercial transport (37° 30′), for very high cruising speeds over the longest ranges. This wing was given glass-fibre slats, ten on each outer wing, with Krüger flaps inboard. These high-lift devices were first tested on the 707, as was an exceptional new array of avionics, fuel, propulsion and electro-mechanical systems.

In order to meet passenger loading problems, ten doors were fitted and it was estimated that under normal conditions no more than three would be needed to handle a full load. Plans were also devised for the division of some airport waiting areas into two or perhaps three sections each serving a single door.

In order to reduce any impression of 'herding' the passengers, careful attention was paid to the internal atmosphere and an impression of space was created by the use of wall-to-wall carpeting. High ceilings were installed throughout so that switches for the cabin lights had to be provided in miniature consoles at arm level between the seats.

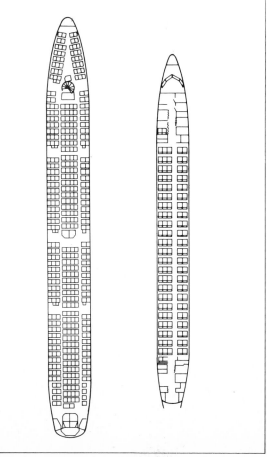

Above: The CP Air Boeing 747-217B *Empress of Asia*, previously named *Empress of Japan*. CP Air, which was formed in 1942, operates services to South America and Asia as well as the USA and Europe
Far left: A Boeing 747 of United parked at the gate at Chicago O'Hare with an excellent view of its jetway and loading facility
Left: A contrast in Boeings – the 747 and the 707-320. The 707 could carry between 181 and 195 passengers – the 747 carries 500 at economy class

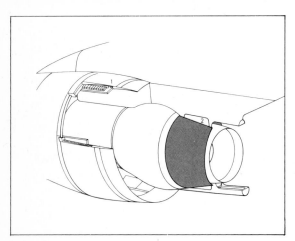
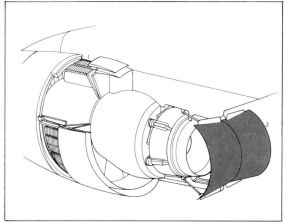

Top left: Two of the four Pratt & Whitney JT9D engines of a British Airways Boeing 747, pylon-mounted in pods on the right-wing leading edge

Top centre: After every flight each of the Pratt & Whitney JT9D engines are carefully checked

Top right: Changing the Pratt & Whitney JT9D on a Lufthansa 747-130 at Tucson airport, Arizona

Above left and right: An alternative engine for the 747 is the Rolls-Royce RB.211-524B notable for its smaller size and better fuel economy

Far left and left: The 747 had to pioneer the technique of reversing large turbofan engines. When the reverse-thrust is in action the fan cascades (1) are exposed and the blocker doors (2) of the hot-stream flow spoiler are deployed

These were banked four-wide in the central group, giving 10% extra width over those normally fitted to conventional jetliners of the time, and the gangways were each 51 mm (2 in) wider than usual. In order to reduce boredom, provision was naturally made for various kinds of music and large-screen movies. Eleven toilets were provided, with another on the upper deck.

Refreshments were provided by means of six walk-through galleys reducing the time for the eight to 12 cabin staff to serve passengers by some 30%.

To build the 747, Boeing cleared a vast tract of forest near Everett, 48 km (30 miles) north of Seattle, built adjoining Paine Field, and began assembly of the aircraft in the world's largest-volume buildings. Parts were shipped from 49 US States, Northrop building much of the fuselage. British companies supplied specialist parts such as windshields and instruments.

There was no prototype, the first aircraft off the production line flying on February 9, 1969 (one month later than scheduled) after a roll-out on September 30, 1968. By this time the Pan American contract had been extended to 23 of the pure passenger version plus two 747F freighters. Another early customer, Continental, had ordered the convertible 747C.

In all, five 747s were committed to an intensive development programme. It was the fourth of these to fly that was first seen in Europe at the 1969 Paris Air Show when N731PA arrived at Le Bourget on

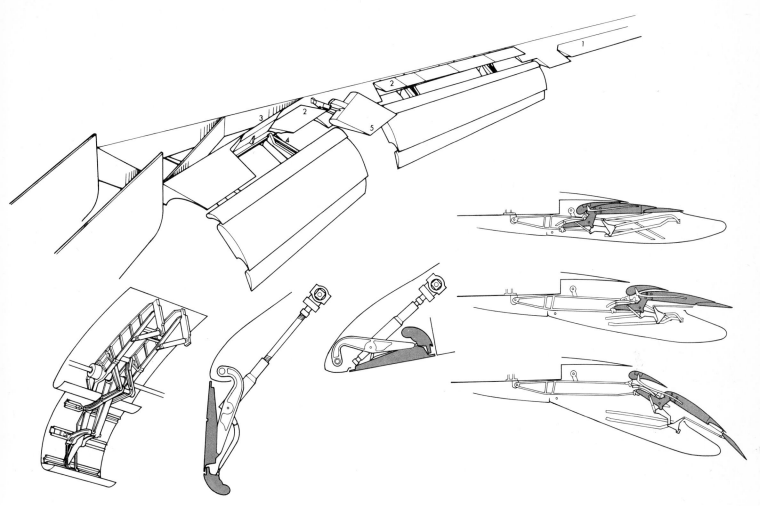

Top: The disposition of the trailing-edge controls, flaps and spoilers: 1 the low-speed aileron; 2 flight spoilers; 3 ground spoiler; 4 ball screw jacks; 5 high-speed aileron
Above left: Krüger flaps seen from below deployed and retracted; they extend from the inner pylon to the fuselage
Above right: Flap settings: top, in the cruise position; centre, at take-off; bottom, deployed for landing. These triple-slotted trailing-edge flaps were of considerable interest because Boeing managed to fit the mechanism into a comparatively restricted space of the wing

trailing-edges. On landing they give an increased area which extends almost continuously from the outer-engine pylon to the fuselage

Above: A good view of a Lufthansa 747 settling into the first segment of climb after take-off

June 3, after a non-stop flight over 8304 km (5160 miles) in 9 hours 8 min.

On December 30, 1969 the 747 received its Federal Aviation Administration type approval and on January 22 the following year the first machine entered service on the Pan American route from New York to London. It was believed, at a time when no dramatic increase in the cost of crude oil was anticipated, that the speed and fuel-efficiency of this pioneer wide-body would actually result in reduced tariffs for the carriage of cargo. The typical transatlantic flight time of 5 hours 45 min represented a reduction of 30 min on the previous best.

At the same time it took a year for the engines to settle down after severe problems with such new questions as ovalization of the casings and the difficulty of starting in cross-winds. The twinned inertial navigation systems were the first in commercial operation consisting of units which each monitor the other to cancel out all possibility of error.

During 1970 an interesting and little-publicized set of trials took place with what at first sight seemed to be a five-engined version. At the request of 12 airlines a complete engine could be carried on a standard pylon under the left wing as had previously been common practice with 707s and VC10s. Engines could thus be transported to maintenance bases or returned to the home base for specialized attention.

Long before certification, Boeing was planning

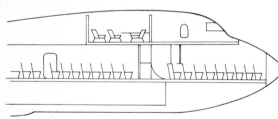

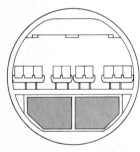

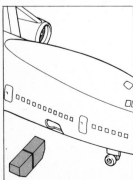

Top: Passengers boarding a Lufthansa 747-236B. There are five pasenger doors on each side of the aircraft, of which the two forward of the wing are usually used
Above centre: Seating for 16 passengers in the upper-deck first-class lounge of a Lufthansa Boeing 747
Above: A novel feature of the 747 is the upper deck which contains the cockpit and first class lounge. This allows the main deck to extend right to the nose
Left above: Baggage and underfloor cargo is carried in left and right LD-3 containers
Left below: LD-3 containers loaded into underfloor holds are then rolled on rails inside

747-200

1 Radome
2 Radar dish
3 Pressure bulkhead
4 Radar scanner mounting
5 First-class cabin, typically 32 seats
6 Windscreen
7 Instrument panel shroud
8 Rudder pedals
9 Control column
10 Flight-deck floor construction
11 First-class bar unit
12 Window panel
13 Nose undercarriage bay
14 Nosewheel door
15 Steering mechanism
16 Twin nosewheels
17 Radio and electronics racks
18 Captain's seat
19 Co-pilot's seat
20 Flight engineer's panel
21 Observers' seats
22 Upper deck door, left and right
23 Circular staircase between decks
24 Cockpit air conditioning
25 First-class galley
26 First-class toilets
27 Plug-type forward cabin door, No 1
28 First-class seats
29 Cabin dividing bulkhead
30 Anti-collision light
31 Cabin roof construction
32 Upper deck toilet
33 Upper deck seating, up to 32 passengers
34 Window panel
35 Air-conditioning supply ducts
36 Forward fuselage construction
37 Baggage pallet containers
38 Forward under-floor freight compartment
39 Communications aerial
40 Upper deck galley
41 Meal trolley elevator
42 Lower deck forward galley
43 No 2 passenger door, left and right
44 Air-conditioning system intake
45 Wing-root fairing
46 Air-conditioning plant
47 Wing spar bulkhead
48 Fresh water tanks
49 Forward economy-class cabin
50 Wing centre-section fuel tank
51 Centre-section stringer construction
52 Cabin floor construction
53 Fuselage frame and stringer construction
54 Main fuselage frame
55 Air distribution duct
56 Air-conditioning cross-feed ducts
57 Risers to distribution ducts
58 Machined main frame
59 Satellite navigation aerial
60 Right wing inboard fuel tank
61 Fuel pumps
62 Engine bleed-air supply
63 Krüger flap operating jacks
64 Inboard Krüger flap
65 Right inner engine
66 Right inner engine pylon
67 Leading-edge Krüger flap segments
68 Krüger flap drive mechanism
69 Krüger flap motors
70 Refuelling panel
71 Right wing outboard fuel tank
72 Right outer engine
73 Right outer engine pylon
74 Outboard Krüger flap segments
75 Krüger flap drive mechanism
76 Extended range fuel tank
77 Surge tank
78 Right wingtip
79 Navigation light
80 VHF aerial boom
81 Fuel vent
82 Static dischargers
83 Outboard, low-speed, aileron
84 Outboard spoilers
85 Outboard slotted flaps
86 Flap drive mechanism
87 Inboard, high-speed, aileron
88 Trailing-edge beam
89 Inboard spoilers
90 Inboard slotted flap
91 Flap drive mechanism
92 Centre fuselage construction
93 Right undercarriage bay housing
94 No 3 passenger door
95 Wing-mounted main undercarriage bay
96 Flap drive motors
97 Undercarriage beam
98 Fuselage-mounted main undercarriage bay
99 Main undercarriage jack

100 Floor panels
101 Seat rails
102 Cabin window trim panels
103 Centre cabin economy-class seating, typically 82 passengers
104 Nine-abreast seating
105 Air-distribution ducts
106 No 4 passenger door, left and right
107 Centre cabin galley
108 Overhead baggage racks
109 Main air supply duct
110 Rear cabin galley
111 Rear cabin seating, typically 114 passengers
112 Economy-class seating
113 Overhead baggage racks
114 Cabin roof panels
115 Control cable runs
116 Rear fuselage construction
117 Rear cabin seats
118 Rear cabin toilets
119 Wardrobes
120 Rear pressure dome bulkhead
121 Fin root fairing
122 Right tailplane
123 Static dischargers

124 Right elevator
125 Fin leading-edge construction
126 Fin spar construction
127 Fin-tip fairing
128 VOR aerial
129 Static dischargers
130 Upper rudder segment
131 Lower rudder segment
132 Rudder jacks
133 Tailcone fairing
134 APU exhaust
135 Auxiliary power unit (APU)
136 Left elevator inner segment
137 Left elevator outer segment
138 Static dischargers
139 Tailplane construction
140 Elevator jacks
141 Tailplane sealing plate
142 Aft fuselage frames
143 Fin attachment
144 Tailplane centre section
145 Moving tailplane jack
146 APU air duct
147 No 5 passenger door, left and right
148 Rear fuselage window panel
149 Rear under-floor freight hold

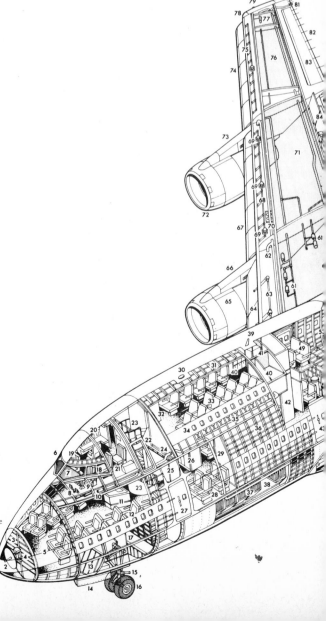

150 Freight and baggage pallet
    container
151 Fuselage frame and stringer
    construction
152 Trailing edge fillet
153 Fuselage-mounted undercarriage
    pivot
154 Trailing edge beam
155 Left inboard slotted flap
156 Flap tracks
157 Flap track fairings
158 Inboard spoilers
159 Flap drive shaft
160 Flap down position
161 Fuselage- nounted main
    undercarr age bogie
162 Wing spar and rib construction
163 Wing root attachment plate
164 Front spar
165 Engine bleed air supply pipe
166 Leading-edge ribs
167 Landing lamps
168 Inboard Krüger flap
169 Krüger flap motor and drive
170 Wing-mounted main undercarriage
    leg

171 Four-wheel main undercarriage
    bogie
172 Main undercarriage side brace
173 Wing-mounted undercarriage jack
174 Wing skins
175 Wing stringer construction
176 Inboard engine mounting beam
177 Pylon attachment strut
178 Left inner pylon construction
179 Heat exchanger
180 Engine intake
181 Rolls-Royce RB.211-524B engine
182 Engine driven gearbox
183 Outer fan ducting
184 Core engine exhaust
185 Integral fuel tankage
186 Inboard, high-speed, aileron
187 Aileron jack
188 Outboard slotted flap
189 Flap track fairing
190 Flap down position
191 Outboard spoilers
192 Flap tracks
193 Flap track mounting beams
194 Wing spar and rib construction
195 Leading-edge construction

196 Krüger flap segments
197 Krüger flap mechanism
198 Outboard engine mounting beam
199 Left outer engine pylon
200 Heat exchanger air duct
201 Left outer engine cowlings
202 Thrust reverser cascades
203 Thrust reverser cowling door, open
204 Door operating jacks
205 Outboard Krüger flap segments
206 Krüger flap mechanism
207 Outer wing construction
208 Aileron jacks
209 Outboard, low-speed, aileron
210 Static dischargers
211 Fuel vent
212 Wingtip fairing
213 Navigation light

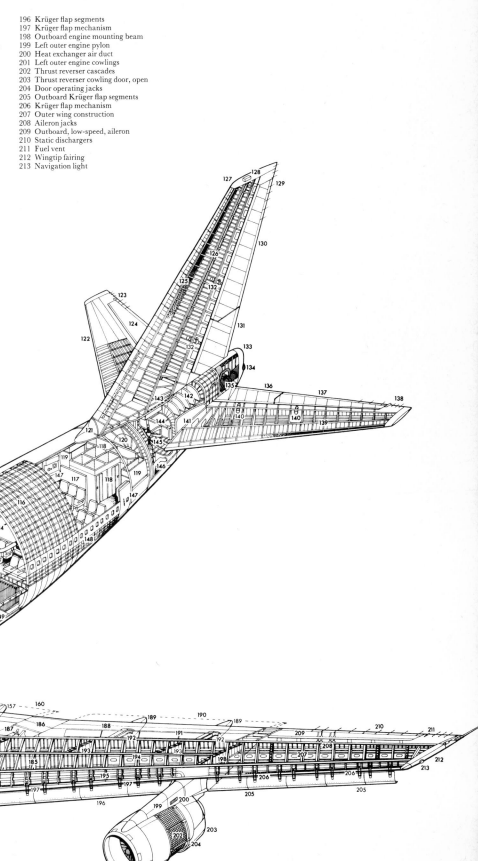

variants of the 747. The initial model was designated the 747-100 and it was followed on October 11, 1970 by the 747-200 with JT9D-7A engines allowing increased gross weight. These longer-range aircraft entered service with KLM in 1971. It was not long before this variant appeared in a re-engined form with JT9D-7F turbofans with 680 kg (1500 lb) extra thrust.

Three further variations of the 747-200B were launched in quick succession with different power-plants. A thrust-increase of 1361 kg (3000 lb) marked the next change brought about by the installation of the JT9D-70 and these gave way to the General Electric CF6-50E2s of the subsequent model while the first British engines adopted for the 747 were the Rolls-Royce RB.211-524Bs. For the 747-200C the JT9D-7F was used. All variants retained the same dimensions.

It was not until the 747-200F was introduced that any change in the basic structure was made and this version, although having the fuselage common to the series as a whole up to that time, has an upward-hinged nose and optional side cargo door. It is a single example of this version that flies the round trip operated by Lufthansa from Frankfurt to John F Kennedy Airport, 365 days each year.

A complete structural redesign with a shortened fuselage and Pratt & Whitney JT9D-7A turbofans produced the special performance 747SP introduced in 1973. Not only was the length 14.2 m (47 ft) less but the type was identified by a considerably larger tail. Structure weight was

Right: The flight-deck of the Boeing 747
1 Approach-chart holder
2 Radar display and controls
3 Stabilizer (tailplane) trim switch
4 Autopilot-disengage switch
5 Pitch trim
6 Rudder trim
7 Machmeter and airspeed
8 Autopilot pitch and turn commands
9 Attitude director
10 Flight compass director
11 Parking brake
12 VSI (vertical speed)
13 Altimeter
14 Flight-system mode annunciator
15 Clock
16 Overhead panel: hydraulic power, engine ignition, alternative gear selection, anti-icing, lighting
17 Marker-beacon lights
18 Stabilizer control lever (manual systems); indicator wheel on side of pedestal
19 Stand-by attitude-director
20 Master warning panel
21 Speed-brake
22 Main instruments engines 1,2,3,4 (vertical rows)
23 Engine starting
24 Reverser indicators
25 Stand-by compass
26 Urgent warnings
27 Throttles
28 Overshoot mode select switches for flight director and autothrottle
29 Flap position indicator (leading-edge devices)
30 Air temperature
31 Autopilot control panel
32 Flap position indicator (trailing-edge devices)
33 Landing-gear indicators
34 Landing-gear selector
35 Control-surface position indicator
36 Radio compass
37 True-airspeed indicator
38 Flap selector
39 Radar and communications
40 Rudder pedals incorporating wheel brakes

Left: The Boeing production line in the gigantic new plant at Everett, with 747s at various stages of construction

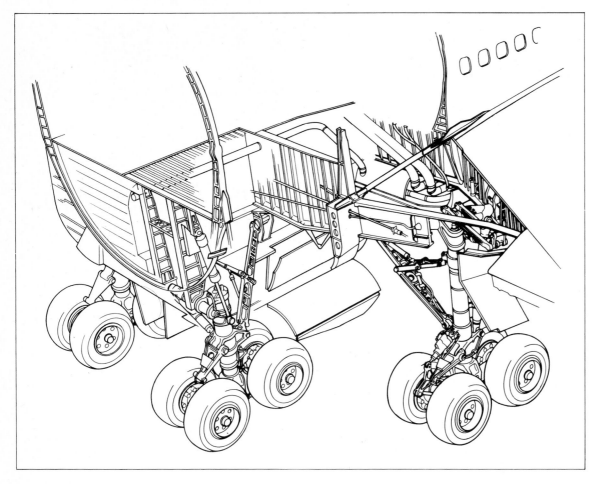

reduced, and the design optimized to operation over extremely long sectors. Among its first operators were Iran Air and Pan American.

Looking to the future for the 747 family it seems likely that it will eventually appear with extended wingtips in combination with active ailerons and in the meantime Boeing have followed a policy of investigation into a stretched version. The demand for such a version has been delayed by the adoption of progressively denser seating arrangements. Up to the present this has been achieved partly with the aid of slimmer seat units making possible an increase of 70 over the original number. A machine with a length increase of 7 m (23 ft) could increase the seat capacity by a further 130.

However, the longer the delay in introducing a stretched version the greater will be the chances that a demand will be made for a more modern aircraft. To meet this a programme would have to be initiated that would provide updated avionics and cockpit displays and lightweight powerplants.

The original Rolls-Royce powerplants were RB.211-524B engines but provision is made for their replacement with RB.211-524D4s. These, delivering 24 040 kg (53 000 lb) st, are more economical and when they become available in 1981 will be fitted with a low-pressure intermediate turbine module of a new type and a redesigned fan. Even the original 524B was found by British Airways to cut fuel burnt per trip by 7%.

The machine constructed in secret for the Saudi Arabian government – a 747SP basically completed towards the end of 1979 – is also powered by
146

Rolls-Royce and it is this machine that was said to have been sent for fitting out with an advanced communications system by E-Systems. It is the same contractor which is responsible for another version of the 747, the E-4B, an advanced airborne command post for the United States government.

However, there is no reduction in the powerplant lead competitively enjoyed by Pratt & Whitney and this will doubtless be enhanced by the JT9D-7Q in use by Northwest Airlines and certificated only in 1979. Nevertheless the General Electric turbofan continues to feature in an increasing number of orders.

The grand total of these towards the end of 1979 stood at 504, those of the 747-200 class proving the most popular at 240 as against 176 for the first 747-100 variant. The smallest number on order at the moment is for the short-range 747SR of which all 14 were intended for Japan, to be equally divided between All Nippon and JAL.

Slow progress continues for sales of the SP and those operated by Pan American have been fitted with new recliner seats in the first-class section while versions are now available with a 2041-kg (4500-lb) increase in payload or an alternative capability for an extended range. Three such 747s were sold to the People's Republic of China.

Small numbers of the cargo version have continued to attract orders from a wide number of customers ranging from a single specimen for Air Afrique to six for Seaboard. It is this model that has straight-in capability and a maximum load potential of approximately 100 tonnes.

Top: The Boeing 747 twin-wheel nose unit, incorporating a landing light. It retracts forward
Above and above left: Main gear comprises four four-wheel bogies, two under the wings retracting inwards and two near the wing trailing edge, mounted side-by-side under the fuselage, retracting forward. There are disc brakes on all main wheels
Below: The 747 gas-turbine APU (auxiliary power unit) to provide power for the electrical, hydraulic, environmental and many other systems before the main engines are started

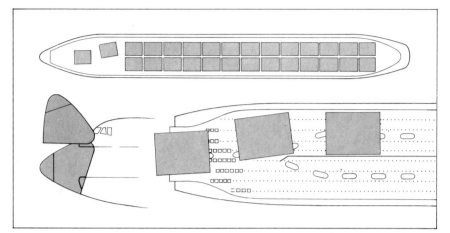

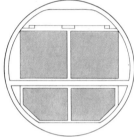

Left: A Boeing 747SP (Special Performance) displaying all its 18 wheels comes in to land

Top left: The freighter version loads through the nose, and containers are moved over support rollers onto drive units which carry them to the rear of the hold
Left: The 747-200F can accommodate both standard baggage containers in the lower hold and cargo containers above
Above: Pitts Specials of the US Aerobatic team being front-loaded into a Lufthansa 747-200F freighter. One Lufthansa 200F makes a Frankfurt–New York round trip every day of the year

747-100B

Type: long-haul large capacity transport
Maker: Boeing Commercial Airplane Co
Span: 59.6 m (195 ft 8 in)
Length: 70.51 m (231 ft 4 in)
Height: 19.33 m (63 ft 5 in)
Wing area: 511 m² (5500 sq ft)
Weight: maximum 322 050 kg (710 000 lb); empty 169 190 kg (373 000 lb)
Powerplant: four 21 296-kg (46 950-lb) st Pratt & Whitney JT9D-7A two-shaft turbofans; alternative engines, CF6 and RB.211 of various models
Performance: maximum cruising speed 967 km/h (601 mph) at 9150 m (30 000 ft); range with 442 passengers and baggage and full reserves, 8330 km (5180 miles)
Payload: 69 625 kg (153 500 lb); seats for up to 442 passengers
Crew: 3 to 4
Production: 176 by 1980

747-200B

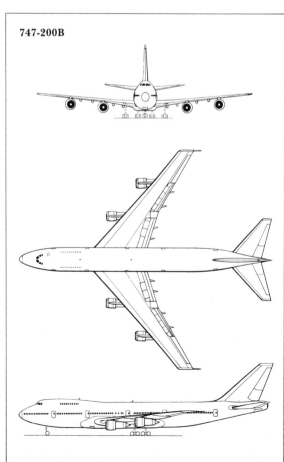

747-200B

Specification similar to 747-100B except in following particulars:
Weight: maximum 362 880 kg (800 000 lb) or with highest-thrust engines 371 950 kg (820 000 lb); empty 175 995 kg (388 000 lb)
Powerplant: four JT9D, CF6 or RB.211 turbofans of various types with ratings of 22 680 kg (50 000 lb) to 24 040 kg (53 000 lb) st
Payload: 71 670 kg (158 000 lb)
Production: 228 by 1980

747-200C

Specification similar to 747-100B except in following particulars:
Weight: empty 165 110 kg (364 000 lb)
Payload: 102 510 kg (226 000 lb)
Production: 13 by 1980

747-200F

Specificaton similar to 747-200C except in following particulars:
Weight: empty 154 200 kg (340 000 lb)
Payload: 113 400 kg (250 000 lb)
Production: 30 by 1980

DC-10, McDonnell Douglas

FIRST FLIGHT 1970

THE majority of airliners are more commonly born out of the anticipation by the manufacturers of a customer's potential needs, but in the case of the DC-10 it was the reverse. The project began in April 1966 when American Airlines decided to circulate, to a chosen seven of America's transport-aircraft constructors, a list detailing requirements that appeared to be indicated by a study of the forecast airport congestion problems over a future period of several years. One of the obvious conclusions to be drawn from this was that part of the answer lay in the use of 'wide-body' aircraft with a consequent reduction in the movements at air terminals.

Although this solution seems patently obvious it must be remembered that large-capacity machines, due to their increased weight, also call for operation from airfields with very strong and probably long runways. It was, therefore, firmly stated that any aircraft designed to meet the new specification must be capable of operation from the type of field then in use, so the technical considerations seemed to point to the resultant airframe being powered by twin turbofan engines.

Though Lockheed appeared to have damaged the project's chances by selling the L-1011 to Eastern and Trans World Airlines, the DC-10 was launched weeks later, in February 1968, with an order from American, closely followed by United.

At Long Beach, California, a mock-up was assembled and it was immediately possible to appreciate in practical terms the size of the main passenger cabin with its high ceiling and a width of

Above: The DC-10 Series 30 with its three General Electric CF6-50 engines for intercontinental operations. KLM, the Dutch airline, was formed in 1919 with a two-passenger DH.16. With Avianca (Colombia) it is the oldest airline in the world
Right: The three turbofan engines of the Series 30 DC-10, two hung on underwing pylons and the third between fuselage and fin

148

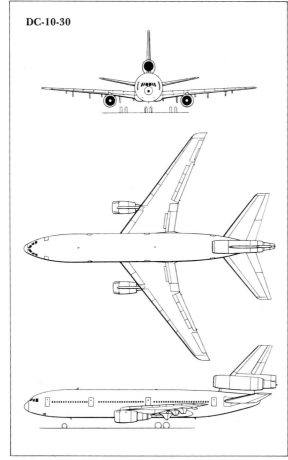

DC-10-30

DC-10 Series 10

Type: large capacity medium- and long-range transport
Maker: McDonnell Douglas Corporation
Span: 47.34 m (155 ft 4 in)
Length: 55.3 m (181 ft 5 in)
Height: 17.53 m (57 ft 6 in)
Wing area: 357.7 m² (3861 sq ft)
Weight: maximum 206 384 kg (455 000 lb); empty 109 438 kg (241 270 lb)
Powerplant: three 18 597-kg (41 000-lb) st General Electric CF6-6D1 turbofans
Performance: cruising speed 940 km/h (584 mph) at 9449 m (31 000 ft); range 4355 km (2706 miles)
Payload: 46 130 kg (101 700 lb); seats for up to 345 passengers
Crew: 5
Production: 139

Series 30

Specification similar to Series 10 except in following particulars:
Span: 50.39 m (165 ft 4 in)
Length: 55.35 m (181 ft 7¼ in)
Height: 17.55 m (57 ft 7 in)
Wing area: 364.3 m² (3921 sq ft)

Weight: maximum 259 450 kg (572 000 lb); empty 120 914 kg (266 570 lb)
Performance: cruising speed 956 km/h (594 mph) at 9449 m (31 000 ft); range 7413 km (4606 miles)
Payload: 47 400 kg (105 500 lb)
Production: 191

Series 40

Specification similar to Series 30 except in following particulars:
Length: 55.54 m (182 ft 2½ in)
Weight: maximum 251 744 kg (550 000 lb); empty 122 737 kg (270 590 lb)
Powerplant: three 22 000-kg (48 500-lb) st Pratt & Whitney JT9D-20 or -59A turbofans
Performance: maximum speed 956 km/h (590 mph) at 9449 m (31 000 ft); range 6485 km (4030 miles)
Payload: 45 700 kg (100 750 lb)
Production: 31 by September 1979

almost 6 m (20 ft). However, the story prior to the mock-up stage had not been happy. During the two years that had passed since the inception of the idea, several designs had been submitted, only to be retracted a short time later. It was during one of these changes of plan that it was decided to power the aircraft, not by the two engines at first suggested but by three. The additional engine was accommodated in a visually rather crude mounting at the base of the vertical tail surfaces. Despite the fact that this complicated engine maintenance and replacement, it was judged the most aerodynamically efficient solution.

The construction of the prototype, the first of five development aircraft, began during January 1969 and it was finally rolled out for flight testing on August 10, 1970, closely followed by two more in August and December.

These were all of the basic model intended for operation within the United States to cover distances in the 480 to 5795 km (300 to 3600 miles) range and were known as the Series 10. Meanwhile the sales office had been circulating details of the new wide-body. Soon it was announced that orders had been obtained for 14 DC-10s from the European consortium of KLM, SAS, Swissair and UTA, known as the KUSS Group. These orders were, in fact, for the next model, the heavier, longer-range DC-10 Series 30. The idea behind this version was that it should be used for intercontinental operations, and it was for this duty that engines of increased power were fitted.

To support the increased weight, a third main landing gear unit was added under the fuselage. This fourth leg, with two wheels, was set almost in line with the main four-wheel bogies. Tankage and wing span were increased.

The first deliveries of the Series 10 model took place on July 29, 1971 when American Airlines – which had fathered the idea in the first place – and United were simultaneously equipped with the new type. The first passenger flight was carried out by American when the airline initiated the scheduled daily Los Angeles-Chicago service on August 5 of the same year.

There was a fair degree of sub-contracting in the manufacture of the DC-10. This had existed from an early stage in the production programme, even with the assembly of the first machine. The forward section of the fuselage was delivered from the San Diego works of Convair and this was soon joined by further fuselage sub-assemblies.

The pace of production was ensured by employing about 100 sub-contractors responsible for components ranging from actuators for undercarriage doors made by Mitsubishi Heavy Industries in Japan, the upper fin and rudder by Aeritalia at Naples, and the fuselage shell by General Dynamics. Wings were assigned to de Havilland Canada at Toronto, but the plant was later bought and became Douglas Aircraft of Canada.

When the first pair of production machines were handed over, 127 orders for the type had already been received. However it appeared that the immediate zenith of the passenger transport business had been passed, and consequently some of the options that had been taken out in the first flush of

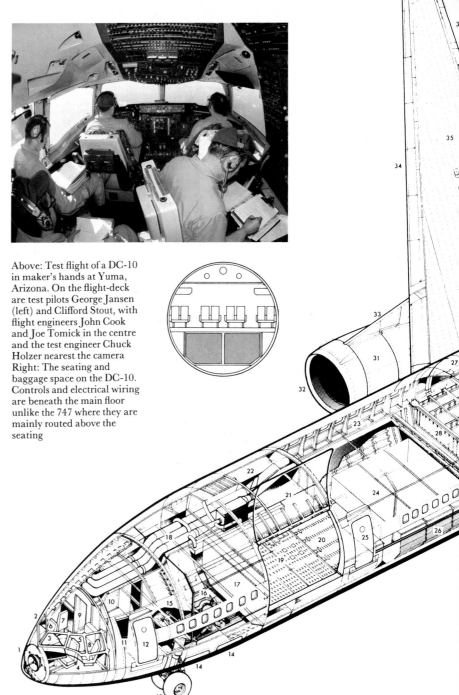

Above: Test flight of a DC-10 in maker's hands at Yuma, Arizona. On the flight-deck are test pilots George Jansen (left) and Clifford Stout, with flight engineers John Cook and Joe Tomick in the centre and the test engineer Chuck Holzer nearest the camera
Right: The seating and baggage space on the DC-10. Controls and electrical wiring are beneath the main floor unlike the 747 where they are mainly routed above the seating

DC-10 Series 30 CF

1 Weather radar
2 Windshield
3 Instrument console
4 Flight deck
5 Captain's seat
6 First officer's seat
7 Flight engineer's position
8 Supernumerary crew seat
9 Flight deck door
10 Forward right toilet
11 Forward left toilet
12 Crew and passenger forward door
13 Twin wheel nose gear
14 Air-conditioning access doors
15 Forward cargo bulkhead
16 Air-conditioning bay
17 Forward lower galley area
18 Air-conditioning trunking
19 Cargo deck lateral transfer area
20 Cargo deck pallet channels
21 Main cargo door
22 VHF antenna
23 Frame-and-stringer fuselage

24 Main deck cargo
25 Passenger door
26 Forward lower compartment
27 Centre-section fuselage main frame
28 Centre-section front beam
29 Shear-web floor support over centre-section fuel tank
30 Cargo/passenger compartment dividing bulkhead
31 Right engine pod (Rohr subcontract)
32 Engine intake
33 Nacelle pylon
34 Leading-edge slats
35 Integral wing fuel tank
36 Right navigation lights
37 Low-speed outboard aileron
38 Fuel ventpipe
39 Wing spoilers/lift dumpers
40 Double-slotted flaps
41 All-speed inboard drooping aileron
42 Passenger doors
43 Centre-section fuselage mainframe
44 Cabin air ducts
45 Centre undercarriage bay
46 Keel box structure

47 Fuselage/wing attachment points
48 Wing torsion-box construction
49 Leading-edge structure
50 Nacelle pylon
51 Engine intake
52 General Electric CF6-50 turbofan
53 Exhaust outlet
54 Four-wheel main undercarriage
55 Leading-edge slats
56 Outboard slat extended
57 Left navigation lights
58 Low-speed outboard aileron
59 Fuel vent pipe
60 Outboard flap hinge fairings
61 Fuel pipes
62 All-speed inboard drooping aileron
63 Inboard flap hinge actuator and fairing
64 Undercarriage support structure
65 Flap construction
66 Wing root fairing
67 Fuselage-attached flap track
68 Centre cargo compartment
69 Cabin floor support
70 Overhead luggage lockers
71 Eight-abreast coach-class seating

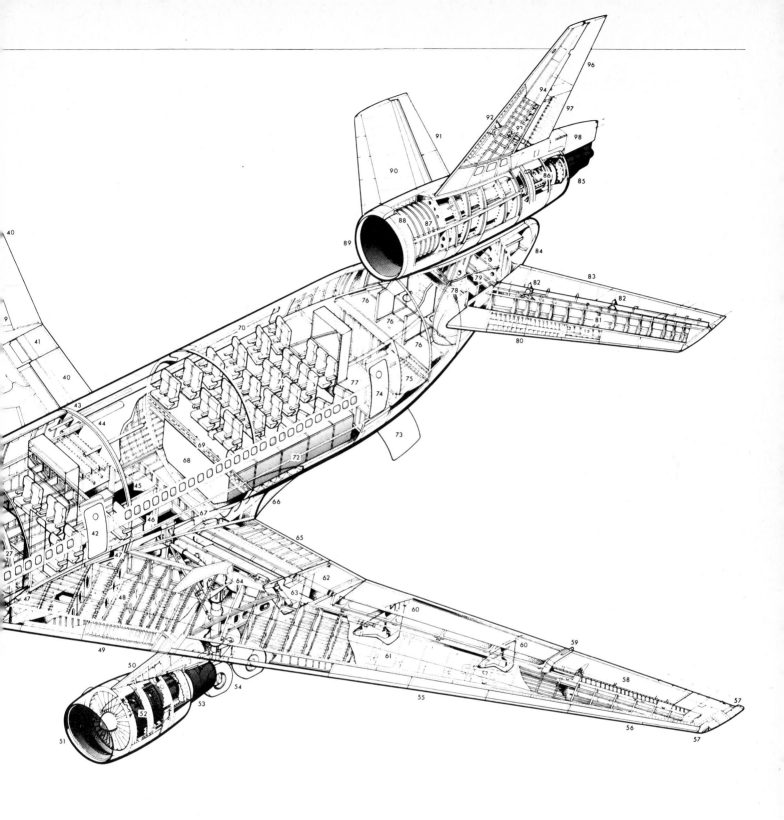

72 Baggage containers
73 Bulk cargo hold floor
74 Rear passenger door (left and right)
75 Rear toilet (left and right)
76 Three toilets/washrooms
77 Underfloor bulk cargo hold
78 Rear pressure bulkhead
79 Tailplane centre section (Garrett or AiResearch APU below)
80 Tailplane leading edge
81 Tailplane construction
82 Elevator actuators
83 Dual elevators
84 Tail cone
85 Exhaust outlet
86 General Electric CF6-50 turbofan
87 Inlet duct
88 Intake hot-air duct
89 engine intake
90 Right tailplane
91 Dual elevators
92 Tailfin leading edge
93 Rudder actuator
94 Tail fin torsion box construction
95 VOR

96 Upper rudder sections
97 Lower rudder sections
98 Tail pylon

Left: Final assembly of the DC-10 at the Douglas plant at Long Beach, California

enthusiasm were deliberately dropped. Therefore it was anticipated that by the end of 1971 there would be five DC-10s operating on scheduled service, augmented by a further 20, 12 months later, so that the number for which firm orders existed was reduced to 96.

Those few machines in service soon gained a reputation for quietness and cleanliness of operation. However, some members of the American Air Line Pilots' Association did express misgivings about certain features of the design. Some of their criticisms seemed to be justified because of an incident that took place as early as November 1971 when grave doubts were expressed about the security of some of the door-locking mechanisms.

Orders continued to be placed, however, and the customers included Laker Airways and THY (Turkish Airlines). These airlines bought the Series 10, though delivery was now in sight for the Series 30, and this gradually became the more popular type.

The next variant to be announced, the Series 40, had as its powerplant Pratt & Whitney engines of an even higher rating than the previous General Electric CF6-50, obtained through the complication of water injection.

Next came the DC-10 Series 30CF, a Convertible Freighter for 380 passengers or 70 626 kg (155 700 lb) of cargo. The first flight of this version took place on February 28, 1973. In a surprisingly short space of time the deliveries of the production CF began, the first taking place on April 17, when Overseas National and Trans International each

received one.

The conversion from passenger to freight carrier was intended to be an overnight operation and, in addition to the removal of the seats, the procedure included a general stripping-out of the passenger facilities. This could also include removal of the refreshment points and dismantling the lavatories to achieve extra space. The stability of the cargo was ensured by tie-down points and restraining nets attached to the seat rails, while freight was handled via a system of rollers and adjustable guide-rails. To admit bulky items a large side door was provided with a hinging top so that it could be swung up to clear the larger items. As a convenience to operators the fixing and loading systems could be stowed under the floor of the passenger

Above: A Douglas DC-10-40, the variant first built to a Japan Air Lines order and powered by Pratt & Whitney JT9D-59A turbofans. First flight with this powerplant was July 25, 1975
Below: *Ciudad de Mexico*, one of the two DC-10-30s used by Aeromexico in 1979. The airline was founded in 1934 and nationalized in 1959

Left: Air New Zealand DC-10 ZK-NZL. It was an aircraft identical to this, registered ZK-NZF, which crashed tragically on Mt Erebus in the Antarctic on November 28, 1979

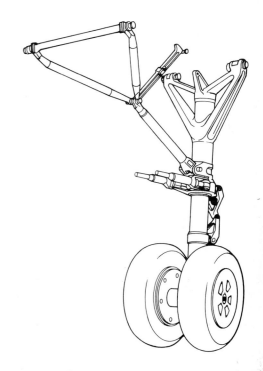

Below: The Abex/Dowty nosegear which was the first part-British undercarriage to be used in a US aircraft for 30 years

compartment so that conversion could be carried out away from the main base.

By the midsummer of 1973 McDonnell Douglas were ready to deliver their 100th production aircraft. They had also received orders totalling 197 airframes with options for a further 37 from 29 operators, most of whom required aircraft of the Series 30 type plus a few cargo convertibles while the remainder ordered the original model.

All seemed set for further progress when disaster struck over France. At 1238 hours on March 3, 1974 a DC-10 of THY Turkish Airlines crashed a few miles out from Paris in the Ermenonville Forest. The death-toll of 346 was the highest in aviation history. 'Apparent in-flight depressurization' was the immediate diagnosis. The result was

a long list of new safety precautions ordered by McDonnell Douglas. General Dynamics disclaimed any responsibility for the design and went on to say that their part was merely that of the manufacturer. Ironically the same year saw the announcement during the summer of a total 250 orders and options.

The investigations that followed the French crash seemed to indicate that the sequence of events that immediately preceded the fatal flight was as follows: following take-off, at about 3800 m (12 500 ft) the freight door of the aft compartment suddenly burst open with explosive force and struck the tailplane as it was flung rearwards. At the same time the baggage compartment suffered a sudden decompression and the floor collapsed

Below: A Lufthansa DC-10-30 with its distinctive livery taxies down the runway. In 1980 the airline, formed in 1954 as the successor to Deutsche Lufthansa, was operating 11 such aircraft on its intercontinental routes

under the pressure of the passenger area above it; this destroyed the control runs that passed through the floor with subsequent total loss of flight control. This was by no means the first failure of a DC-10 baggage compartment door; in one earlier incident over the United States a coffin had fallen out.

Consequently, on May 25, 1979, when a DC-10 shed an engine at take-off from Chicago O'Hare, it threw the world's airlines into a panic. The Federal Aviation Administration (FAA) immediately grounded all DC-10s pending investigations. The most popular theory was that the accident was due to the failure of the engine mountings. However, American Airlines was blamed for faulty maintenance procedures and the design was given a clean bill of health.

Top: An Alitalia DC-10-30 in the maintenance hangar with its General Electric engine in the foreground. This was one of eight DC-10s operated by the airline in 1980
Centre: A good indication of the size of the GE CF6-50, as a technician runs it through a series of tests. More than any other turbofan in airline use the CF6 has a slim core driving a large-diameter front fan handling a tonne of air every two seconds. It is fitted with Borescope ports at every compressor and turbine stage and around the combustor, which help reduce maintenance costs as the engine does not have to be disassembled for visual checks
Above: A CF6-50 is tested at the Hamburg overhaul division of Lufthansa. Similar engines power Lufthansa's twin-engined A300s

From 1980 McDonnell Douglas are hoping to deliver heavier examples of the DC-10 fitted with engines giving an increased thrust and both Varig and Laker have been offered options on this variant. In the interests of greater efficiency these airliners will be fitted with an improved wing fillet, which appeared on some of the earlier machines delivered in the late 1970s.

Future plans include a stretched model ready for service in 1983; this will be in the Super 60 series and the prototype is scheduled to fly in 1980.

Three versions are anticipated of which the DC-10-61 will be a domestic machine for use within the US, fitted with the wing of the 30 model but with a fuselage lengthened by 12.19 m (40 ft). For these versions JT9D-7R4 or CF6-80-type engines are planned, marking a new family of powerplants and systems. Like the 61 which will seat 390 passengers, the other two variants, the 62 and 63 will feature wings set at a new angle of incidence to reduce drag and floor angle.

The first of these will have a capacity similar to that offered by the DC-10 Series 30 with an extended length of 8.23 m (26 ft 8½ in). The increase of loaded weight will be met by replacement of the twin-wheel landing gear by a four-wheel centre unit while active ailerons will allow an increase in the total span of 4.27 m (14 ft).

Features of the 63 model of the DC-10 will include aerodynamic advances from the 62 joined to the fuselage of the 61, although it is planned at present to retain the same weight as the 62.

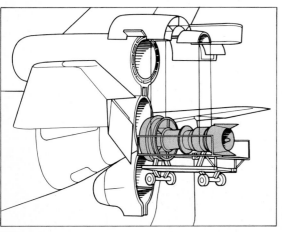

Right: The slats, double-slotted flaps and spoilers on the DC-10. They are shown in light grey in their cruise position and blue deployed for landing. These secondary surfaces are necessary for adequate lift on take-off and landing. The centre diagram shows a section of a DC-10 wing with the slat position on the left and the flaps on the right

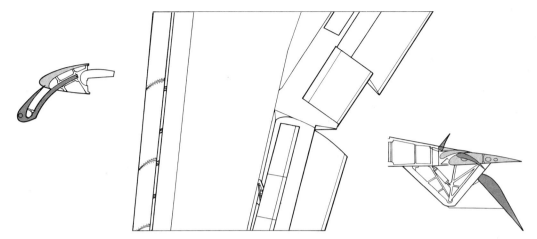

Far left above: Preparing to change the General Electric CF6-50C engine of a Lufthansa DC-10-30
Far left below: The complicated procedure for changing the centre engine. The tailcone is swung down, and the inner sections of the elevators are disconnected and allowed to hang down
Left: In the interest of safety all DC-10 mechanical, hydraulic and electronic components receive close inspection. In May 1979 inadequate maintenance procedures were blamed for a fatal crash

A300B, Airbus Industrie

FIRST FLIGHT 1972

BY 1965 various European aircraft industries were considering the possibility of combining to produce a large-capacity passenger aircraft to fill the entirely new role of an 'air bus'. The key to such an aircraft was the totally new level of engine thrust and fuel efficiency provided by the new generation of large high-ratio turbofan engines. By October of the following year the first design proposals were available for study.

The responsible consortium consisted of delegates from Aérospatiale, Deutsche Airbus (a combination of MBB and VFW-Fokker) and Hawker Siddeley (later to become part of British Aerospace). Like the original studies such as the HBN-100 (Hawker-Brequet-Nord) and Sud Galion, the original design was a 300-seater, hence the desig-

nation A300. In 1968 this was scaled down in size to about 250 seats but instead of being called A250 it was redesignated A300B.

In order to finance the new venture, repayable loans were invited from several interested governments or national banking groups. A levy on the sales figures ensured the repayments once production was in progress. The Aérospatiale organization was elected leader in the field of design studies, responsible for the production of the nose section including the flight-deck, and the jet-engine pylons, the centre wing inside the fuselage and the final assembly. Deutsche Airbus were assigned responsibility for the production of the fuselage and tail. For purely political reasons the British government pulled out of the programme in 1969, foolish-

Right: Airbus Industries' demonstration aircraft, pulling g (note wingtip vortex)
Below: Eastern Air Lines A300B4 with landing gear lowered. This aircraft is the basic long-range Airbus. It is fitted with Krüger flaps on the wing leading edges to improve take-off and landing performance and in 1980 was the most fuel-efficient transport aircraft in the world

ly failing to appreciate the need for such an aircraft. Despite this, Hawker Siddeley accepted responsibility for the entire main wing, and was in a position to fund this participation with its own money.

For the powerplants another group of companies combined including Rolls-Royce, MAN-Turbo and SNECMA. Following the lukewarm British attitude, the chosen engine was the General Electric CF6-50, assembled by SNECMA with some parts made in Germany by MTU. VFW-Fokker contributed the moving surfaces of the wing assembly, Messier-Hispano the landing gear and, later, CASA of Spain provided portions of the tail assembly and the main fuselage doors.

Not only was the Airbus Industrie organization

Above: An Indian Airlines A300B2 still bearing French registration before delivery in 1977. The B2 was the first production version of the A300B. This aircraft was later registered VT-EDV and became one of five operated in 1980 by Indian Airlines on its vast network throughout the sub-continent.
Right: Lufthansa A300B2 *Rudesheim am Rhein* at Frankfurt-am-Main Airport

F-WLGB

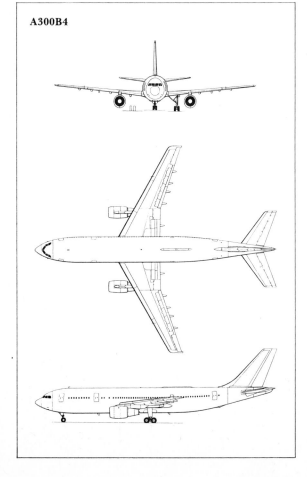

A300B4

A300B2-100

Type: short/medium-range transport
Maker: Airbus Industrie
Span: 44.84 m (147 ft 1¼ in)
Length: 53.75 m (175 ft 9 in)
Height: 16.53 m (54 ft 2¾ in)
Wing area: 260 m²
(2799 sq ft)
Weight: maximum
142 000 kg (313 055 lb); empty
85 910 kg (189 400 lb)
Powerplant: two 23 034-kg
(51 000-lb) st General Electric
CF6-50C turbofans
Performance: maximum
cruising speed 935 km/h
(582 mph) at 8354 m
(28 000 ft); range with full
payload 1610 km (1000 miles)
Payload: 34 600 kg
(76 260 lb; seats for up to 336
passengers
Crew: 3
Production: 40

A300B1

Specification similar to B2-
100 except in the following
particulars:
Length: 50.96 m (167 ft
2¼ in)
Weight: maximum
132 000 kg (291 000 lb); empty
70 520 kg (155 470 lb)
Production: 1

A300B2-200

Specification similar to B2-
100 except in the following
particulars:
Weight: empty 77 427 kg
(170 697 lb)
Production: 26 (including
future deliveries)

A300B2-300

Specification similar to B2-
200 except in the following
particulars:
Powerplant: two 24 040-kg
(53 000-lb) st Pratt &
Whitney JT9D-59A turbofans
Production: 12

A300B4-100

Specification similar to B2-
200/300 except in the
following particulars:
Weight: maximum
157 000 kg (347 230 lb); empty
79 070 kg (174 319 lb)
Performance: typical cruise
at 9145 m (30 000 ft)
917 km/h (570 mph); range
with payload 4818 km
(2994 miles)
Payload: 35 900 kg
(79 170 lb)
Production: 104 (including
orders)

A300B4-200

Specification similar to B4-
100 except in the following
particulars:
Weight: maximum
165 000 kg (363 760 lb)
Performance: range with
269 passengers and baggage
and full reserves 5095 km
(3165 miles)
Production: 97 (including
orders and C4)

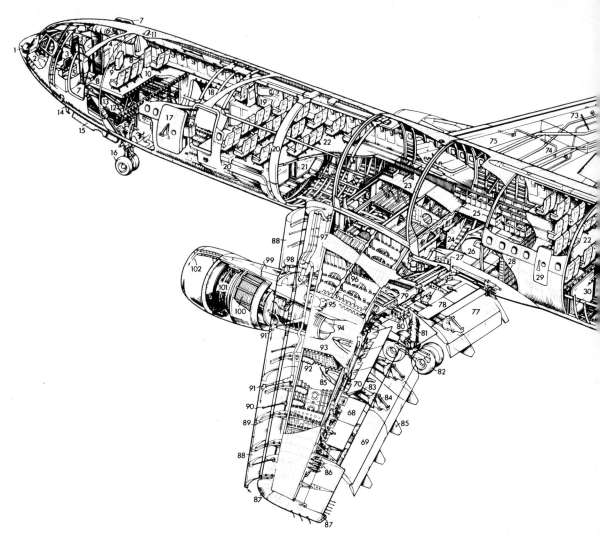

responsible for the design, development and manufacture of the machine, but also for marketing. To finance this operation a second consortium was formed, this time from French and German banks.

In the United Kingdom the first the public at large saw of the design was when a mock-up of part of the fuselage was exhibited at the SBAC Display at Farnborough in 1968. It was a strange choice since the main British design responsibility was for the wing box from Hawker Siddeley. However, the dummy was complete with furnishings and features which in the eventual product were to be added at Hamburg after the completed aircraft had flown from Toulouse.

Two prototypes were built, both of the A300B1 type, slightly smaller than the production aircraft. The first flew at Toulouse-Blagnac on October 28, 1972, and the second on February 5, 1973. From the start the flight development programme was totally successful, and in most respects was beyond criticism. The B1 was shorter than subsequent models by 2.65 m (8 ft 8 in). Although the powerplants were the General Electric CF6-50C, the design was such that any engine offering similar thrust could be used since the external pylon locations offered no problems in installation.

By late 1972 the lengthened A300B2 was on the line, and the first two aircraft, for certification, flew on June 28 and November 20, 1973. The first production aircraft, which flew on April 15, 1974, differed little from the two earlier B2 aircraft, and one month later it entered service on the London to Paris route. By this time one of the original B1

162

A300B 2

1 Weather radar scanner in upward-hinged radome
2 Dual control columns and rudder pedals
3 Flight deck for three crew members (plus optional observer seat)
4 Forward galley
5 Forward toilet
6 Water tank
7 Forward passenger-entry doors with attached escape-chutes (each side)
8 Folding seats for cabin crew
9 Galley service trolley
10 Control cables carried through under-floor beams
11 VHF blade antenna
12 Nose gear retraction jack
13 Nose gear drag strut
14 Overboard waste drain
15 Nose gear doors
16 Forward-retracting nosewheels
17 Main passenger-entry doors with attached escape-chutes (each side)
18 Power-operated forward cargo hold door
19 Escape-chute pack on right door
20 Cabin air-conditioning ducts
21 Type A2 cargo containers in forward hold
22 Eight-abreast passenger seating
23 Wing torsion-box carry-through structure
24 Air-conditioning equipment bay under torsion-box
25 Pressure-floor longitudinal beams
26 Right undercarriage door
27 Central walkway in undercarriage bay
28 Undercarriage bay aft pressure bulkhead
29 Emergency exit doors (each side)
30 Type A2 cargo containers in rear hold
31 VHF and ADF antennae in external fairing
32 Power-operated rear cargo door
33 Rearmost hold for non-containerized cargo
34 Manual plug-door for rearmost hold

35 Seven-abreast seating in aft passenger cabin
36 Overhead hat-racks
37 Air-conditioning valve gear and air outlet
38 Rear passenger-entry doors (each side)
39 Water tank
40 Optional seats at rear of cabin, or galley unit
41 Rear toilets (two each side)
42 Toilet collector tank
43 Water service panel
44 Overboard waste drain
45 Rear pressure dome
46 HF surface antenna
47 Fairing over fin-spar anchorages
48 Compressed air duct from APU
49 Tail bumper
50 Removable tailplane leading edge
51 Tailplane pivot on reinforced fuselage frame
52 Tailplane inter-spar torsion-box, carried through fuselage
53 Tailplane hinge (Teflon swivel-bearing)
54 Triple elevator-actuating jacks
55 APU access doors, open
56 Detachable tail cone
57 APU exhaust outlet
58 Garrett TSCP 700-5 auxiliary power unit
59 Rudder hinges (Teflon swivel bearings)
60 Multi-spar fin torsion-box
61 Triple rudder-actuating jacks
62 Rudder-section at topmost hinge
63 Static discharge wicks (at tips of all surfaces)
64 Detachable fin leading edge
65 Low-speed aileron
66 Flush air intake for fuel-vent system
67 Outer integral fuel tank
68 Two-piece airflow spoilers
69 Outboard two-piece tabbed Fowler flaps (extended)
70 Three-piece air-brakes, open
71 Fuel pumps (two per tank)
72 Refuelling points
73 Fuel contents indicators
74 Inner integral fuel tank
75 Fuel pipe circuitry

76 All-speed aileron (depressed)
77 Inboard tabbed Fowler flap section (extended)
78 Inboard two-piece lift-dumpers
79 Undercarriage load-bearing beam structure
80 Triple actuating jacks for all-speed aileron
81 Inwards-retracting main gear leg
82 Four-wheel main gear bogie
83 Flap track beam
84 Flap carriage
85 Flap track fairing
86 Triple actuating jacks for low-speed aileron
87 Navigation lamps
88 Three-piece full-span leading-edge slats (extended)
89 Slat tracks
90 Slat actuating jacks
91 Slat anti-icing hot-air ducts
92 Sealed cans in fuel tank, receiving retracted slat-tracks
93 Full-span inter-spar torsion-box structure, with integral fuel tanks
94 Engine jet efflux nozzle
95 Engine fire extinguisher bottles
96 Auxiliary inner wing spar
97 Hot-air ducts
98 Retractable slat section, allowing pylon coverage
99 Engine pylon, cantilevered to wing spars
100 Fan-air reverser cascades
101 General Electric CF6-50C two-spool turbofan engine
102 Intake-lip anti-icing hot-air duct

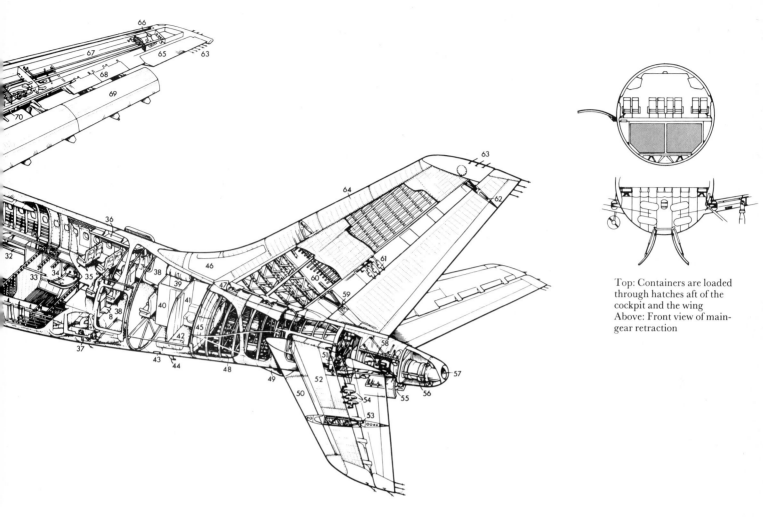

Top: Containers are loaded through hatches aft of the cockpit and the wing
Above: Front view of main-gear retraction

Far left: Assembling an overhauled Pratt & Whitney JT9D engine at the Lufthansa Technical Centre at Hamburg
Left: The seating layout of a Lufthansa Airbus A300B2. The interior can be varied from the airline's standard 220 seats to an economy single-class configuration with 336 in either the B2 or B4 – virtually doing the job of the big trijets
Below: The General Electric CF6-50 engine for the A300 has some tough competition from both Pratt & Whitney and Rolls Royce with their JT9D and RB.211 engines

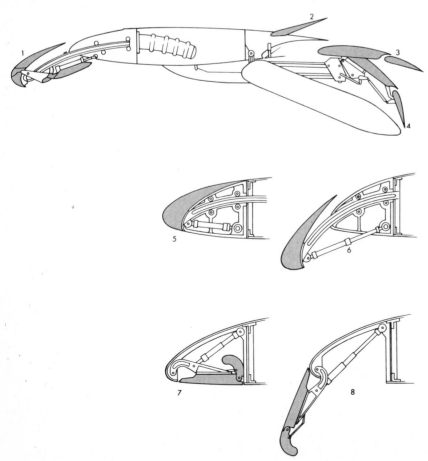

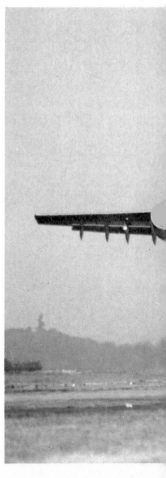

Above: The cockpit of an Indian Airlines A300B2-100, showing its registration VT-EDV in the centre. Seating is for a flight-crew of three

Above right: The engineer's panel on the right-hand side of the flight-deck

Right: In take-off mode the A300B shows its extremely efficient slender slightly-swept wing with long-span Fowler flaps. Leading-edge slats are unbroken by the pylon struts

Left top: Section through the wing shows: leading-edge slat (1), spoiler (2) and double-slotted Fowler flap in take-off position (3) and landing position (4)

Left centre: The leading-edge slat retracted (5) and extended forwards on rollers and curved guides (6) to the high-lift position

Left bottom: The inboard leading edge has Krüger flaps normally retracted (7) but for maximum lift extended (8)

Left and above: A Lufthansa flight simulator. Conversion of flight crews is handled by the busy company Aéroformation at Toulouse, France, which also trains customer technical staff and cabin crew. Many hours are put in on simulators which incorporate external visual scenes and exactly reproduce every feature and function of the aircraft apart from actual flight

prototypes was flying 15 hours a day with Belgian TEA taking pilgrims to Mecca. The order from Air France had been for six models of the mixed-class version capable of carrying 251 passengers. When the first orders were placed options were taken out on a further ten of the type. Lufthansa was another customer during the same year ordering three with an option for another four. Despite the strikingly obvious nature of the aircraft, and Air France's early assessment that it used from 29 to 39% less fuel per passenger journey than a Boeing 727-200 (besides being much quieter), orders remained at what was a remarkably low level for six years. This was allegedly because it was not an American product.

The B2K version which followed was distinguished from the earlier design by having Krüger flaps which had been originally developed for the B4. Unlike the American trijet rivals the A300B has a continuous leading-edge slat unbroken by the engine pylon. In the B2K the inboard end of the slat is neatly completed by a Krüger flap which swings out from the fuselage. The B2K also features the heavy-duty wheels, tyres and brakes that had been earmarked for the B4 with higher gross weight. The B2K was therefore especially suitable for operation from airfields in the tropics. South African Airways, having to contend with hot and high airfields, was the first B2K customer in November 1976.

A fresh designation was also given to the Airbus formerly described as the B4 Stage I, when it became known as the B4-100. It was intended to be

Above: The passenger loading
bridges leading to a
Lufthansa A300B2
Right: A Super Guppy opens
its cavernous maw to deliver
an A300 fuselage to the plant
at Toulouse for final assembly

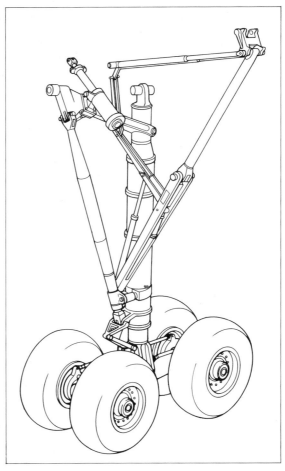

Top: The four-wheel bogie of the A300, a product of Messier-Hispano-Bugatti. Such landing gears are now common with large transports since they offer greater security against blowouts, and distribute weight over a large area
Above: The Toulouse 'feeding trough' with nine A300s in the livery of different customers. Among the aircraft is A300 number 3, which was reserved as the development vehicle for the Advanced A300 programme, and one of the Pratt & Whitney-powered SAS aircraft

Left: The production line at Toulouse, with aircraft in various stages of construction

Right: Thai Airways operates
its long-range A300B4s
between Bangkok, Taiwan,
Japan and Hong Kong
Far right: Air Inter, the
French metropolitan airline,
operated five A300B2s in 1980
Below: An A300 of the
Belgian operator Trans
European Airways
Below right: Bavaria
Germanair operates from
Frankfurt to parts of Europe
and North Africa
Bottom: An A300 sporting the
insignia of airline customers
landing after a sales
demonstration

a longer-range type and was derived from a 'stretched' B2. Fitted with Krüger flaps in order to improve the take-off performance, the main dimensions remained unaltered. There were internal modifications, most notably including a very large new centre-wing fuel tank to provide adequate safety margins over the extended-range routes. This was the version finally taken up by Thailand and Iberia although the first operators were Germanair who flew their first model of this series on a scheduled service on June 1, 1975.

A further range-stretch was made public by an announcement in January 1978 that work had begun on the B4-200 and orders for three had already been received from Air France. Apart from strengthening the landing gear, there was provision for extending the range by carrying extra fuel in optional tanks stowed in the cargo hold. At a certificated weight of 165 tonnes the Airbus B4-200 is matched to sectors of up to 5930 km (3685 miles).

It is the B4-200 that has appealed most to new customers, taking orders from 180 to 380 in the first ten months of 1979 alone. Some, led by the batch for the Scandinavian airline SAS, have Pratt & Whitney JT9D engines. A freight version was considered as well as a military tanker variant, and the former was the next model to be produced, with a large upper-deck cargo door, strengthened floor, computerized loading system and automatic smoke detection. The first C4 rolled out at Hamburg in November 1979 went to the West German airline Hapag-Lloyd.

An interesting feature common to the majority of A300 variants is the provision for pressure refuelling through a pair of points beneath each wing surface outboard of the engine pylons. Thrust reversers are fitted capable of pneumatic activation by means of air bled off the engine, which allows the aircraft to operate from short-runway airfields. Passenger comfort was a priority. As an example, in the all-tourist class aircraft two galleys can be fitted capable of meeting the needs of 281 passengers and in this particular model there is a total of five lavatories. Passenger baggage is normally stowed in compartments under the floor in holds situated fore and aft of the wings. These areas are pressurized and accessible from the outside through doors on the right-hand side. The rear cargo section of the aircraft is also pressurized and livestock can be transported on some medium-haul flights.

In 1978 two new versions were announced, the A300B11 with an increased sweep to the wings and seating for 200 mixed-class passengers for long-range destinations, and the A300B9 with both lengthened fuselage and increased wing span. In 1979 Rolls-Royce belatedly tried to enter the A300B programme, although no customers for RB.211-powered models had been announced by 1980. British Aerospace became a full risk-sharing member of AI in 1979, as did Belairbus, a Belgian consortium. Continued development of the A300B family had by 1980 led to composite structural parts, digital avionics and flight-control system and the option of an advanced cockpit with electronic displays and colour radar.

A310, Airbus Industrie

ESTIMATED FIRST FLIGHT 1982

FROM the formation of Airbus Industrie in December 1970 it was the consortium's intention to develop more than a single type of aircraft, the immediate objective being derivatives of the A300B. By 1974 these had crystallized into three main projects: the A300B9 stretched high-capacity aircraft, the B10 reduced-size version for routes not offering sufficient traffic for an A300B2 or B4, and the B11 long-haul aircraft with four smaller engines. After prolonged market research and discussion with potential customers the decision was taken in July 1978 to go ahead with the B10, redesignated A310.

Though naturally having maximum commonality with the A300B2 and B4 then in production the A310 represents a major design and certification task because, as well as having a shorter fuselage, it has a completely new wing. Other changes include a smaller horizontal tail, standard engine pylons able to accept any of the three basic makes of engine on offer and a modified lightweight landing gear.

The basic A310 design was predicted on a fuselage of the same carefully optimized cross section but shortened by 13 frames; then the rear pressure bulkhead was moved back inside by two frames to leave the available interior just 11 frames shorter. Having established this extremely efficient fuselage the decision was taken to match it to a minimal wing optimized to the lowest possible cruise fuel consumption. In this Airbus Industrie took the directly opposite course to Boeing with its 767, whose wing is actually larger than that of the A300B, and instead of being optimized to trip fuel, is based on extreme 'hot and high' take-offs and a climb to high cruise altitude.

While the A300B has the newest and most efficient wing flying on any airliner, that of the A310 is of even later concept and has the higher aspect ratio of 8.8, compared with 7.9 for the Boeing 767 and 7.73 for the A300B. Section profile is totally supercritical, and cruising efficiency will be unquestionably unrivalled in the 1980s. Baseline wings, both aerodynamic and structural, were investigated at British Aerospace, Aérospatiale and MBB, and the final design incorporates features from all partners. Detail engineering took place in 1978–80 at British Aerospace where the main wing box is being produced. Both inner and outer flaps are double-slotted (on the 767 only the inners are of this type) and another point scored over the 767 appears to be elimination of outboard ailerons.

Structurally the A310 follows A300B philosophy, which has been shown to set the very highest standards in the industry, with the incorporation of advanced composites such as are now being introduced to the A300B airframe, notably in the use of carbon-fibre in the rudder and spoilers, fin leading edge, tail/fuselage fairing and floor beam struts, with Kevlar flap-track fairings, wing/body fairing and landing-gear doors. Like the latest A300Bs the flight-control system and avionics is totally digital and the flight-deck will be almost identical to its larger brother. While Boeing could offer customers no choice in a 'take it or leave it' cockpit based on electronic displays, Airbus Industrie has offered more choice with an alternative of a

170

more traditional cockpit similar to that of A300Bs at present in service.

Launch of the A310 sparked off violent competition between General Electric, lead engine supplier on the A300B, and Pratt & Whitney. The original A310-100 series was planned as a short-hauler, but all early customers preferred the longer-range A310-200 family. This is now in production as the A310-201, with CF6-45B2A engine; -202, with CF6-80A; -220, with Pratt & Whitney JT9D-7R4C; and an even longer-range -300 series which had not been ordered in early 1980 but offers a maximum weight of 140 600 kg (310 000 lb) and range with full passenger load (214) using the CF6-80A engine of 6550 km (4070 miles), very much further even than the TC

Below: An A310 in the livery of Air Afrique. The A310 will have microprocessors controlling the operation of the flaps, slats, flight trajectory and engines, for minimal energy consumption. These systems will have all to agree for such operations as landing, and the pilots can overide them in an emergency. The CRT display linked to the system will give a visual display of what each 'chip' has decided

A310-200

Type: short/medium-range transport
Maker: Airbus Industrie
Span: 43.90 m (144 ft 0¼ in)
Length: 47.21 m (154 ft 10¾ in)
Height: 15.81 m (51 ft 10 in)
Wing area: 219.9 m² (2367 sq ft)
Weight: maximum 132 000 kg (291 020 lb); empty 76 469 kg (168 585 lb)
Powerplant: two 21 773-kg (48 000-lb) st GE CF6-80A1 or 21 274-kg (46 900-lb) st JT9D-7R4C turbofans
Performance: economical cruise 830 km/h (515 mph) at 10 670 m (35 000 ft); range with 214 passengers and baggage, and full reserves, 5582 km (3470 miles)
Payload: 31 890 kg (70 290 lb); seats for 214 mixed-class passengers
Crew: 3
Production: 63 orders with 66 options by January 1980

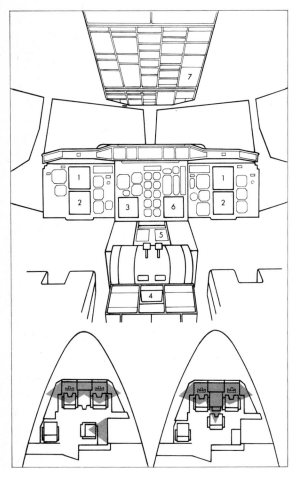

A310

1 Radome
2 Radar scanner
3 Pressure bulkhead
4 Radar scanner mounting
5 Windscreen panels
6 Windscreen wipers
7 Instrument panel shroud
8 Control column
9 Rudder pedals
10 Cockpit floor level
11 ILS aerial
12 Access ladder to lower deck
   equipment bays
13 Pitot tubes
14 Captain's seat
15 First officer's seat
16 Overhead systems control panel
17 Engineer's control panel
18 Circuit breaker panel
19 Flight engineer's seat
20 Cockpit air-conditioning duct
21 Observer's seat
22 Cockpit bulkhead
23 Wardrobe/locker
24 Nose undercarriage wheel well
25 Retraction jack
26 Twin nosewheels
27 Steering jacks
28 Nosewheel doors
29 Forward toilet
30 Galley
31 Right entry door
32 Cabin attendant's folding
   seat
33 Curtained cabin divider
34 Cabin attendant's seat
35 Left main entry door
36 Door latch
37 Door surround structure
38 Radio and electronics racks
39 Fuselage frame and stringer
   construction
40 Floor beam construction
41 Forward freight hold
42 Freight hold door
43 VHF communications aerial
44 Right engine nacelle
45 Curtained cabin divider
46 First-class passenger compartment,
   20 seats
47 Overhead baggage lockers
48 Air-conditioning ducting
49 Baggage pallets
50 Pressurized fresh water tanks
51 Slat drive gearbox
52 Wing centre section spar
53 Tourist-class seating 197 seats
54 Air-distribution ducting
55 Overhead stowage bins
56 Right nacelle pylon
57 Slat screw jacks
58 Screw jack drive shaft
59 Refuelling connections
60 Fuel system piping
61 Right wing integral fuel tanks
62 Leading-edge slats
63 Slat fence
64 Leading-edge de-icing
65 Right navigation lights
66 Wingtip fairing
67 Static discharge wicks
68 Fixed portion of trailing edge
69 Right spoilers
70 Flap drive mechanism
71 Airbrakes
72 Fuel jettison pipe

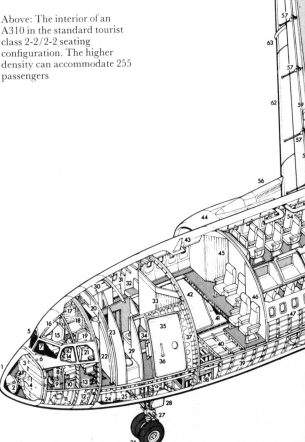

version of 767. Rolls-Royce is also offering its RB.211-524B4 engine, in the proposed A310-240, but this had not been selected by the early part of 1980.

Other variants include the A310C series of convertibles and A310F series of pure freighters, using the same cargo floor, door and handling system as the A300C4 and F4. Of course, another major advantage over the 767 is the ability to carry standard wide-body underfloor LD-3 cargo and baggage containers, as well as standard above-floor 88 × 125 cargo pallets which fit a 767 only lengthways (after fitting a wider door).

Thanks to the fact the A310 is a derivative aircraft the bill for development is in the order of $900 million, less than half that needed for the 767. Go-ahead was thus possible on two big orders from important customers, Swissair and Lufthansa, for first delivery in 1983.

The Swiss operator selected the Pratt & Whitney engine, but despite the most intense efforts by that engine supplier (especially with Air France) both other versions so far selected by March 1980 will have GE engines, the customers being Air France and KLM. Not yet announced were the engine choices of British Caledonian, Martinair, Air Afrique and Sabena. The last-named, the Belgian flag-carrier, followed participation of a Belgian industrial group, called Belairbus, in the A310 manufacturing programme.

Despite this indecision, the A310 is likely to be of major concern to American aircraft designers and operators in the 1980s.

Above left: The new forward-facing crew cockpit of the A300/310 showing: 1 the electronic attitude director indicator; 2 electronic horizontal situation indicator; 3 caution/warning cathode-ray tube (CRT) display; 4 systems CRT controller; 5 caution/warning panel and CRT controller; 6 systems CRT; 7 overhead panel
Inset left: The crew positions in the earlier A300s, indicating crew vision
Inset right: Crew positions in the forward-facing cockpit with the flight engineer seated between the two pilots

Above: The interior of an A310 in the standard tourist class 2-2/2-2 seating configuration. The higher density can accommodate 255 passengers

73 Outer double-slotted Fowler flap
74 Right all-speed aileron
75 Inboard double-slotted flap
76 Lift dumper/airbrake
77 Flap drive shaft
78 Wing attachment fuselage main frames
79 Right overwing emergency exit
80 Fuselage centre-section construction
81 Centre-section floor beams
82 Wing carry-through structure
83 Ventral air-conditioning pack
84 Left overwing emergency exit door
85 Pressure floor above wheel well bay
86 Right main undercarriage retracted position
87 Undercarriage door jack
88 Equipment bay walkway
89 Undercarriage bay bulkhead
90 Flap drive motor
91 Hydraulic reservoir
92 Eight-abreast tourist class seating
93 DF loop aerial fairing
94 Cabin wall trim panels

95 Fuselage frame and stringer construction
96 Rear freight hold door
97 Baggage pallets
98 Freight hold rear bulkhead
99 Cabin floor panels
100 Seat attachment rails
101 Seven-abreast rear cabin seating
102 Central overhead stowage bins
103 Curtained rear cabin divider
104 Aft galley unit
105 Fin root fillet
106 HF notch aerial
107 Right tailplane
108 Right elevator
109 Fin leading edge
110 Fin construction
111 Fintip fairing'
112 Static discharge wicks
113 Rudder construction
114 Triplex rudder hydraulic jacks
115 APU intake duct
116 Garrett GTCP331 auxiliary power unit
117 Tailcone fairing
118 APU exhaust duct

119 Left elevator construction
120 Elevator triplex hydraulic jacks
121 Static discharge wicks
122 Left tailplane construction
123 Moving tailplane sealing fairing
124 Tailplane centre section
125 Fin attachment joints
126 Tailplane trim screw jack
127 Fin support structure
128 Rear pressure bulkhead
129 Rear toilet compartments
130 Cabin attendant's folding seat
131 Rear entry door
132 Cabin window panel
133 Bulk cargo hold
134 Fuselage skin plating
135 Wing trailing-edge fillet
136 Left inboard flap
137 Lift dumper/airbrake
138 Undercarriage side struts
139 Main undercarriage pivot fixing
140 Inboard flap drive mechanism
141 Flap track fairing
142 Aileron triplex hydraulic jacks
143 Left all-speed aileron
144 Left airbrakes

145 Flap down position
146 Flap guide rails
147 Flap track fairings
148 Fuel jettison pipe
149 Left roll spoilers
150 Fixed portion of trailing edge
151 Static discharge wicks
152 Wingtip fairing
153 Left navigation lights
154 Wing rear spar
155 Front spar
156 Left leading-edge slats
157 Leading-edge de-icing
158 Slat fence
159 Screw jacks
160 Slat guide rails
161 Wing rib construction
162 Left outer wing fuel tank
163 Telescopic de-icing air duct
164 Wing stringer construction
165 Wing skin joint strap
166 Main undercarriage leg strut
167 Retraction jack
168 Left main undercarriage four-wheel bogie
169 Nacelle pylon attachment joint

170 Engine pylon
171 Exhaust nozzle
172 Fan air duct exhaust
173 Reverser cascade, closed
174 Bleed air piping
175 General Electric CF6-80A turbofan
176 Engine fan blades
177 Intake duct
178 Intake de-icing air pipes
179 Detachable engine cowlings
180 Bleed air system pre-cooler
181 Inboard leading-edge slat
182 Bleed air delivery pipes
183 Inner wing integral fuel tank
184 Three-spar inboard wing construction
185 Wing root Krüger flap
186 Leading-edge wing root fillet

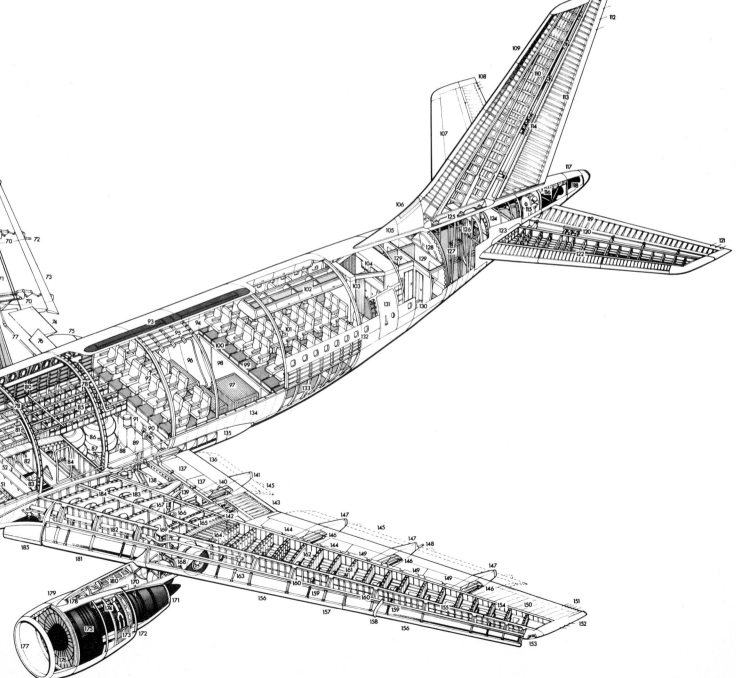

Il-86, Ilyushin

FIRST FLIGHT 1976

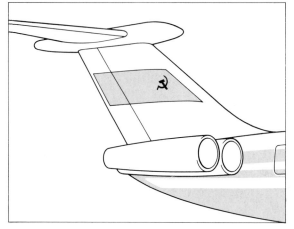

DURING the summer of 1971 Genrikh Novozhilov announced that his design team was working on a new project for a medium-range transport in the wide-bodied class capable of carrying 200 or more passengers. It was to be built under the supervision of his 'Ilyushin' bureau. At the time the details were to be finalized and even the number of powerplants was still under discussion. A little under a year later an exhibition in the Soviet Union featured a model of the new Ilyushin which appeared to be projected as a machine with four rear-fuselage-mounted turbofans. It was confirmed that the Il-86 was the type finally chosen as a successor for the Tupolev Tu-154 airliner recently in production and in Aeroflot service.

The general appearance of the new type was, when it arrived at the end of 1976, quite different from that indicated by the model. Some observers claimed to detect, in fact, something of a superficial resemblance to the McDonnell Douglas DC-10. What probably prompted this comparison with the US design was the use of an extra landing leg under the fuselage. On the Soviet design, however, it carried a four-wheel bogie similar to the wheel arrangement on the main legs, a widely-used design feature intended to distribute the weight of large aircraft.

The chief change was to the engine mountings. They were now of the pylon type and carried the four engines under the wings. This allowed the high-mounted tailplane to be lowered from its position at the top of the fin to a location at the after end of the fuselage. Internally the design was

similar to many in western service with a two-deck configuration with seats only in the upper segment of the circular-section fuselage. The area below was used for baggage and freight, with three stairways connecting the two levels.

Seating was nine-abreast with twin gangways between each group of three. Those aircraft catering for several classes had extra room in the forward, first-class sector by arranging the seating six-abreast, with eight across the remaining parts. Of these there was a total of three with the divisions achieved by means of storage spaces and the galleys. In the internal design much greater use had been made of metal and natural fibres than might be expected in a western aircraft. The reason for this was to provide an additional safety pre-

174

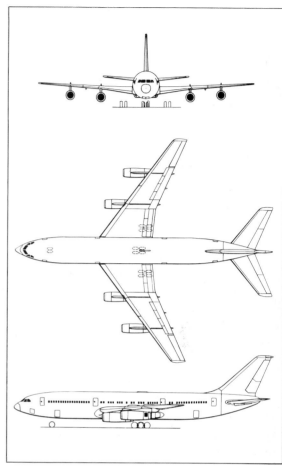

Il-86

Type: high-capacity, short/medium-range airliner
Maker: Soviet state factories in Voronezh, Kharkov, Kiev and Poland
Span: 48.06 m (157 ft 8 in)
Length: 59.54 m (195 ft 4 in)
Height: 15.81 m (51 ft 10½ in)
Wing area: 320 m² (3444 sq ft)
Weight: maximum 206,000 kg (455 000 lb); empty 111 230 kg (245 262 lb)
Powerplant: four 13 000-kg (28 660-lb) st Kuznetsov NK-86 turbofans with thrust reversers and noise attenuators
Performance: maximum speed (estimated) 950 km/h (590 mph) at 11 000 m (36 000 ft); range with payload 3600 km (2235 miles)
Payload: 42 000 kg (92 600 lb); seats for up to 350 passengers
Crew: 3 to 4
Production: not available

Top left: The interior of the USSR's first wide-bodied transport. The Soviet Union makes extensive use of natura¹ fibres for seating and fittings
Left: The Il-86 prototype rumbles into Paris in 1977

Top: The Il-86 has received a high-priority production status in the USSR, and the first Aeroflot unit to receive it is the North Caucasus Directorate which is responsible for holiday services on the Black Sea coast
Above: The Kuznetsov NK-86 engines of the Il-86 finally ended up mounted on pylons on the leading edge of the wings

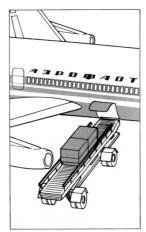

Left: Loading a cargo container. In contrast to Western practice the Il-86 passengers will carry their baggage up the first stairway from the apron and stow it with winter coats in underfloor compartments; then they climb stairs to the main deck

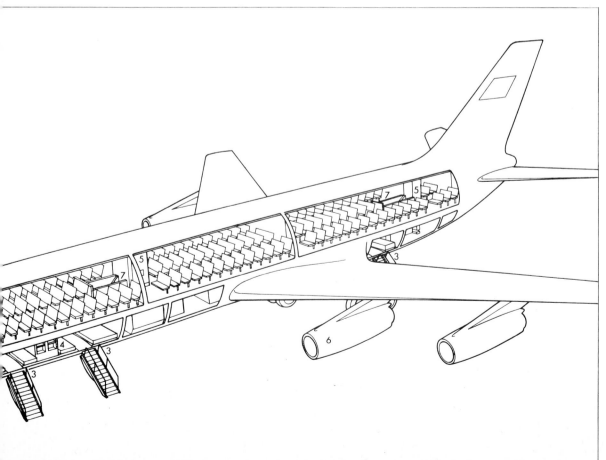

Left: 1 Flight-deck for crew of three; 2 Mixed accommodation for up to 350 passengers. First-class seating in the front; 3 Integrated airstairs; 4 Stowage for baggage, winter coats and cargo; 5 Galley; 6 Kuznetsov NK-86 turbofans; 7 Stairs from baggage area.
Air and ground crews with experience of the Il-62 or Tu-154 are in training to operate the Il-86, but there is no indication of how many are intended for service

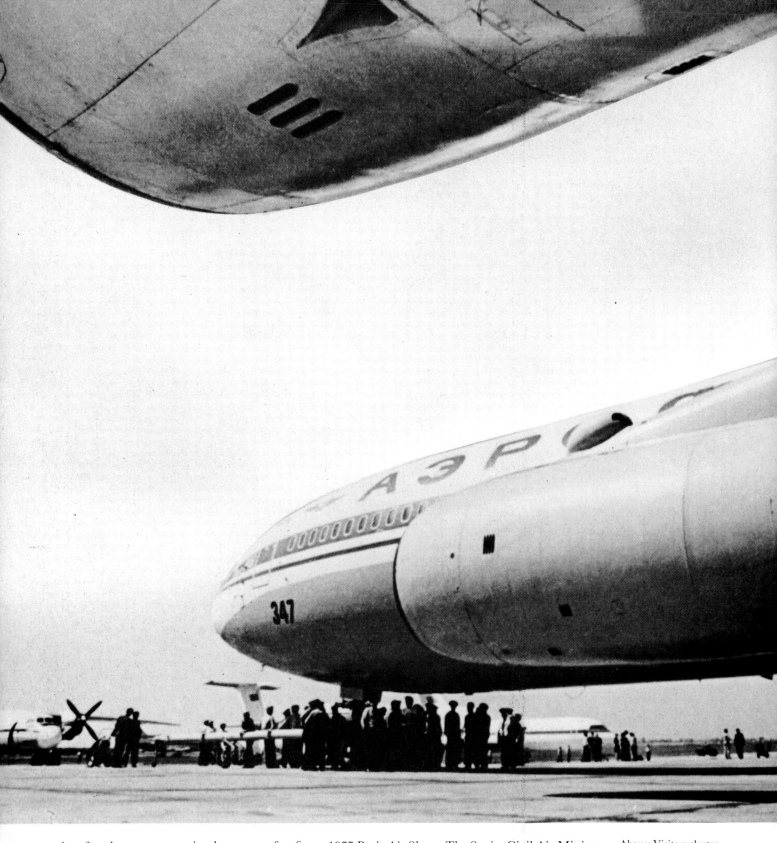

caution for the passengers in the event of a fire following a crash.

The first flight took place on December 22, 1976 when Captain Kuznetsov took off from the Moscow Central airport at Khodinka for a 40-min flight to the official test centre. Officials present on this occasion remarked on the take-off run of 1700 m (5575 ft). A press agency announcement issued during the next year stated that the test programme included more than 100 inflight investigations. The series tests would continue for the remainder of the year, it said, and were scheduled for completion by the 60th anniversary of the October Revolution, November 7, 1977. Despite the heavy commitments to the test programme, the prototype aircraft was exhibited and flown at the

1977 Paris Air Show. The Soviet Civil Air Minister announced that the new airliner would be in service with Aeroflot in time to carry passengers arriving in the USSR for the controversial 1980 Olympic Games in Moscow.

Three prototypes were completed and the first production model, 86002, flew on October 24, 1977. This continued the numbering sequence begun by the prototype 86000. Production involves a fair degree of sub-contracting through a widely-flung range of state aircraft factories, the greater number of them being situated in Poland. The break-down of assemblies consists in the main of all the major components, in addition to the engine pylons and pods. The parts are assembled at Voronezh, the location of the wing construction

Above: Visitors cluster around the nosegear of the Il-86. The 12-wheel landing gear bears a very heavy load, but the Soviet Union has always made great efforts to make its transports compatible with poor runway surfaces

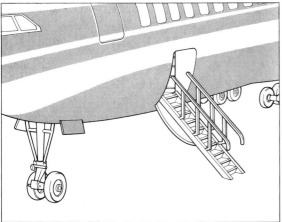

Top: A military truck is used to tow out the first Il-86
Above: The production line for the Il-86. There are no indications of how many the Soviet Union plans to build but they have important emergency military potential
Left: The integral airstairs for direct loading of pre-ticketed passengers are an important feature for poorly equipped airports, but have meant a reduction of about 3 m (10 ft) in cabin length and a consequent increase in weight

plant. These are produced with slats and flaps with the multi-section spoilers ahead of the main flap sections already in place. The complete tail unit is built at Kiev and then sent to Voronezh for final assembly.

Among the features which excited comment at Le Bourget in the summer of 1977 was the number and close spacing of the windows, similar to those of Concorde or Boeing jetliners; similarly of interest was the pair of upper-fuselage straps from the trailing portion of the wing indicating the presence of a tail parachute, which would not be fitted to production machines. Some of the windows at that time were replaced by a series of louvres at several stations which seemingly showed that this particular model was not pressurized. However, further investigation indicated that these were in fact airlocks, probably introduced in association with flight-observation cameras employed in studies of the airflow over the wings.

The powerplants were reported to be a variant of the NK-8 low-bypass-ratio turbofan used in the Il-86M and Tu-154. These engines suggested that Genrikh Novozhilov's design team had had second thoughts, since it was generally agreed that the first engines considered were the Soloviev D-30KP type. Unquestionably engines of higher bypass ratio are needed, and long discussions have already been held with Rolls-Royce but these had yielded no result by 1980.

During the development programme the maximum weight of the Ilyushin underwent a steady increase partly due to the extra fuel tank capable of an additional 20 000 litres (4500 Imp gal) in the fuselage centre section. The result was a major increase in the range.

Layout of the flight deck incorporated read-out displays on the navigational panels and a moving map display. However some observers felt that the general presentation did not conform to the latest ideas on simplification of pilot displays.

Earlier reports suggested that the intention of the designers was to complete over 1000 test hours before the first deliveries were made. It has been stated that each airframe is capable of 40 000 hours of flying time.

The Ilyushin Il-86 is a very large aircraft and there is a temptation to compare it with contemporaries like the Boeing 747, or the Airbus Industrie A300B. In fact it comes midway between the two in capacity, but as a basic design has much older aerodynamics and propulsion, comparable with the British VC10 and Trident of 1958–59, with pre-critical high-sweep wing and engines of low bypass ratio. Its main advantage to Aeroflot is its ability to operate from airports where the equipment is poor, lacking thick taxiways and air jetties leading up to the terminal.

Investigation has already taken place into the possibilities of a longer-range version capable of intercontinental transportation. Such a model would require redesigned wings and increased span and to be powered by modern turbofans of the high-bypass-ratio type similar to the RB.211. However engines like this have not so far been revealed by the Soviet Union.

Above: The Il-86 at Paris. Its engines are slightly old-fashioned, and plans to build high-bypass-ratio engines on later versions have not yet been officially confirmed

Boeing 767

ESTIMATED FIRST FLIGHT 1982

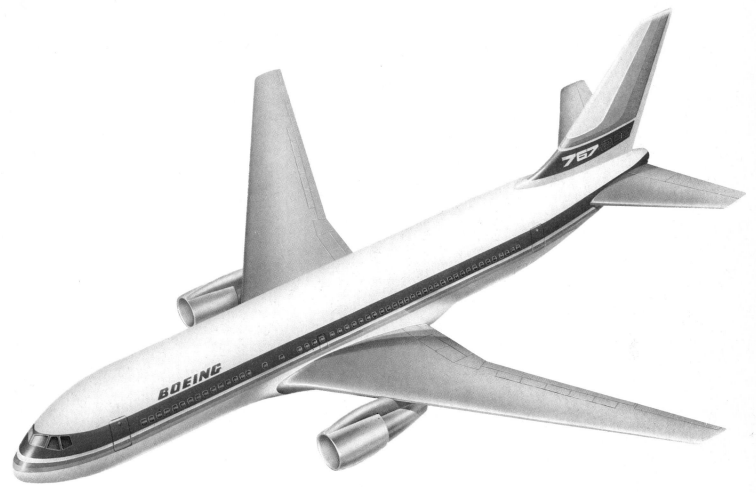

THE Boeing Company made the first announcement of its intention to produce a new type of advanced wide-bodied airliner incorporating the latest forms of technology in early 1978. There were several projects listed but the chief among these was the Model 767 of which greater details were made public during the following summer. It was the outcome of 12 years of studies, generally under the family designation 7X7 and then 7N7, without any go-ahead being possible.

An order had already been received for this design in the form of 30 machines to be delivered during the midmonths of 1982. They would be expected to replace the aircraft that will have by that time been in use for a minimum of 15 years. One of the primary reasons for this change, apart from a normal, progressive up-grading of service will be improved fuel economy. The new types will be capable of operating without loss of efficiency but at a lower fuel cost per passenger-mile, with an increased fuel economy of about 35%, similar to that introduced by the A300B in 1974.

In addition to these obvious advantages the mid 1980s will see the introduction of entirely new noise level regulations so the decibels emitted by the two-motor Boeing 767 will have to be appreciably lower than those for the four-jet 747 and very much less than that of small twin-jets today.

Noise has only been one problem in the design of this aircraft; another of the main considerations has been the maximum weight the runway can support at each airport on an airline route, a consideration which makes a bogie undercarriage

767-200

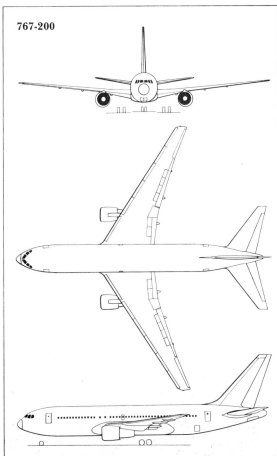

Boeing 767

Type: medium-range wide-bodied airliner
Maker: Boeing Commercial Airplane Co
Span: 47.24 m (155 ft)
Length: 48.51 m (159 ft 2 in)
Height: 15.85 m (52 ft)
Wing area: 283.3 m² (3050 sq ft)
Weight: maximum (200MR) 127 006 kg (280 000 lb); empty 73 356 kg (161 720 lb); (200TC) maximum 136 078 kg (300 000 lb); empty 73 981 kg (163 100 lb)
Powerplant: two 20 094 kg (44 300 lb) st Pratt & Whitney JT9D -7R or General Electric CF6-80A high bypass ratio turbofans
Performance: maximum speed 1030 km/h (640 mph) at 8840 m (29 000 ft); range with max payload (200MR) 3763 km (2338 miles), (200TC) 5208 km (3236 miles)
Payload: 26 762 kg (59 000 lb); seats for up to 255 passengers
Crew: 4
Production: orders for 96 with options on 44

Above: The 767 is unusual in having a very large wing area, 30% bigger than that of the comparable A310

Above: The spacious interior of the 767. Boeing claim seven-abreast seating is better then the eight-abreast in the A300 or A310, but this is challenged by Airbus Industrie

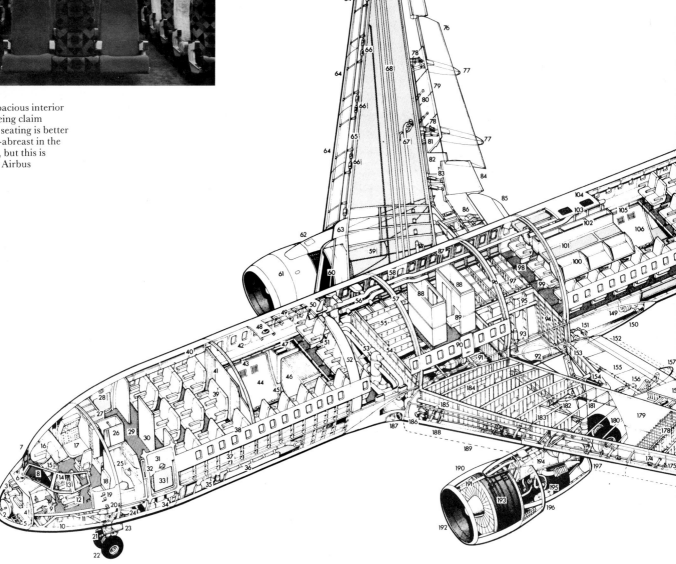

Boeing 767-200

1 Radome
2 Radar scanner dish
3 VOR localizer aerial
4 Front pressure bulkhead
5 ILS glideslope aerials
6 Windscreen wipers
7 Windscreen panels
8 Instrument panel shroud
9 Rudder pedals
10 Nose undercarriage wheel bay
11 Cockpit air-conditioning duct
12 Captain's seat
13 Opening cockpit side window
14 Centre console
15 First officer's seat
16 Cockpit roof systems control panels
17 Flight engineer's station
18 Observer's seat
19 Pitot tubes
20 Angle of attack probe
21 Nose undercarriage steering jacks
22 Twin nosewheels
23 Nosewheel doors

24 Waste system vacuum tank
25 Forward toilet compartment
26 Crew wardrobe
27 Forward galley
28 Right overhead sliding door
29 Entry lobby
30 Cabin divider
31 Left entry door
32 Door control handle
33 Escape chute stowage
34 Underfloor electronics racks
35 Electronics cooling air system
36 Skin heat exchanger
37 Fuselage frame and stringer
38 Cabin window panel
39 Six-abreast first-class seating compartment, 18 seats
40 Overhead stowage bins
41 Curtained cabin divider
42 Sidewall trim panels
43 Negative pressure relief valves
44 Forward freight door
45 Forward underfloor freight hold
46 LD-2 cargo containers, 12 in forward hold

47 Centre electronics rack
48 Anti-collision light
49 Cabin roof frames
50 VHF aerial
51 Seven-abreast tourist-class seating
52 Conditioned air riser
53 Air-conditioning distribution manifolds
54 Wing spar centre-section carry through
55 Floor beam construction
56 Overhead air-conditioning ducting
57 Front spar/fuselage main frame
58 Right emergency exit window
59 Right wing integral fuel tank
60 Thrust reverser cascade door, open
61 Right engine nacelle
62 Nacelle pylon
63 Fixed portion of leading edge
64 Leading-edge slat segments, open
65 Slat drive shaft
66 Rotary actuators
67 Fuel system piping
68 Fuel venting channels
69 Vent surge tank

70 Right navigation light (green)
71 Anti-collision light (red)
72 Tail navigation strobe light (white)
73 Static dischargers
74 Right outer aileron
75 Aileron hydraulic jacks
76 Single-slotted outer flap, down
77 Flap hinge fairings
78 Flap hinge control links
79 Outboard spoilers, open
80 Spoiler hydraulic jacks
81 Rotary actuator
82 Flap drive shaft
83 Aileron hydraulic jacks
84 Inboard aileron
85 Inboard double-slotted flap, down
86 Flap hinge control linkage
87 Fuselage centre-section construction
88 Mid cabin toilet compartments
89 Cabin attendants folding seat
90 Left emergency exit window
91 Ventral air-conditioning plant, and left and right
92 Mainwheel doors

93 Door jack
94 Wheel bay pressure bulkhead
95 Right wheel bay hydraulic reservoir
96 Rear spar/fuselage main frame
97 Pressure floor above right wheel bay
98 Cabin floor panels
99 Seat mounting rails
100 Overhead stowage bins
101 Cabin roof lighting panels
102 Centre stowage bins
103 VOR aerials
104 Fuselage skin plating
105 Negative pressure relief valves
106 Rear freight door
107 Seven-abreast tourist class seating
108 Rear toilet compartments
109 Cabin attendants folding seat
110 Rear galleys
111 Overhead sliding door counterbalances
112 Rear pressure dome
113 Fin root fillet
114 Tailfin construction

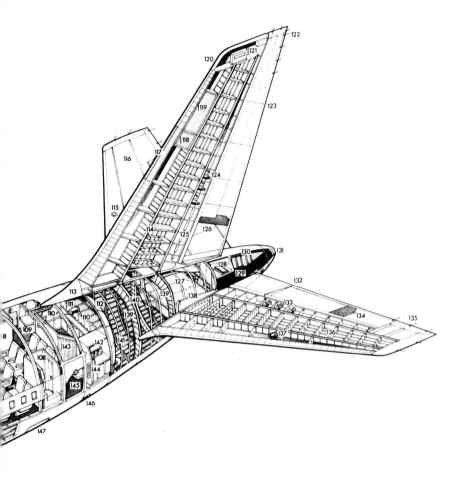

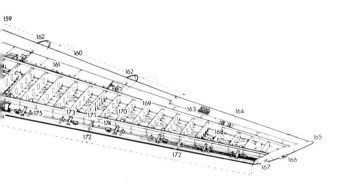

essential. The form this takes on the 767 is fairly conventional. It consists of tricycle gear with twin wheels on the steerable nose leg and two four-wheel bogies for the main landing gear.

In order to lift this weight into the air without runs of inordinate length the wings have to be designed to give a moderate take-off using high-lift slats on the wing leading edge and high-efficiency flaps on the trailing edges. The Boeing 767 is designed to take a variety of turbofans, all naturally of the high bypass ratio type. All these powerplants are mounted on pylons under the leading edge of the wings. Fuel is carried in a single tank within each wing, the two having a combined capacity of 83 280 litres (18 319 Imp gal). The internal arrangements draw on the experience gained with the Boeing 747. All the passenger accommodation is on the upper deck which divides the circular-section fuselage at just below the mid-point.

The forward section of this floor is occupied by the flight deck. Avionic and electric equipment are stored under the floor at a point forward of the front freight section where they are available for ease of maintenance and inspection.

Boeing went to great lengths to refine the fuselage cross-section. After more than a further two years of studies a seven-abreast layout was chosen, narrower than the A300B and A310. Boeing believe that the lower drag of the slightly narrower body will more than outweigh the greater internal volume of the competing aircraft. The same basic fuselage is common to the proposed Boeing 777, a very similar machine powered by three turbofan engines and intended for use over medium to long ranges.

Since the first quantity order for Boeing 767s came from United Air Lines it seems likely that this will be the pioneer operator of the type. Crew training is scheduled to begin in the near future and it seems likely that before long a cargo version of the 767 may be announced.

The standard machine at present envisaged has the available under-floor area fitted for cargo and baggage which can be loaded through either the forward or rear freight door of equal standard size. A larger forward cargo door of 1.75 m by 3.4 m (5 ft 9 in by 11 ft 2 in) is optional and allows for the loading of Type 2 pallets. The cargo area can hold up to 22 LD-67 or 11 LD-3 containers.

115 Fin 'logo' spotlight	139 Fin attachment frames	161 Outboard spoilers	184 Inboard auxiliary fuel tank
116 Right tailplane	140 Tailplane trim control jack	162 Flap hinge link fairings	185 Engine bleed air ducting
117 Leading-edge HF aerial	141 Rear fuselage frame and stringer	163 Honeycomb control surface	186 Slat drive motor
118 HF aerial coupler	construction	construction	187 Landing and taxiing lamps
119 Television aerial	142 Left rear galley unit	164 Left outer aileron	188 Inboard leading-edge slat
120 Fintip aerial fairing	143 Curtained cabin divider	165 Tail navigation strobe light (white)	189 Slat open position
121 Tail VOR aerials	144 Door operating handle	166 Anti-collision light (red)	190 Left engine cowlings
122 Static dischargers	145 Rear entry door	167 Left navigation light	191 Intake de-icing air duct
123 Rudder	146 Pressurization outflow valve	168 Left vent surge tank	192 Left engine intake
124 Rudder hydraulic jacks	147 Bulk cargo door	169 Rear spar	193 Pratt & Whitney JT9D-7R4
125 Balance weights	148 Rear underfloor freight hold, ten	170 Wing rib construction	turbofan engine (General Electric
126 Rudder honeycomb construction	LD-2 containers	171 Front spar	CF6-80A optional fit)
127 Tailplane centre section	149 Air turbine driven hydraulic pump	172 Leading-edge slat segments	194 Engine mounting pylon
128 APU intake plenum	150 Trailing-edge wing root fillet	173 Slat guide rails	195 Oil tank
129 Gas turbine APU	151 Inboard flap rotary actuator	174 Rotary actuators	196 Fan air exhaust duct
130 Tailcone	152 Inboard double-slotted flap	175 Slat operating links	197 Hot stream exhaust nozzle
131 APU exhaust	153 Main undercarriage mounting	176 Pressure refuelling connectors	
132 Two-segment elevator	beam	177 Left wing integral fuel tank	
133 Elevator hydraulic jacks	154 Retraction jack	178 Wing stringers	
134 Honeycomb control surface	155 Inboard spoilers	179 Wing skin plating	
construction	156 Flap hinge control link	180 Four-wheel main undercarriage	
135 Static dischargers	157 Hinge link fairing	bogie	
136 Tailplane construction	158 Left inner aileron	181 Mainwheel leg	
137 Fin 'logo' spotlight	159 Flap 'down' position	182 Undercarriage leg side struts	
138 Tailplane sealing plate	160 Outer single-slotted flap	183 Left wing dry bay	

The cabin is divided internally into three sections. The smaller portion immediately aft of the flight deck is used for about 18 first-class passengers and the two larger portions for the tourist class. The main first-class cabin incorporates the four toilets with galleys situated at each end of the cabin area.

Following the order from United, Boeing announced the 767-200TC, a transcontinental-range version with increased gross weight. It is powered by General Electric CF6-80 turbofans, while Pratt & Whitney JT9D-7R4s can be mounted according to customer requirements.

Some 62 had been ordered by mid 1979, including 30 for American Airlines (with options for 20 more) and 20 for Delta.

Manufacturing sub-contracts have been awarded to Grumman Aerospace for the wing centre section and adjacent lower fuselage and fuselage bulkheads. Vought have been sub-contracted to build the horizontal tail, while Canadair have the rear fuselage. More interestingly Boeing have co-production agreements with Aeritalia and CTDC (Civil Transport Development Corporation). CTDC is a conglomerate formed from the Japanese firms of Fuji, Kawasaki and Mitsubishi. The Italians will build the control surfaces, flaps, leading-edge slats, wingtips, elevators, fin, rudder and nose radome. CTDC will be responsible for the manufacture of the wing fairings, main landing-gear doors, centre and rear fuselage body panels, exit hatches, stringers, dorsal fin and passenger and cargo doors.

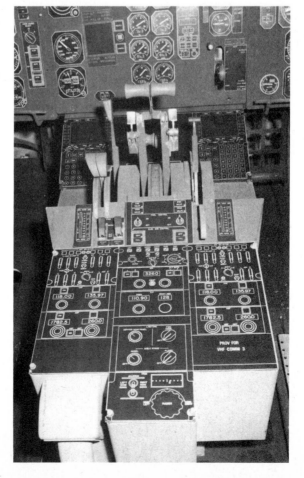

Above: A light mobile crane installs the inboard section of a 767 wing. This aircraft is destined for American Airlines
Left: A mock-up of the 767 cockpit. In common with the 757 it uses new technology like the Rockwell-Collins AFCS (automatic flight control system) which will differ between the two aircraft only in its software. Advanced flight-management and thrust control systems are included, and electronic displays will remove the need to keep monitoring dial instruments

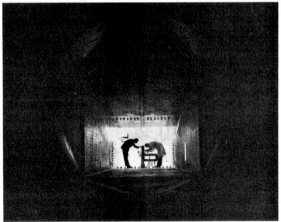

Top: Streamers billow in front of a General Electric CF6-80 engine during a reverser test. The flaps and slats are also deployed during this wind tunnel test

Left: A litter of drawing boards and work benches in front of a 767. Though the aircraft is built in sections by numerous sub-contractors it will be assembled at the Boeing plant at Everett

Above: Technicians prepare the wind tunnel during tests on the 767 airframe, which in early 1980 suddenly revealed an instability problem, putting more pressure on Boeing's aerodynamicists

SST Projects and Advanced Transports
FIRST FLIGHT 1968

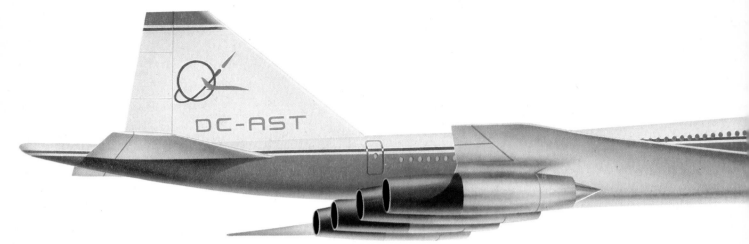

THE first serious experiments in SST (supersonic transport) were carried out by Bristol Aircraft and Sud Aviation in 1959–61, from which in 1962 stemmed the collaborative Concorde. The first SST to fly however was the Russian Tupolev Tu-144 which was remarkably similar to Concorde in appearance. The prototype took to the air in 1968, the year before Concorde. Concorde, however, has had a completely successful career, unlike its Russian rival.

Preparation for new SST projects continued in the US even after the abandonment of the programme of the early 1970s, and a feature common to most of these was the use of a NASA proposal. This was the arrow wing which minimizes wave drag allowing the waves to stream back from the nose and not cross the leading edge of the wing.

An SCV (supersonic cruise vehicle) such as this has demonstrated a lift:drag ratio of 9 in the wind tunnel and in 1980 McDonnell Douglas planned to increase this to 10.3 for a design intended to be ready within the decade.

But other solutions exist and these have to be viewed in the light of such considerations as the advantages of simplicity. One example is a straightforward modification of the ogive form of Concorde and this is incorporated in a British Aerospace proposal with leading-edge devices and a canard.

Various suggestions have been made to comply with Federal Air Regulation Part 36 which covers noise. These include the use of hotter, large-scale Olympus core motors with a very small bypass ratio, a complex mixer nozzle and an ejector with acoustic lining.

Another method of suppression from Lockheed employs the mounting of vertically superimposed jets above and below the wing thus leaving the trailing edge free for flaps and with improved flutter characteristics. The lower motor suppresses the noise of the upper.

Since an SCV spends only a percentage of its operation at supersonic speeds, its handling at subsonic speeds has to be ensured by large areas of high-lift devices on the landing approach, but the heat created while travelling at cruising speed reduces the allowable stress levels of the structure. The McDonnell Douglas study aims at no more than an acceptable Mach 2.2 while the BAe project aims only at Mach 1.9 – slower than Concorde.

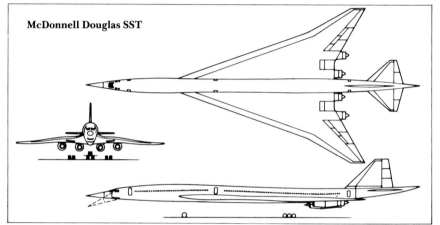

McDonnell Douglas SST

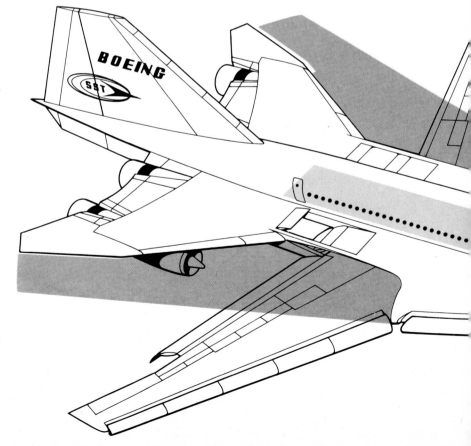

Above, left and right: All the major US aircraft designers and builders made studies of an SST. McDonnell Douglas and Lockheed proposed an aircraft not unlike the Anglo-French Concorde, but with Mach 3 cruise (steel/titanium structure) and a bigger payload. The daunting development cost and the apparent environmentalist opposition persuaded the companies to concentrate on more conventional aircraft and shelve these projects

Below: This Boeing design used variable-geometry wings for high-speed flight and low-speed landings. The cabin tapered but was 56.8 m (186.5 ft) long and had a width varying between 345 cm (136 in) and 508 cm (200 in). In the 1960s it was a dramatic design, but even at that stage it was dogged by astronomical development costs. Boeing tried to persuade airlines to book positions on the production line for their 'orders' by placing refundable deposits of $750 000 (£270 000 at 1967 rates) per aircraft. The domestic airlines in the USA thought it politically expedient to join the scheme, but foreign operators were not enthusiastic. Congress was reported to be prepared to underwrite loans to Boeing and fund some of the development costs. Boeing reached the stage of ordering 4989.5-kg (11 000-lb) titanium billets for the wing pivot lugs. However estimates and costs began to climb, and when Congress became worried at the political strength of the so-called environmental lobby the project was shelved.

Technically it is of considerable interest. The wings have an area of 1828 m^2 (6000 sq ft), but when they are moved back for high-speed flight they combine with the tail to give an area of 2743.2 m^2 (9000 sq ft). The powerplants are four General Electric GE4/J5 turbojets each with 27216 kg (60 000 lb) of thrust with afterburning. Cruising they would carry 350 passengers and three crew for 6475 km (4023 miles) at 2858 km/h (1776 mph). Despite their massive cost Boeing were able to report in 1967 that European and American airlines had placed orders for 115 aircraft

These aircraft follow the more or less accepted form of the monoplane as it has existed since the first successful monoplanes, but there are other projects involving new and revolutionary shapes.

One of these is a flying wing, not new in itself for the idea was considered by Junkers in 1910, but in the projected form weighing almost three times as much as a Boeing 747 and capable of containing within its airfoil the entire payload. Such an airliner could be a pure freighter or combine this role with passenger transport.

Just how such a large machine would be powered is open to speculation but in view of its size it is thought that nuclear power would be the answer, and Boeing has already issued a paper setting out the advantages of such a theory.

Once it had been established that the reactor would be safely contained in the event of a crash it would be relatively simple to design one that was capable of generating temperatures sufficient for driving a turbofan. This could give an unrefuelled range equivalent to as much as 10 000 hours duration. Naturally, a reactor of this size could only be used in a very large transport aircraft but despite its great weight there would be no problem incorporating one in an airliner capable of taking perhaps 1700 passengers. Much of the basic engineering was worked out in the mid-1950s.

In an inflationary world, however, nuclear propulsion is unlikely. As a more practical proposal Lockheed-Georgia is working on turbofan transports whose entire secondary power is electric.

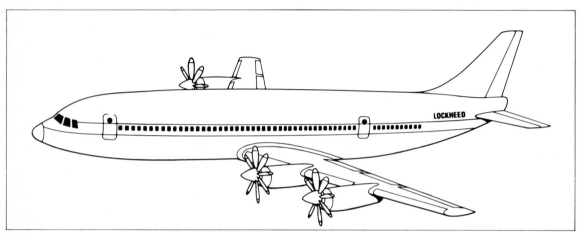

Left: A Lockheed and NASA concept for a high-speed turboprop version of the TriStar. The rather curious idea of putting propellers on a jet airframe reflects the pressures on both manufacturers and airlines to make savings in operating costs

Right: Upper-surface blowing on the Boeing YC-14. This system of augmented lift uses the Coanda effect which pulls the jet thrust sharply downwards over the wing and produces a dramatic improvement in lift
Below: A McDonnell Douglas concept for a freight carrier. The payload is carried in the wings, and the engines are mounted forward of the leading edge to give augmented lift

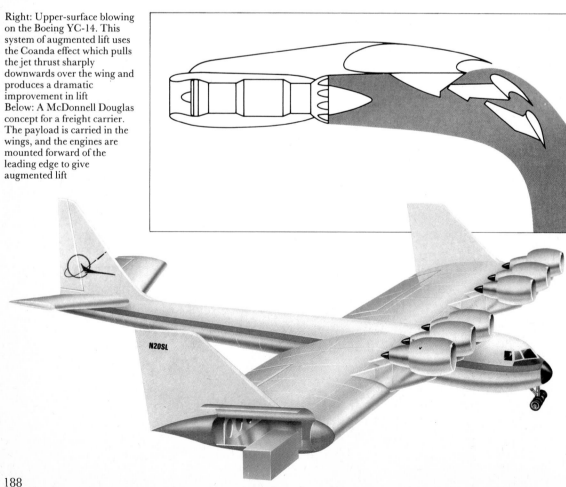

Using new magnet technology and high-voltage direct current an 'all-electric' airliner is calculated to be able to save just over 20% of the fuel burned by today's aircraft.

One of the problems of supersonic flight is the stress and heating that the airframe suffers during sustained high speed flight. The fuel costs can be borne since the aircraft is making money by travelling faster than conventional airliners. However, while the use of exotic alloys in new honeycomb-like panels may produce a strong lightweight material, it is also very expensive.

Other revolutionary aircraft proposals include a Lockheed hypersonic transport with an anticipated speed of around 6400 km/h (4000 mph) over a range of 9250 km (6000 miles). This would have a combined propulsion system with turbojets for take-off and landing and to accelerate the machine to a speed where an alternative airbreathing system would take over to hold it at cruising speed. A liner of this type would be capable of taking 200 passengers from Los Angeles to Tokyo in under 2 hours 20 min.

Transonic business jets are also likely to come into use during the 1980s. Ideally these would have a range in the transcontinental class. Such aircraft have been proposed with VTOL capability. The wing would perform the dual functions of a conventional lifting surface for the greater part of the flight but for take-off and landing it would be rotated in the manner of a helicopter rotor.

Not all future projects are concerned with high speed, for it is an inescapable fact that in the field of mass passenger transportation, the SST will usually need longer runways and many international airports are hard pressed for space.

Research is currently being conducted in the United States and Japan that will be applied to a proposed new aircraft type. The Japanese machine is scheduled to fly in 1982 and this National Aerospace Laboratory Q/STOL is similar in concept to the NASA/Boeing QSRA. The Japanese NAL Kawasaki four-turbofan airliner employs upper-surface blowing (USB) and has a planned capacity for 150 passengers. It may well prove the basis of a new trend in tomorrow's airliners, though operators are unlikely to find lower speeds and increased costs attractive, except where normal airports are out of the question.

Below: An artist's impression of the Lockheed X-wing. This design uses a rotor for vertical take-off and landing, but in horizontal flight the rotor can be locked to become a fixed wing. In high-speed helicopter flight it can reach 322 kmh (200 mph), but as a fixed-wing machine it could reach a maximum speed of around Mach 0.9. Though its role is at present seen as a military machine it might revolutionize inter-city travel

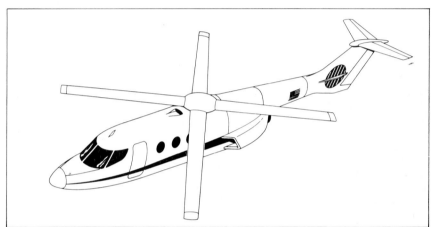

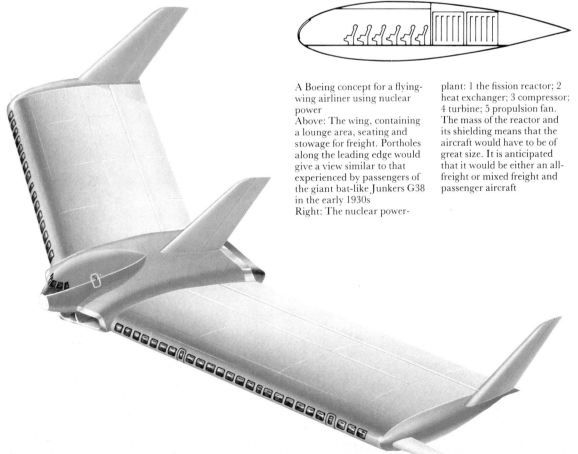

A Boeing concept for a flying-wing airliner using nuclear power
Above: The wing, containing a lounge area, seating and stowage for freight. Portholes along the leading edge would give a view similar to that experienced by passengers of the giant bat-like Junkers G38 in the early 1930s
Right: The nuclear power-plant: 1 the fission reactor; 2 heat exchanger; 3 compressor; 4 turbine; 5 propulsion fan. The mass of the reactor and its shielding means that the aircraft would have to be of great size. It is anticipated that it would be either an all-freight or mixed freight and passenger aircraft

189

Hydrogen-fuelled Airliners

ESTIMATED FIRST FLIGHT 1985

Left: A model of a hydrogen-powered transport designed by Lockheed
Right: Though the original space remains in the wing to take fuel it is difficult to insulate this thermally and so LH$_2$ has to be housed in giant tanks either in the body or on the outer wings
Below: A McDonnell Douglas concept of an LH$_2$ hypersonic airliner, capable of cruising at six times the speed of sound

THE 1980s find the air transport industry faced with an approaching oil shortage and its allied problem of increasing costs. In 1979 for instance one airline, America's United Airlines, had a fuel bill in excess of $1000 million and the position is unlikely to improve.

The industry is aware of these problems and, in a search for an alternative fuel, has considered liquid hydrogen for future transport aircraft. Synthetic, manufactured fuel is another possibility but on almost every count except safety, liquid hydrogen is superior in both the subsonic and supersonic speed range.

Transport aircraft fuelled by liquid hydrogen (LH$_2$) would have a lower gross weight with smaller wings and engines but larger fuselages – or else they would have giant fuel tanks outboard on the wings. They would produce a lower engine noise and less sonic-boom overpressure. In an age acutely ecology-conscious the pollution level would be less with no hydrocarbons ejected into the atmosphere but about double the quantity of water vapour.

Other advantages include less costly airframes, a longer engine life with less need for frequent maintenance. Engines would also be easier to maintain because hydrogen burns more cleanly than oil-based fuels.

The National Aeronautics and Space Administration of the USA have considered schemes for a hypersonic aircraft which could fly 200 passengers between Paris and Los Angeles in two hours 20 min. A supersonic aircraft could fly at Mach 2.7, while the subsonic version would carry 400 passengers in a wide-body fuselage.

LH$_2$ has greater energy per unit mass than today's fuels, but its density is so much lower that, for any given mission, the volume of tankage – even ignoring the thermal insulation for the intensely cold liquid – would have to be far greater than for an aircraft using hydrocarbon fuel. Either the fuselage would be enormous, with LH$_2$ adjacent to passengers, or tankage would be in streamlined nacelles on the wings.

Much of the pioneer work in this area is being done by engineers at the Lockheed California Company. In order to give a smooth but also an informed transition from ordinary jet fuel to LH$_2$ an experimental airline has been proposed to look into the working problems of transports with the

alternative fuel. The machines would be Lockheed L-1011 TriStars modified for their new role. This would involve flying between four widely-separated cities such as Pittsburgh, Frankfurt, Riyadh and Birmingham, and then back to Pennsylvania.

Four machines are envisaged as sufficient to take a minimum 45 360 kg (100 000 lb) payload over a range of 6600 km (4000 miles). The air terminals selected would be fitted out to provide refuelling facilities at a rate of 18.14 tonnes of LH$_2$ per day which would require a liquefaction plant capable of meeting the demand.

The preliminary planning for these proposals has already taken place in the late 1970s. While such aircraft technology as the fuel system and pumps could probably be completed within two

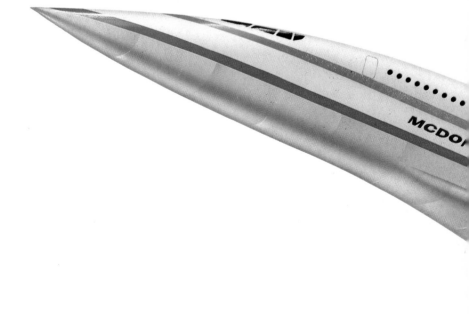

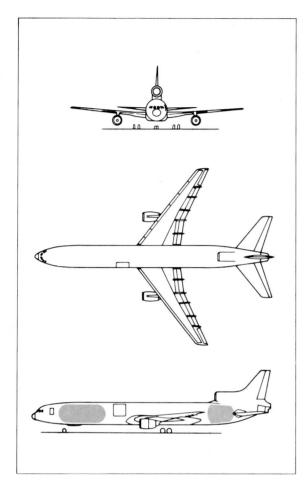

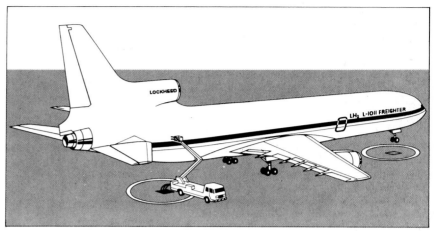

years the engine development might take until the mid 1980s to finalize with flight trials in the late 1980s. An airline could therefore be operating before the end of the current decade provided that the development process for liquid hydrogen is carried out as a parallel programme.

The greater part of the time would be taken up in the design and fabrication of the plant, since the method of commercial liquefaction is already largely completed. In order to ensure that the plant is capable of producing the requisite amount per day the steam-iron process would be used to make hydrogen from coal. A pilot plant already exists in Chicago under the combined development supervision of the US Department of Energy and the American Gas Association.

Above: Refuelling a liquid hydrogen-powered L-1011. The service truck has connected two hoses from the hydrant pit, one is used to pump LH_2 while the other is a return line for gaseous hydrogen displaced from the aircraft tanks by the incoming LH_2. The cold GH_2 is returned to the airport liquefaction plant for re-use

Slew-winged Airliners

FIRST FLIGHT 1979

V ARIABLE-geometry aircraft are now an accepted part of aeronautical engineering, but one of the latest experiments is in the field of the slew or skew-wing aircraft, also called the 'Yawed wing' by the Boeing company. A small test vehicle with twin jets, the AD-1, was delivered to NASA's Dryden Research Center in March 1979.

The basic form of the slew-winged aircraft consists of a one-piece wing positioned on the fuselage so that it can be pivoted with one wing moving forward, and the other back, thus offering less drag. Take-off and landing is effected with the wing situated straight across the fuselage.

As a commercial airliner such a design would fly only a little faster than the speed of sound at about Mach 1.1 or Mach 1.2, would give an improvement in the transonic lift:drag ratio over that of conventional aircraft and would also give a gain in speed of almost 50%.

Although the speed of a slew-winged airliner would not be so great as a current SST (supersonic transport) design, it would be easier to build and would produce a lower noise level. The sonic boom would be weakened due to the optimum pressure distribution and the sound would therefore be largely muffled before reaching the ground. An airliner of this sort would be less mechanically complex than say, a variable geometry one; and the trim/drag penalties would be less severe.

It is suggested that some control problems would be encountered, mainly because remotely piloted test vehicles, which fail to give the 'pilot' any visual reference points at high slew angles, have failed to

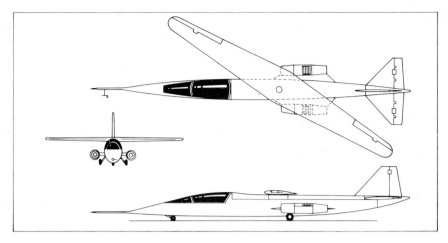

show the type of handling characteristics that may be met. To answer these questions the low-cost, piloted demonstrator, AD-1, was ordered from Ames Industrial, the US distributor of Microturbo engines, two of which – 100-kg (220-lb) thrust TRS18 versions – are fitted.

Trials were scheduled to begin in 1980 and the wing will be progressively traversed through 60° from the first neutral position.

The AD-1 is intended to act as a scaled-down model of a projected 200-seat airliner with twin decks and turbojet engines faired into the rear fuselage. It is anticipated that a second step in the development programme will be the modification of an F-8 Crusader with a slew-wing to determine the performance at higher speeds.

AD-1

Type: research aircraft
Maker: NASA
Span: 9.84 m (32 ft)
Length: 11.82 m (38 ft)
Height: 1.98 m (6 ft 6 in)
Wing area: 8.64 m (93 ft)
Weight: maximum 907 kg (2000 lb); empty not available
Powerplant: two 100-kg (220-lb) thrust TRS18-046 turbojets
Performance: not available
Payload: not available
Crew: 1
Production: 1 by 1980

Left: NASA's AD-1 oblique-wing research aircraft in flight at the Dryden Flight Research Center in California
Below: The wing positions of an oblique-wing SST. The variable geometry allows the aircraft to take off with maximum lift and then move to a high speed alignment of the wings for minimum drag, but the fact that all axes (pitch, roll and yaw) are interdependent may prove a major problem

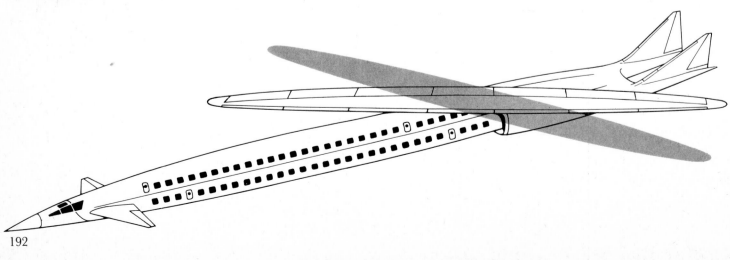

Po-2, Polikarpov

FIRST FLIGHT 1927

THE Polikarpov Po-2 was designed in 1926 by the young Russian aeronautical engineer Nikolai Polikarpov. It was intended as a light training biplane and had a fabric-covered wood/metal airframe and was powered by a 100-hp M-11 five-cylinder radial engine. The first aircraft refused to fly at all during tests and was extensively redesigned and put into series production as the U-2 (later redesignated Po-2 in honour of its designer).

The U-2/Po-2 was ordered in quantity and remained in production from 1928 until 1952 in the Soviet Union and Poland, where it was known as the CSS 13. The total number built was unknown, but is believed to be in excess of 40 000 aircraft, which makes the Po-2 one of the world's most produced aircraft, along with the Ilyushin Il-2 and Il-10 (41 400) and the Yakovlev Yak-1, -3, -7, and -9 (37 000).

The U-2 biplane made history in 1938 when an aircraft piloted by G Vlasov located a team of Russian scientists who had been drifting on ice floes in the North Pole for nine months.

Few, if any, other aircraft have fulfilled as many widely varying roles as the Polikarpov Po-2, which has served as a trainer, sportsplane, liaison aircraft, artillery spotter, parachute dropper, glider tug, air ambulance, transport, reconnaissance aircraft, light bomber, ground-attack aircraft, floatplane, skiplane and agricultural aircraft, – the last role gaining it the designation Po-2AP and name of *Kukuruznik* (corn cutter). The fire-fighting version was named *Lesnik* (forest guard). Some were

modified by the addition of a cabin for use in the light transport role, or as an air ambulance.

The Soviet State airline Aeroflot used thousands of Po-2s for crop-dusting and spraying. In Russia the aircraft became known as the 'sewing machine' because of the distinctive note of its M-11 engine. Although designed as an open-cockpit aircraft, cabin versions were built which could accommodate two passengers or stretcher cases behind the pilot's position. When the Air Standards Co-ordinating Committee of NATO met in 1954 to agree on a system of reporting names to identify Soviet aircraft types, they chose the appropriate name of Mule. Production was then ending. But Po-2s still fly with clubs in the USSR, China, Czechoslovakia, Poland, Romania and Yugoslavia.

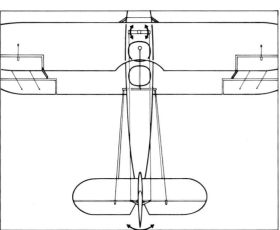

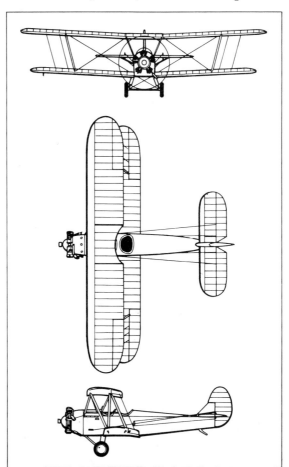

Top: The Polikarpov Po-2 Mule is still in use more than 50 years after its first flight. Known popularly as the Kukuruznik (Corn Cutter) it served throughout the war and is now used for ambulance, air-taxi and survey work. Most versions in service today are Polish-built

Above: The simple controls on the Po-2; though these are crude by modern standards they are easy to maintain and make the Po-2 a good training and utility aircraft which can be flown by comparatively unskilled pilots

Po-2

Type: training, liason, utility, agricultural and ambulance biplane
Maker: State Industries, USSR
Span: 11.4 m (37 ft 5 in)
Length: 8.15 m (26 ft 9 in)
Height: 2.92 m (9 ft 7 in)
Wing area: 35.4 m² (381 sq ft)
Weight: maximum 981 kg (2163 lb); empty 608 kg (1340 lb)
Powerplant: one 110-hp M-11 radial piston engine
Performance: maximum speed 149 km/h (93 mph); range 530 km (329 miles)
Crew: 2
Production: minimum 40 000 estimated

FC.2, Fairchild

FIRST FLIGHT 1927

THE Fairchild Airplane Manufacturing Company was founded by Sherman Fairchild in 1925 and two years later production began of the FC.2 light transport aircraft. It was powered by a 220-hp Wright Whirlwind radial engine and could carry four passengers at a speed of 185 km/h (115 mph). The FC.2 was a pioneer American airliner and was used by Pan American Airways for their first airmail service between Key West, Florida and Havana, Cuba on October 19, 1927.

From the FC.2 was developed the more powerful Fairchild FC.2W, powered by a 450-hp Pratt & Whitney Wasp engine. This tough, reliable aircraft became a mainstay of North American airline operations in the late 1920s. A high-wing monoplane of mixed wood and metal construction, it served airlines such as Pan American, PANAGRA (Pan American Grace) and Colonial Air Transport on passenger, mail and cargo routes throughout the Americas. One FC.2W was used by Bell Telephone Laboratories for early experiments in airborne radio communication; another was selected by John Henry Mears and Captain Charles Collyer for their 1928 round-the-world flight. The Fairchild, named *City of New York*, set off from New York on June 29, 1928 and completed the circumnavigation in 23 days 15 hours 21 min.

The Fairchild Model 71 was a 1928 development of the FC.2W with the same Wasp engine, but with accommodation for six passengers. Folding wings and interchangeable float, ski or wheel undercarriages were offered. A subsidiary company, Fairchild Aircraft Limited, was established at Longueuil, near Montreal, Canada in 1929 to manufacture the aircraft which was widely used in Alaska with Pacific Alaska Airways and in Central America by Pan American Grace Airways. A metal-skinned version of the Fairchild 71 was produced in Canada as was the improved Model Super 71, which was the first aircraft of original design to be built by the Canadian company. Unlike the previous model it featured a parasol-mounted wing with the pilot's cockpit removed to the rear of the trailing edge behind the six-seat passenger cabin. A ten-seat aircraft, the Fairchild (Canada) 82-B, was designed to meet the needs of Canadian bush operators in 1935.

In the draft of civil aircraft which took place in World War II, the USAAF took charge of three 1928 Model FC-2W-2s.

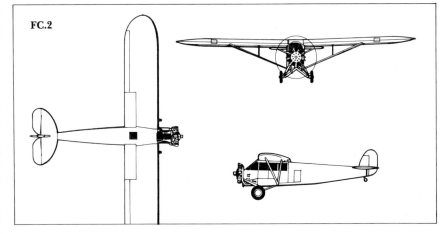

FC.2

FC.2W

Type: utility and cargo aircraft
Maker: Fairchild Engine & Airplane Co
Span: 15.24 m (50 ft)
Length: 9.45 m (31 ft)
Height: 2.74 m (9 ft)
Wing area: 17.1 m² (184 sq ft)
Weight: maximum 2087 kg (4600 lb); empty 1097 kg (2418 lb)
Powerplant: one 450-hp Pratt & Whitney Wasp radial engine

Performance: maximum speed 225 km/h (140 mph): range 1609 km (1000 miles)

Payload: seats for 4 passengers
Crew: 1
Production: 100 (FC.2, FC.2W); 90 (Model 71)

Top: A Fairchild FC.2 of Pan American Grace Airways (PANAGRA), which inaugurated a mail service in the late 1920s. This eventually linked the Canal Zone with Argentina via Chile and Peru
Above: A close-up of the Pratt & Whitney Wasp radial engine. The blister on the left of the cockpit is designed to give improved vision to the front and below – vital for rough airstrips or agricultural work

Robin, Curtiss

FIRST FLIGHT 1928

Left: A colourful Curtiss Robin seen at the Reno Air Races in September 1968
Below: The Robin in its more prosaic role as an agricultural spraying aircraft. The chemicals are fed into the tank aft of the cockpit and dispensed via the spray boom, with its wind vane valves on the leading edge

IN 1927 Curtiss developed a three-seat cabin monoplane for the expanding personal and private aircraft market. With a steel-tube fuselage and wooden wings it was a conservative design. The pilot was seated behind a stick with two passengers side-by-side to the rear of him.

The choice of engine was very surprising. This was the war-surplus 90-hp Curtiss OX-5. It was in fact once alleged that the Robin was produced just to use up Curtiss' stock of these old engines.

Another unusual feature of the early Robins were their wing struts. These used circular-section steel tube streamlined by the attachment of broad fairings which were supposed to act as aerofoils to produce lift. These were soon replaced with streamlined steel tubing. Early undercarriages used rubber-cord shock absorbers in streamlined boxes; these too were replaced – by oleo-pneumatic shock struts.

Four Robin prototypes were built and the first one flew in 1928. Curtiss produced 769 Robins, reaching a peak of 17 per week in 1929.

The Robin B was undoubtedly the most popular of the type, but in the depression of 1930 the price of these aircraft dropped to $2495. Other types of Robins were as follows: the Comet Robin, powered by a 150-hp Comet radial; the Robin B-2; Robin C, with 185-hp Curtiss Challenger engine; Robin C-1, the main Challenger-powered model; Robin C-2, with 170-hp Challenger; Robin CR, used to test the Crusader engine but never put into production; Robin W, with lower-cost engine; Robin J-1, J-2 and J-3; Robin M, converted Bs; Robin 4Cs, four-seat version.

Serving mostly as private-owner types, Robins broke the world's refuelling endurance record three times – 420 hours 21 min in 1929; 553 hours 28 min in 1930; and 653 hours 34 min in 1935. The most famous Robin was the former B model flown from New York to Ireland in 1938 by Douglas 'Wrong-Way' Corrigan. He had declared the intention of flying non-stop to Los Angeles, but turned east and flew the Atlantic instead.

Many Robins remained in service after World War II employed in roles such as crop-spraying and bush flying, where slow-flying capabilities were an asset. Nowadays, however, Curtiss Robins are cherished antiques. By 1980 some 40 were active in the US, making it the most numerous example of the few prewar Curtiss designs still flying.

Robin

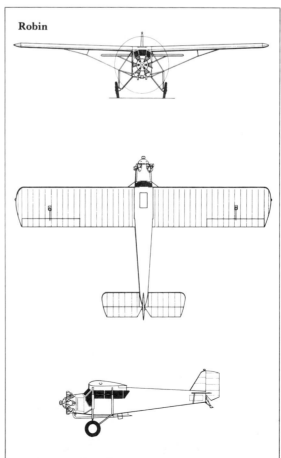

Robin B

Type: cabin monoplane
Maker: Curtiss Aeroplane Co
Span: 12.49 m (41 ft)
Length: 7.83 m (25 ft 8½ in)
Height: 2.37 m (7 ft 9½ in)
Wing area: 20.71 m² (223 sq ft)
Weight: maximum 1107 kg (2440 lb); empty 668 kg (1472 lb)
Powerplant: one 90-hp Curtiss OX-5 V-8 air-cooled engine
Performance: maximum speed 162 km/h (101 mph) at 1525 m (5000 ft); range 772 km (480 miles)
Payload: seats for 2 passengers
Crew: 1
Production: approx 325

Bellanca AirCruiser

FIRST FLIGHT 1932

G IUSEPPE Bellanca arrived in New York from Milan in 1912 to seek his fortune in aircraft manufacture, having built (and crashed) his first aircraft in Italy in 1908. In 1917 he built America's first cabin monoplane which matured into the Wright-Bellanca *Columbia* in which Clarence Chamberlin and Charles Levine crossed the Atlantic from New York to Berlin two weeks after Charles Lindbergh's solo flight in 1927 (Bellanca had refused to sell the aircraft to Lindbergh on the grounds that he was an unknown pilot!). From the *Columbia* was developed Bellanca's first successful series production aircraft – the Model CH-300 Pacemaker which was produced between 1928 and 1935 in two models, one with a 330-hp Wright Whirlwind engine, the other (CH-400 Pacemaker Senior) with a 450-hp Pratt & Whitney Wasp. Both were six-seat cabin monoplanes distinguished readily by the airfoil-sectioned lifting struts which became a Bellanca trademark. One hundred and seven were built.

Produced concurrently with the Pacemaker, the Bellanca Model 31 Skyrocket was a more powerful eight-seat derivative first flown in 1930. Several Skyrocket models were produced, powered by radial engines of 450 to 550 hp. A cargo version was built in Canada after World War II by North-West Industries Ltd to meet the needs of Canadian bush fliers.

Two larger single-engined aircraft were also built by Bellanca in the early 1930s – the 15-seat Airbus which cruised at 241 km/h (150 mph), and the 11 to 14-passenger AirCruiser Model 66-75 which first appeared in 1932. The AirCruiser, with its wide airfoil section struts, was effectively a sesquiplane, and was used by many pioneering airlines in the United States. It became the backbone of small transport companies after the 1930 McNary-Watres Act stimulated interest in passenger-carrying by awarding payments to airmail carriers on the basis of their aircraft's load-carrying capacity, whether or not that capacity was actually used for mail. The AirCruiser was powered variously by 715-hp Wright Cyclone, 750-hp Pratt & Whitney Hornet and 875-hp Wright Cyclone radial engines, and was supplied to the Cuban Government in 1935 as a general purpose transport aircraft for the Cuban air force. In the 1930s Bellanca aircraft were renowned for their speed and comfort.

196

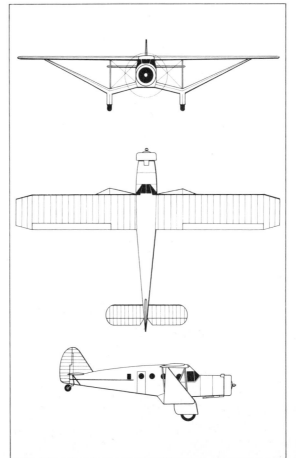

Top: The Bellanca AirCruiser with its wide airfoil-section struts was effectively a sesquiplane. It first appeared in 1932 and was popular both as a passenger carrier and mailplane
Above: A modified Pacemaker seen in the summer of 1972. Alterations include fitting floats and tapering the wing struts

66-75 AirCruiser

Type: passenger transport/utility aircraft
Maker: Bellanca Airplane Co
Span: 19.8 m (65 ft)
Length: 13.2 m (43 ft 4 in)
Height: 3.65 m (12 ft)
Wing area: 61.8 m^2 (665 sq ft)
Weight: maximum 5171 kg (11 400 lb); empty 2857 kg (6300 lb)
Powerplant: one 715-hp Wright Cyclone, 750-hp Pratt & Whitney Hornet, or 875-hp Wright Cyclone radial engine
Performance: maximum speed 265 km/h (165 mph); range 1143 km (710 miles)
Payload: seats for 14 passengers
Crew: 1
Production: not available

Norseman, Noorduyn

FIRST FLIGHT 1935

THE Norseman was a conventional high-wing monoplane with fixed undercarriage. Construction was a mixture of wood and metal covered with fabric. The fuselage was a welded steel-tube framework, a structure similar to that adopted for the tailfin, rudder and elevators, while the wings and tailplane were of wooden two-spar construction, again covered with fabric.

This aircraft was flown by the Canadian Car & Foundry Company but subsequently Noorduyn acquired the production rights. The wooden wing was replaced by a metal unit on a prototype, mated to a lengthened fuselage. Initially the type was powered by a Wright Whirlwind R-975-E3 radial engine rated at 450 hp, and in this form entered service as the Norseman Mk II, which was designed to fly with floats or skis in place of wheels. The usual propeller was a two-blade Hamilton Standard with three blades optional. Provision was made for eight passengers to be accommodated on removable bench-type seats or for six individual upholstered seats, or the cabin could be stripped bare for cargo.

Before World War II the type was flying in Mk II, III and IV forms with the Royal Canadian Mounted Police, Mackenzie Air Service and Dominion Skyways. The Norseman IV, which emerged in 1937, became the major production variant and was powered by a 600-hp Pratt & Whitney R-1340-S3H-1 Wasp nine-cylinder radial. The first of a number of Royal Canadian Air Force contracts came in 1940 when 38 Mk IVs were ordered as radio/navigational trainers. Seven ex-

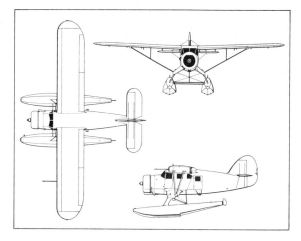

amples were supplied to the USAAF as YC-64s, which later led to an order for almost 750 UC-64s. A few of these found their way to the US Navy, while six further examples were produced for the US Army Corps of Engineers equipped to carry six passengers.

Noorduyn Aviation stopped aircraft manufacture in 1946, its assets being taken over by the Canadian Car & Foundry Company. The new owner continued Norseman production until 1950, the final production variant being the Mk VI. The 1950s and 1960s saw bush operators in North America and small airlines throughout Central America, Iceland, Scandinavia, part of Africa, India and the Philippines operating more than 100 Norsemen.

Norseman IV

Type: light STOL transport
Maker: Noorduyn Aviation Ltd
Span: 15.75 m (51 ft 8 in)
Length: 9.68 m (31 ft 9 in)
Height: 3.07 m (10 ft 1 in)
Wing area: 30.19 m^2 (325 sq ft)
Weight: maximum 3357 kg (7400 lb); empty 1928 kg (4250 lb)
Powerplant: one 600-hp Pratt & Whitney R-1340-S3H-1 or R-1340-AN-1 Wasp 9-cylinder radial engine
Performance: maximum speed 249 km/h (155 mph) at 1525 m (5000 ft); range 747 km (464 miles)
Payload: seats for 8 passengers
Crew: 1
Production: approx 900

Below: A Noorduyn Norseman of the Canadian operator Pacific Western Airlines. From modest beginnings in 1945, PWA has risen to be the third largest airline in Canada

Widgeon, Grumman

FIRST FLIGHT 1940

THE Widgeon is one member of a family of amphibian flying boats built in America by Grumman in the late 1930s and 1940s. Designated the G-44, the Widgeon first flew, before the US entry in World War II, in July 1940, some three years after its predecessor the Goose.

The type was designed to provide a four-seat amphibious transport for private and executive use, but the initial production examples were supplied to the United States Coast Guard Service for antisubmarine patrol work and as a three-seat utility transport which was designated the Grumman J4F-1.

The 25 J4F-1s were followed by 16 OA-14s for the United States Army Air Force, but the most important version developed for military use was the J4F-2. After World War II a civil version designated the G-44A was developed, using a modified hull to provide better handling characteristics on water. Some 50 examples were eventually produced.

Many Widgeons no longer required for military service became available and were converted for airline or executive use, especially in North America. Short-range passenger services and sight-seeing flights were flown by New Zealand Tourist Air Travel from Auckland in the mid 1950s until the late 1960s. The operation was taken over by Mount Cook Airlines, and this company flew them for a further six years.

The French manufacturer Société de Constructions Aéro Navales produced 40 G-44As under licence both for the French navy and for civil use. The civil types were supplied to the United States, their French-fitted Mathis 220-hp engines being replaced by 300-hp Lycoming radials in a model which was known as the Garrett Super Widgeon.

McKinnon Enterprises, well known for conversions of the Grumman Goose, produced a model called the Super Widgeon featuring 270-hp Lycoming flat-six engines. More than 70 McKinnon conversions were built, with optional features including retractable wingtip floats and other extras. Three of the New Zealand Tourist Air Travel aircraft were converted to Super Widgeon standard by the installation of two 260-hp Continental engines. Widgeons were used in service by the air forces of Canada, Brazil and also by the Portuguese navy

198

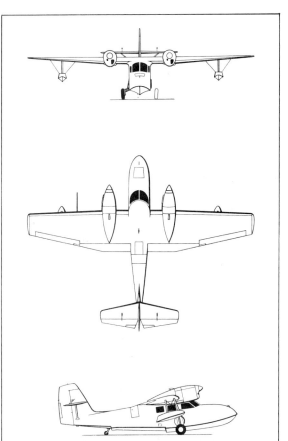

Widgeon

Type: amphibian flying boat
Maker: Grumman Aircraft Engineering Corporation
Span: 12.19 m (40 ft)
Length: 9.47 m (31 ft 1 in)
Height: 3.48 m (11 ft 5 in)
Wing area: 22.76 m² (245 sq ft)
Weight: maximum 2055 kg (4525 lb); empty 1470 kg (3240 lb)
Powerplant: two 200-hp Ranger 6-440C-5 6-cylinder inverted inline air-cooled engines
Performance: maximum speed 257 km/h (160 mph) at 1525 m (5000 ft); range 805 km (500 miles)
Payload: seats for up to 5 passengers
Crew: 1
Production: 286

Top: a Grumman Super Widgeon of New Zealand Tourist Air Travel based at Auckland. These aircraft were used on short-range passenger services and sight-seeing flights
Above: A Canadian-registered Widgeon; the type is a useful taxi for towns based on the Great Lakes

Aerovan, Miles

FIRST FLIGHT 1945

THE Aerovan began life in 1944. Designer George Miles wanted to design a cheap low-powered freighter suitable for either military or civil purposes, which he also saw as a flying scale model for the larger types of freighter he was proposing. The result was a high-wing aircraft with external aerofoil flaps which was powered by two 150-hp Blackburn Cirrus Major engines. For easy freight-loading the entire rear of the plastic-bonded wooden fuselage was hinged to form a large loading door. The high tail boom was of all-metal construction and carried three fins and rudders. Since the Aerovan had a tricycle undercarriage there was ample headroom for loading freight underneath the tail boom.

From its first flight in 1945 the Aerovan flew and performed well, showing itself able to lift nearly 1016 kg (1 ton) of payload – a feat never before achieved with an aircraft powered by merely two 150-hp engines.

The production version had a slightly longer tail boom than the prototype and different-shaped windows, but otherwise no changes were made. Aerovans became popular in the UK and overseas and were used to carry all sorts of cargo, including animals. Standard Aerovans had two 150-hp Blackburn Cirrus Major III engines, one was fitted with two 145-hp Gipsy Major 10s, and another flew experimentally with two 195-hp Lycomings, with extra 20 mph and 50% improved climb rate.

Aerovan experiments included carrying a mock-up of a nacelle for the Armstrong Siddeley Mamba turboprop engine, and fitting external aerofoil ailerons in line with the flaps. One Aerovan was also fitted with a very high aspect-ratio wing in the late 1950s.

One development, considered in 1945 but never completed, was to be a flying boat, with the fuselage nacelle deepened to make a single-step hull, still keeping the back door above the water-line. Two retractable floats for stability in the water were mounted on outriggers on the sides of the hull. The wing, engines and tail from a standard land-based Aerovan would have been used in both cases.

One related development, a prototype of which flew briefly in 1947, was the Merchantman. This was a four-engined freighter midway in size between the Aerovan and the bigger Bristol Freighter.

Below: An idea of the excellent pilot visibility in the Miles Aerovan is given by this picture of a pre-delivery aircraft
Bottom: An Aerovan of East Anglian Flying Services based at Southend-on-Sea. The rear doors and high tail made for quick loading of freight or passengers

Aerovan

Type: light freight or passenger aircraft
Maker: Miles Aircraft Ltd
Span: 15.24 m (50 ft)
Length: 11 m (36 ft)
Height: 4.12 m (13 ft 6 in)
Wing area: 36.23 m² (390 sq ft)
Weight: maximum 2540 kg (5600 lb); empty 1393 kg (3070 lb)
Powerplant: two 150-hp Blackburn Cirrus Major III engines
Performance: maximum speed 193 km/h (120 mph) at 610 m (2000 ft); range 644 km (400 miles)
Payload: seats for 9 passengers
Crew: 1
Production: 48

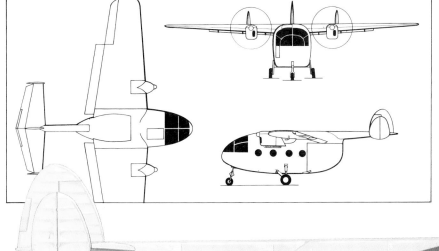

G-AJKM

East Anglian Flying Services

Beaver, de Havilland Canada

FIRST FLIGHT 1947

Y the end of World War II, there was a requirement for a modern purpose-built utility transport to serve in backwood, undeveloped areas. For many of these regions the only means of communication is by air. This is particularly true in Canada's extreme north, an area demanding strong and reliable aircraft with good short-field performance and an alternative of floats or skis.

Following its success with the Chipmunk primary trainer, de Havilland Canada turned its attention to this requirement with the DHC-2 Beaver, designed as a seven-seat transport powered by a Pratt & Whitney 450-hp Wasp Junior. First flight took place in August 1947 with Canadian type certification coming seven months later. To obtain STOL (short take-off and landing) performance DHC chose slotted flaps which when lowered completely are complemented by slotted ailerons with a 15° droop. Large cabin doors are featured on each side of the fuselage, big enough to allow a standard 205-litre (45-Imp gal) drum to be loaded aboard.

The cabin floor is strong enough to support heavy freight loads and the cabin rear wall contains hatches which will permit the stowage of long cargo items. Optional undercarriages included floats, skis, or combined wheel/ski units, while an amphibian version featured floats with retractable wheels.

Like other types designed for the same utility role, the Beaver can be used as an air ambulance, crop-duster, aerial surveyor and paratroop transport. In 1953 one aircraft – the Beaver 2 – was fitted with a 550-hp Alvis Leonides radial engine and featured a taller fin and rudder.

It was to be ten years though before a major change in Beaver development took place, with the advent of the Beaver 3. A longer cabin was produced by extending the fuselage to bring the cockpit further ahead of the wing, although the major change was the installation of a Pratt & Whitney PT6 turboprop powerplant. Initial deliveries of the Turbo-Beaver were in mid 1963.

Turbo-Beavers can also be recognized by the swept fin and rudder of increased area. Nine passengers can be carried in the fuselage with a tenth one alongside the pilot. More than 1680 Beavers were built, over 1000 of these being supplied to military operators.

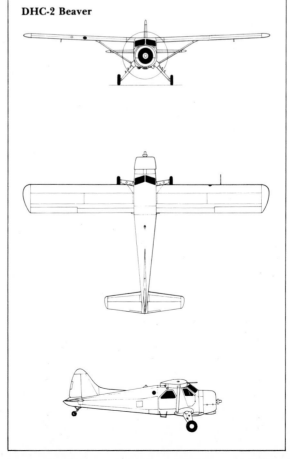

DHC-2 Beaver

Top: One of three Beavers operated by Wilderness Airline of Williams Lake, British Columbia. Floats are essential, for two of the airline's depots are on lakes
Above: The attractive lines of the Turbo Beaver with its larger rudder and swept fin. It is powered by a Pratt & Whitney PT6

DHC-2 Turbo-Beaver

Type: utility light transport
Maker: de Havilland Canada Ltd
Span: 14.6 m (48 ft)
Length: 10.75 m (35 ft 3 in)
Height: 2.74 m (9 ft)
Wing area: 23.22 m² (250 sq ft)
Weight: maximum 2435 kg (5370 lb); empty 1360 kg (3000 lb)
Powerplant: one 578-ehp Pratt & Whitney PT6A-6 or PT6A-20 turboprop
Performance: maximum cruising speed 252 km/h (157 mph); range with maximum fuel and 45 min reserves 1090 km (677 miles)
Payload: seats for up to 10 passengers
Crew: 1
Production: approx 1690

Drover, de Havilland Australia

FIRST FLIGHT 1948

WHEN production of the venerable de Havilland Dragon biplane ended, the company's Australian subsidiary soon set to work designing a rugged replacement for the sort of arduous duties demanded by that country's outback. Durability and a safe performance after the loss of one engine were among the principal design aims, and the outcome was a three-engined aircraft. It was the first three-engined all-metal aircraft to fly in Australia.

Inevitably the design was in one sense a development of the Dove, but there was little resemblance in close detail, except around the cabin and in the fairly large windows. The Drover used three 145-hp Gipsy Major 10 Mk 11 engines (the same as that used in many marks of Chipmunk trainer) instead of the Dove's two larger Gipsy Queen 70s. Performance requirements, with one engine failed, were such that the designers had considered a four-engined aircraft, but they eventually settled on three engines. Three involved no weight penalty in the wing and little extra drag but could still produce a 50% power increase over a twin.

The prototype Drover first flew in January 1948, with chief test pilot Brian Walker at the controls, and he gave a good report of the handling and performance from the outset. Production got under way, with first deliveries being made the following year. Prospects for Drover sales initially looked good, but with the beginning of Vampire jet production, and a slow flow of Drover orders, only 20 were built. The Mk I was succeeded by a version with double-slotted flaps, the Mk II. Major operators in New Guinea or Australia were Qantas, Trans Australia Airlines, the Department of Health, Department of Civil Aviation, Fiji Airways, New Hebrides Airways and Air Melanesia. Best known operator was the Royal Flying Doctor Service, which flew them in Queensland and New South Wales. Seven of the latter's aircraft were re-engined with 180-hp Lycoming O-360-AIA engines to become Mk III Drovers, with Hartzell feathering propellers.

One of only two Drovers with British registrations is now preserved at Southend, Essex.

Seating arrangement allows for accommodation for up to eight passengers with a flight crew of either one or two. The ambulance version could carry two stretcher patients and two passengers.

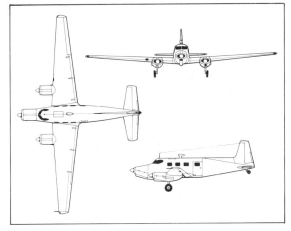

DHA-3 Mk III

Type: light transport
Maker: de Havilland Aircraft Pty Ltd
Span: 17.37 m (57 ft)
Length: 11.12 m (36 ft 6 in)
Height: 3.28 m (10 ft 9 in)
Wing area: 30.2 m² (325 sq ft)
Weight: maximum 2948 kg (6500 lb); empty 2086 kg (4600 lb)
Powerplant: three 180-hp Lycoming O-360-A1A 4-cylinder horizontally opposed air-cooled engines
Performance: maximum speed 254 km/h (158 mph) at 2438 m (8000 ft); range 1448 km (900 miles)
Payload: seats for 8 passengers
Crew: 1
Production: 20

Left: A Mk III Drover of the Royal Flying Doctor Service of New South Wales, Australia. It is powered by three Lycoming O-360-A1A engines
Below: The Mk I and II Drovers had three 145-hp Gipsy Major 10 Mk II engines, the same powerplant used in many marks of the Chipmunk trainer

An-2, Antonov

FIRST FLIGHT 1947

THE Antonov An-2 (codenamed Colt by Nato) is a classic example of an aerial-utility work-horse, with more than 12 000 produced in the Soviet Union and Poland since 1949. The type was originally designed to meet a Soviet agricultural and forestry ministry requirement. Powered by a Shvetsov ASh-21 engine of some 630 hp, the proto-type flew in 1947.

Initially, the Colt was called the SKh.1 (from *Selskokhozyaistvennyi-1* – agricultural/economic). Production examples featured the 1000-hp ASh-62 radial engine and became known as the An-2. The biplane's reliability for all sorts of general-purpose work was soon apparent and operations as a passenger and freight transport were quickly ex-tended to take in survey and photographic sorties, ambulance, parachute-training and rescue work. In Soviet air force service the type is used as a trainer for paratroops, radio-operators and navigators, and as a light freighter.

The basic version is the An-2P, accommodating up to 14 paratroops, or ten passengers, or six stretchers with attendants and four other seats. An agricultural version, the An-2S features an under-fuselage pump to dispense crop-spraying chemicals via spray bars under the lower wing from a 1360-litre (300-Imp gal) tank. The An-2M, which en-tered service in 1965, provided an engine-driven system discharging powder or liquid from a larger 1950-litre (430-Imp gal) hopper. This version also included other changes: fin and rudder are notice-ably more square-cut, the tailplane is larger and the aircraft can be flown by a single pilot.

In 1960 production began in Poland; the An-2P was a passenger version of the basic An-2T trans-port. A seaplane version of the P was developed as the An-2V with a reversible-pitch propeller. The An-2L water-bomber was derived from the V, having provision within the floats for water pick-up and evacuation. The An-2V is also known as the An-6, while the designation An-4 is applied by Antonov to the An-2ZA (a high-altitude meteorological research variant). This version, featuring an extra cockpit incorporated in the fin for ice observations, is powered by an ASh-62IR/TK with an external turbocharger to main-tain 850 hp at altitudes of 10 000 m (32 800 ft). Licence-production of the An-2 has been carried out in China from 1957, and Poland and China remained the producers during the late 1970s.

202

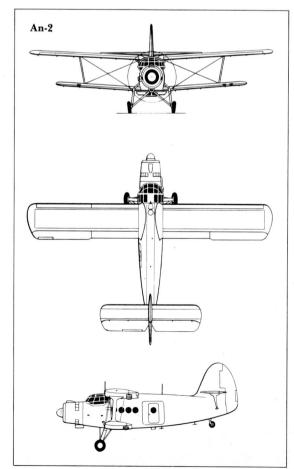

An-2

Top: An Aeroflot An-2S painted yellow as a safety precaution during low-flying agricultural spraying operations
Above: A Hungarian An-2; the type is used in vast numbers in the Communist bloc for both civil and military applications

An-2P

Type: light utility transport
Maker: Antonov Design Bureau; WSK-PZL-Mielec
Span: 18.18 m (59 ft 8½ in)
Length: 12.74 m (41 ft 9½ in)
Height: 6.1 m (20 ft)
Wing area: 43.6 m² (469 sq ft)
Weight: maximum 5500 kg (12 125 lb); empty 3450 kg (7605 lb)
Powerplant: one 1000-hp Shvetsov ASZ-62IR 9-cylinder radial air-cooled engine
Performance: maximum speed 258 km/h (160 mph) at 1750 m (5740 ft); range at 1000 m (3280 ft) with 500 kg (1102 lb) payload 900 km (560 miles)
Payload: seats for up to 14 passengers
Crew: 2
Production: minimum 18 000 (of all models)

DHC-3 Otter, de Havilland Canada

FIRST FLIGHT 1951

FOLLOWING the success of the company's first two original designs, namely the Chipmunk primary trainer and the Beaver utility transport, aimed primarily at the Canadian backwoods, de Havilland Canada looked at the possibility of a larger but similar aircraft to do the same type of job in other outback regions of the world.

The King Beaver, as the design was initially called, was 3 m (10 ft) longer, had a 3-m (10-ft) wider span, and was 50% heavier, with a 50% bigger wing area and 50% greater maximum take-off weight. Ten or 11 passengers could be accommodated as opposed to the Beaver's seven, while power was supplied by a 600-hp Pratt & Whitney R-1430 Wasp. Canadian type certification came in late 1952, less than 12 months after the first flight, and the name Otter was chosen.

The cabin floor is stressed to carry cargo and a hatch in the floor can be used for freight or paratroop dropping, or as a camera port. As with other utility types, skis or floats may be fitted as an alternative undercarriage. There is an amphibious version with float/wheel combination units which feature hydraulic wheel retraction (into the floats). Up to six stretchers may be fitted in the cabin, leaving space for six attendants or 'walking wounded' in an aerial-ambulance layout. A higher maximum speed of 267 km/h (166 mph) and a lower empty weight of 1692 kg (3703 lb) are features of the turbine-powered version developed in Alberta in the mid 1970s by Cox Air Resources.

A more powerful version of the Pratt & Whitney PT6A turboprop engine used in de Havilland's own Turbo-Beaver is used in the Cox Turbo Single Otter (so named to avoid confusion with DHC's Twin Otter). Modification of the prototype was begun in 1976, at which time a market for as many as 75 units was estimated from a total Otter population of more than 200. The Turbo Otter can carry more fuel and a greater payload, with maximum range up from 1520 km (945 miles) to 1682 km (1045 miles).

Like its smaller predecessor the type soon proved to be attractive to the world's armed forces. It was used by the US Army and Navy as well as by Canada, Australia, India, Norway and many African and Far Eastern countries. Nine nations have operated Otters and Beavers in Antarctica. By 1971, 20 years after the first flight, almost 50 Otters remained in worldwide airline service.

Above: Aircrew walk out to their DHC-3 Otters assigned to the United Nations for liaison and observation in troubled areas
Left: An amphibian version of the Otter; though the floats create considerable drag they are very useful in the wilder areas of northern Canada

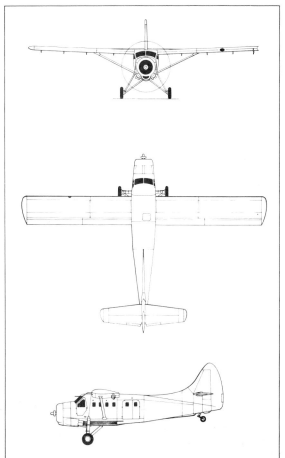

DHC-3

Type: light transport
Maker: de Havilland Canada Ltd
Span: 17.75 m (58 ft 10 in)
Length: 12.75 m (41 ft 10 in)
Height: 3.83 m (12 ft 7 in)
Wing area: 34.8 m² (375 sq ft)
Weight: maximum 3629 kg (8000 lb); empty 2010 kg (4431 lb)
Powerplant: one 600-hp Pratt & Whitney R-1340 S1H1-G Wasp 9-cylinder radial engine
Performance: maximum speed 257 km/h (160 mph); range 1410 km (875 miles)
Payload: seats for up to 11 passengers
Crew: 1
Production: minimum 400

Twin Beech, Beechcraft

FIRST FLIGHT 1937

THE Beech Model 18 had one of the longest production runs of any aircraft, lasting no less than 32 years from 1937. In that time more than 9000 were made, of which over 5200 were military versions delivered during World War II, while 2000 were civil aircraft produced after the war.

The first Model 18 was designed in 1936 as a passenger transport with accommodation for six people. The Beech 18 prototype made its maiden flight in January 1937, and aircraft produced prior to World War II were designated the 18, A18 and B18. The first military C-45 was delivered to the US Army Air Corps in the first half of 1940, and subsequent types included the C-45/UC-45 and TC-45J. The C-45G and H models were converted from T-7 and T-11 Kansan trainers, the RC-45H and TC-45H were photographic and training versions, while the RC-45H and TC-45J performed the same roles for the US Navy.

The navy's JRB-1, 2, 3 and 4 versions were utility transports, while the SNB-1 trainer was virtually the same as the T-11 Kansan, and the SNB-2 another version of the AT-7 navigator trainer. The AT-7/T-7 was derived from the commercial B-185S, and the AT-11/T-11 sported a lengthened glazed nose housing a bomb-aimer, plus a small bag for carrying weapons. A photographic survey version was designated the F-2.

Foreign air forces throughout the western world flew Model 18s after the war. They were used by the RAF and Royal Navy as the Expediter I and II. Some 30 foreign air forces were still flying the basic C-45 version in the mid 1960s.

After the war, civil versions included the C18 and D18. Of these, over 1000 were built. An improved E18 Super 18 was revealed in 1954. The E18 Super 18 had a much improved interior giving a greater degree of comfort to the passengers. The wings were modified structurally and more powerful powerplants fitted. Navigational equipment could be fitted to suit the customers' specialized requirements and two auxiliary rockets were optional. The G18 appeared late in 1959. The G18S had a slightly increased wing span and a reinforced structure. With uprated engines, the performance of this aircraft was a considerable improvement over the earlier variants. The last production version of all was the Super H18. The main features were new 'half fork' mainwheel legs, a refined exhaust system and lighter propellers. A high-density version of the Super H18, known as the Superliner, seats ten.

By the 1960s the Beech 18 was inevitably very old-fashioned in style and appearance. Its big radial engines and twin fins were very much of the 1930s, but the most dated characteristic was its tailwheel undercarriage. Thus a major modernization step was the nosewheel undercarriage, designed by Volpar and available as an option from 1963. Also available were a rocket-assisted take-off installation, and weather radar.

Several other modernized versions were also produced. These included the Dumod I, seating nine passengers, with a nosewheel undercarriage, modified wingtips for more speed, glassfibre control surfaces, and a larger flight-deck with bigger windows for the passengers. A longer version, the

Dumod Liner, was produced until 1970/71.

The Volpar/Beech 18 features a nosewheel undercarriage in which the mainwheels retract completely, and a lengthened nose. A turboprop development is known as the Volpar Super Turbo 18, with 575-shp Garrett-AiResearch TPE331-25 turboprop engines driving three-blade Hartzell reversible propellers. It also has a revised leading edge for the wing, which sweeps back at a greater angle to smaller wingtips.

Yet more versions include the Pacific Airmotive Tradewind with a nosewheel and single fin and rudder, the Turbo Tradewind with PT6A-6 turbo-props, the Hamilton Westwind II and III with Pratt & Whitney PT6As, and the Rausch Star 250 with a high cabin roof.

Above: A Beech C-45H of the Californian commuter service of Air Cortez. This small operator flies from Ontario, east of Los Angeles, to towns in Mexico
Left: A Hamilton Westwind (Beech 18 conversion) of Connie Kalitta Services, a US third-level airline
Below left: A Twin Beech II at a US west coast airfield. The robust airframe has been stretched, re-engined and altered with new avionics, and remains in service as an air-taxi and commuter aircraft

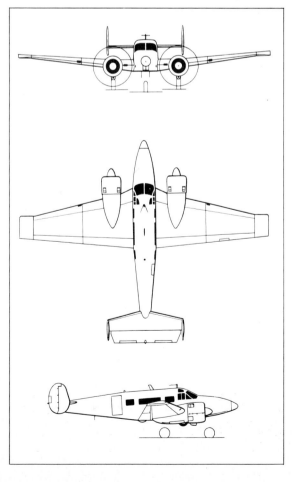

Beech 18

Type: light transport
Maker: Beech Aircraft Corporation
Span: 14.5 m (47 ft 7 in)
Length: 10.08 m (33 ft 1 in)
Height: 2.79 m (9 ft 2 in)
Wing area: 33.54 m² (360.7 sq ft)
Weight: maximum 3979 kg (8750 lb); empty 2617 kg (5770 lb)
Powerplant: two 450-hp Pratt & Whitney R-985-B5 Wasp Junior radial air-cooled engines
Performance: maximum speed 370 km/h (230 mph) at 1525 m (5000 ft); range 1585 km (985 miles)
Payload: seats for up to 7 passengers
Crew: 1 to 2
Production: minimum 9000

Courier, Helio

FIRST FLIGHT 1953

HELIO Aircraft Corporation was founded in 1948 by Dr Otto C Koppen and Dr Lynn Bollinger to develop and produce short take-off and landing aircraft which would offer helicopter-like performance. After experimenting with a much-modified Piper Vagabond lightplane fitted with full-span leading-edge slats, flaps and drooping ailerons, which they called the Helioplane (first flight April 8, 1949), they built the first Helio Courier in 1952. A four-seat high-wing STOL light/utility aircraft, the Courier entered production in 1954. It was powered by a 260-hp Lycoming engine and, because of its unusual aerodynamics, was able to fly in perfect safety and under full control at speeds below 48 km/h (30 mph). Six Couriers were built in 1954 and the aircraft was evaluated by the United States Army as a liaison aircraft and was given the military designation YL-24.

The first quantity production models were the Helio H-391 and H-395 Courier models introduced from 1958. In 1964 the 250-hp and 295-hp Lycoming-engined H-250 and H-295 Super Couriers appeared, the first H-295 flying on February 24, 1965. These models were widely ordered by the United States Government as U-10s for the USAF and for the CIA's (Central Intelligence Agency) clandestine airline Air America, which used them in South-East Asia during the Vietnam war for supply-dropping, spying, drug and gun-running and on psychological warfare missions. The Helio's ability to operate from tiny mountainside airstrips and to loiter at low altitude at ultra-low speeds made them favourite mounts for both USAF and Air America pilots. A tricycle-undercarriage version, the HT-295 Tri-Courier was introduced in 1974, and this aircraft remains in limited production.

Developments of the basic Courier design included the Helio H-500 Twin Courier, and the turboprop-powered HT-550A Stallion and Twin Stallion, all of which have now ceased production. More than 500 Couriers have been built and are widely used by bush fliers on wheels, skis and floats. A Super Courier used by a mountaineering expedition in Peru operated off 30-m (100-ft) long mountainside airstrips at an altitude of 4267 m (14 000 ft), aided by RATO (rocket-assisted take-off) tubes mounted on its fuselage sides, and an arrester hook for landing.

Courier

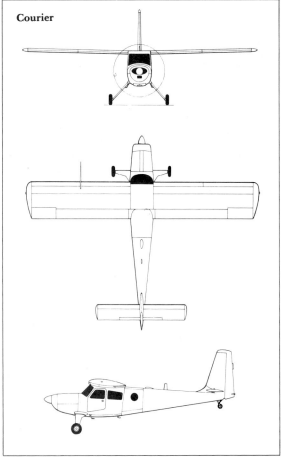

H-295 Super Courier

Type: STOL light utility transport
Maker: Helio Aircraft Co, Division of General Aircraft Corporation
Span: 11.89 m (39 ft)
Length: 9.45 m (31 ft)
Height: 2.69 m (8 ft 10 in)
Wing area: 21.46 m² (231 sq ft)
Weight: maximum 1542 kg (3400 lb); empty 943 kg (2080 lb)
Powerplant: one 295-hp Avco Lycoming GO-480-G1A6 flat-six piston engine
Performance: maximum speed 269 km/h (167 mph); range with full tanks 2027 km (1260 miles)
Payload: seats for 5 passengers
Crew: 1
Production: minimum 500 by 1980

Below: An Australian H-295 Super Courier at Point Cook, Victoria, powered by a 295-hp Lycoming flat-six engine
Bottom: A Helio Courier of Northward Aviation, a Canadian airline which links such remote communities as Aklavik, Pelly Bay, and Old Crow

Fletcher, Aerospace

FIRST FLIGHT 1954

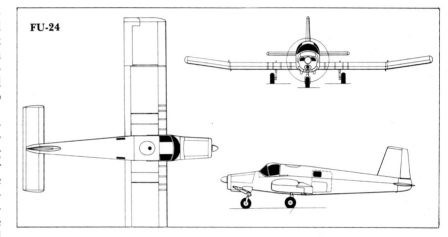

FU-24

WENDELL Fletcher, an American industrialist, visited the South Pacific area in 1952 and solicited orders for a specialist agricultural aircraft which he then had designed in California by John Thorpe. The first Fletcher FU-24 Utility, manufactured by the Sargent-Fletcher company of El Monte, flew on June 14, 1954, powered by a 225-hp Continental O-470-E piston engine.

After 100 FU-24s had been supplied in component form to James Aviation Limited in New Zealand between 1954–1964, all manufacturing rights and production tooling were sold to Air Parts (NZ) Limited who continued to manufacture the basic single-seat version with a 300-hp Rolls-Royce Continental IO-520-F engine. This company, now known as New Zealand Aerospace Industries, has also developed a dual-control model of the FU-24, and the more powerful FU-24-950 which has a 400-hp Lycoming IO-720 engine and can carry a mechanic/loader in a ferry seat for top-dressing operations or, in utility form, up to seven passengers.

The FU-24 is unusual among agricultural aircraft in having a tricycle undercarriage, but New Zealand operators have found the rugged nose-wheel landing gear well-suited to that country's steep, twisting landing strips. The cockpit area is stressed to withstand a 25-g impact – much more than the human body can tolerate – and is protected by a steel truss. New Zealand Aerospace Industries claim the lowest fatality rate for any agricultural aircraft with the FU-24. By mid 1978 production of the aircraft totalled 256, with customers in Australia, Bangladesh, Iraq, New Zealand, Pakistan, Thailand and Uruguay.

In 1978 New Zealand Aerospace Industries developed a turboprop model of the FU-24 known as the FU-1284 Cresco which is powered by a 600-shp Avco Lycoming LTP-101 turboprop and has an additional fuselage section providing an extra $1.33\,m^3$ (47 cu ft) of hopper space aft of the cabin, the additional payload being compensated in the lighter weight of the turbine powerplant. Current versions powered by Pratt & Whitney of Canada PT6A and Garrett-AiResearch TPE331 turboprops are also flying in the agricultural or passenger utility role. The agricultural version can be equipped with a variety of top-dressing, seeding and low- and high-volume spraying equipment.

FU-24-950

Type: agricultural and utility aircraft
Maker: New Zealand Aerospace Industries Ltd
Span: 12.81 m (42 ft)
Length: 9.7 m (31 ft 10 in)
Height: 2.84 m (9 ft 4 in)
Wing area: $27.3\,m^2$ (294 sq ft)
Weight: maximum 2204 kg (4860 lb); empty 1188 kg (2620 lb)
Powerplant: one 400-hp Avco Lycoming IO-720-A1A piston engine
Performance: maximum cruising speed 196 km/h (122 mph); range 709 km (441 miles)
Payload: 1052 kg (2320 lb); up to 7 passengers may be carried in utility form; variety of spraying equipment, capacity 1045 litres (230 Imp gal) or $1.05\,m^3$ (37 cu ft) dry chemicals
Crew: 1
Production: 310 ordered by January 1979

Top: An FU-24 in the colours of New Zealand Aerospace Industries
Left: An FU-24 of Robertson Air Service, New Zealand

E.P.9, Edgar Percival

FIRST FLIGHT 1955

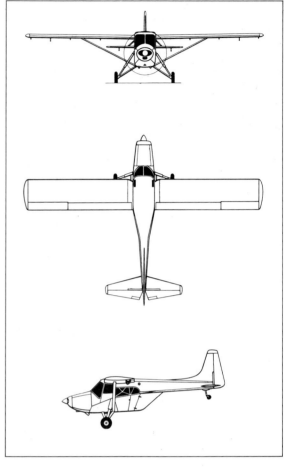

E DGAR Percival who became well-known in the late 1930s for his Percival Gull series of light aircraft, re-entered the British aircraft industry with the E.P.9 in the mid 1950s. It was based on ideas he evolved during a tour of New Zealand and Australia, and was designed for a variety of uses, such as crop-spraying, or stretcher carrying.

The unusual pod-and-boom configuration allowed a very deep front fuselage which could carry 1016 kg (2240 lb) of fertilizer in a hopper discharging through the floor. Pilot and passenger sat high in the front with a good view for low-level flying. Behind them could be carried four passengers, or three stretcher cases with an attendant, or a variety of rural loads. The side and rear clamshell doors were large enough to take bales of straw or wool, 205-litre (45-Imp gal) oil drums and livestock.

The first flight was made in 1955 and by late 1956 20 aircraft had been produced. Several were sold overseas, and two went to the British Army Air Corps.

The E.P.9 proved to be very versatile in service. One was delivered to Germany and fitted out for spraying fruit crops. Insecticide from the 773-litre (170-Imp gal) tank was distributed through holes in underwing booms to spray a swathe 27 m (90 ft) wide at 161 km/h (100 mph). Other aircraft went to Australia, the Bahamas, Libya, New Zealand and Canada, where one was operated on floats.

In 1958 Edgar Percival sold his major shareholding in his company to Samlesbury Engineering, together with his rights to the design for the United States, Canada and Mexico. Over 20 partially

complete aircraft were moved to Squires Gate at Blackpool where the new company, Lancashire Aircraft, completed two aircraft with slightly larger Lycoming engines and three-bladed propellers under the new designation Lancashire Prospector E.P.9.

In 1960 production was moved to Samlesbury. One of the aircraft completed here was fitted with a 375-hp Armstrong Siddeley Cheetah 10 radial, and was one of only two so converted.

The two army E.P.9s became surplus to military requirements and left the Army Air Corps centre at Middle Wallop for civilian homes in 1961. One E.P.9 was fitted out as a six-seater and used as a communications and joyriding aircraft by Skyways until 1968.

E.P.9

Type: light freight or passenger aircraft
Maker: Edgar Percival Aircraft Ltd
Span: 13.25 m (43 ft 6 in)
Length: 8.99 m (29 ft 6 in)
Height: 2.67 m (8 ft 9 in)
Wing area: 21.1 m² (227.6 sq ft)
Weight: maximum 1610 kg (3550 lb); empty 912 kg (2010 lb)
Powerplant: one 270-hp Lycoming GO-480-B1B flat-six engine
Performance: maximum speed 235 km/h (146 mph) at 2440 m (8000 ft); range 933 km (580 miles)
Payload: seats for 5 passengers
Crew: 1
Production: 24

Top left: G-AOFU, the first E.P.9 to be built, was exported to Africa, where it crashed while crop-spraying at Maturabi, Sudan, in November 1962
Above left: A French-registered E.P.9 of Fenwick Aviation. The type is also popular for sport parachuting

208

Ag-Cat, Gulfstream American

FIRST FLIGHT 1957

THE first Ag-Cat G-164 agricultural aircraft flew on May 22, 1957. Designed as a rugged, all-metal machine with biplane configuration to provide the low wing-loading necessary for lifting heavy payloads at low airspeeds, the aircraft was produced for the Grumman company by the Schweizer Aircraft Corporation of Elmira, New York. The first Ag-Cats were powered by 225-hp Continental W-670 radial engines. Versions with 240-hp Gulf Coast W-670 and 300-hp Jacobs R-755 engines were offered in later years, and the Super Ag-Cat G-164B was certificated in 1966 with a choice of three engines: 300-hp Jacobs; 450-hp Pratt & Whitney R-985; or 600-hp Pratt & Whitney R-1340.

The current production model Super Ag-Cat G-164C features a wing of increased span (12.88 m [42 ft 3 in] instead of 10.95 m [35 ft 11 in] on earlier models) and has a gross weight some 1100 kg (2425 lb) higher than the G-164B. The G-164C is powered by a 600-hp Pratt & Whitney R-1340 radial engine.

The Ag-Cat C airframe also forms the basis for the G-164D Turbo Ag-Cat D, which was developed with a Pratt & Whitney of Canada PT6A turboprop engine and is in current production alongside the piston-engined model.

Other Ag-Cats are flying experimentally with 600-shp Lycoming LTP-101 and Garrett-AiResearch TPE331 turboprops and a 650-hp liquid-cooled Chrysler automobile engine converted for aircraft use. Mid-Continent Maintenance Division of Hayti, Missouri has also re-engineered the

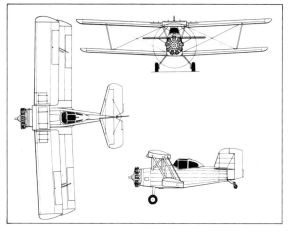

Ag-Cat to take a massive 1200-hp Wright Cyclone R-1820 radial engine. This aircraft, appropriately called King Cat, can operate at a gross weight of 4309 kg (9500 lb) and take off in just 300 m (984 ft). One Ag-Cat underwent conversion by Serv-Aero Engineering. This involved the fitting of a 560-hp Alvis Leonides radial engine.

The Ag-Cat has been exported to more than 40 countries. Two thousand are in operation worldwide and in the first six years of agricultural operation in the United States Ag-Cats logged more than 1 million flying hours without a fatal accident. In May 1980 manufacture of the aircraft was transferred from Schweizer to the parent Gulfstream American factory at Savannah, Georgia.

Ag-Cat G-164C

Type: agricultural biplane
Maker: Schweizer Aircraft Corporation for Gulfstream American Aircraft Corporation
Span: 12.88 m (42 ft 3 in)
Length: 9.14 m (30 ft)
Height: 3.48 m (11 ft 5 in)
Wing area: 36.42 m² (392 sq ft)
Weight: maximum 3855 kg (8500 lb); empty 1696 kg (3740 lb)
Powerplant: one 600-hp Pratt & Whitney R-1340 radial piston engine
Performance: maximum speed 237 km/h (147 mph); range 650 km (404 miles)
Crew: 1
Production: 2280 by January 1979

Top: An Ag-Cat G-164 agricultural aircraft
Above left: Ag-Cat N-4859. The black (or blue) and yellow colour scheme is common for low-flying agricultural aircraft in the USSR and the West
Above: A G-164D Turbo Ag-Cat powered by a Pratt & Whitney PT-6A

JetStar, Lockheed
FIRST FLIGHT 1957

THE Lockheed Model 1329 JetStar was conceived in 1956 and announced in March of the
following year, flying in prototype form as a private
venture six months later, fewer than 250 days after
design work began. The jet-powered utility transport was offered for operation by a crew of two with
accommodation for eight to ten passengers. Initially the aircraft was powered by two British Bristol
Siddeley Orpheus turbojets but one prototype was
re-engined in late 1959 with Pratt & Whitney JT12
turbojets, which were adopted for production aircraft.

Following soon after the Rockwell Sabreliner,
the JetStar is unique among the family of light jet-
transport aircraft in having an all-moving tailplane
for longitudinal control, and in being powered by
four engines. Construction is of conventional aluminium-alloy stressed-skin semi-monocoque fail-
safe structure. Plain ailerons are mechanically
operated with hydraulic boost, while aileron tabs
are electro-mechanical. There are no spoilers fitted
to the wing, which features hinged leading-edge
flaps and double-slotted trailing-edge flaps. Rare
among civil jet transports is the hydraulic speed-
brake fitted beneath the rear fuselage; rudder and
elevators are mechanically operated. Internal fuel
capacity is increased by the use of two non-
removable external tanks fitted on the wings. The
normal cabin-layout features wardrobe, galley and
lavatory, although this can be varied to suit
individual requirements.

Two versions of the JetStar – C-140A and the
VC-140B – were developed for the United States
Air Force and by 1973 more than 150 had been
delivered throughout the world for business and
corporate use, no more orders being accepted after
that year, pending a new longer-range version. A
modification kit developed by AiResearch Aviation
utilizing the Garrett TFE731-3 turbofan (which
offered the traditional fan advantages of greater
fuel economy combined with less noise) was
adopted by Lockheed in its JetStar II, incorporating many other changes.

Perhaps the most obvious visible change is the
redesign of the external fuel tanks, which are now
underslung ahead of the wing. Lockheed claims
that this new shape results in reduced drag,
another advantage being that the aircraft centre of
gravity is more flexible and fuel-flow management
is more easily controlled.

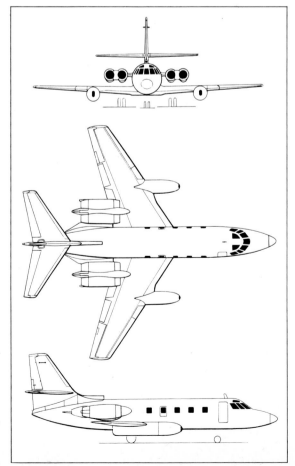

JetStar II

Type: light utility and
business jet transport
Maker: Lockheed Aircraft
Corporation
Span: 16.6 m (54 ft 5 in)
Length: 18.42 m (60 ft 5 in)
Height: 6.23 m (20 ft 5 in)
Wing area: 50.4 m²
(542½ sq ft)
Weight: maximum 20 185 kg
(44 500 lb); empty 10 700 kg
(23 578 lb)
Powerplant: four 1678-kg
(3700-lb) st Garrett-
AiResearch TFE731-3
turbofans
Performance: maximum
speed 880 km/h (547 mph) at
9145 m (30 000 ft); range with
maximum payload and
30 min reserves 4818 km
(2994 miles)
Payload: 1247 kg (2750 lb);
seats for 10 passengers
Crew: 2
Production: I (141), II (40)

Sabreliner, Rockwell

FIRST FLIGHT 1958

THE North American (now Rockwell International) Sabreliner was one of the first business jets on the market. It was, however, developed originally to meet a United States Air Force specification for a combat-readiness trainer and utility aircraft, and it serves with the USAF and Navy as the T-39. The prototype flew for the first time on September 16, 1958, powered by two General Electric J85 turbojet engines. The first commercial version, designated Sabreliner 40 and powered by 1360-kg (3000-lb) thrust Pratt & Whitney JT12A-6A engines, was introduced in 1962. It seated up to seven passengers with a two-man crew; the first customer delivery was made in May 1963, and in all some 125 Sabre 40s were manufactured.

A lengthened Sabreliner 60 seating nine passengers was introduced in 1967 powered by 1497-kg (3200-lb) JT12A-8 engines. In 1970 the Sabreliner 70 with the same engines, but a deeper fuselage offering stand-up headroom was introduced, later to be redesignated Sabreliner 75. This model was fitted with fuel-efficient General Electric CF700-2D turbofan engines as the Sabreliner 75A in 1973, and continues in production.

The Raisbeck Group of Seattle, Washington have developed a new supercritical wing offering increased fuel load and overall performance improvements for the Sabreliner. This wing is available as a retrofit to Sabreliner 60s as the Mk 5 conversion, and has been adopted by the parent company Rockwell International for the latest Sabre 65, which first flew on June 29, 1977, followed on September 8, 1978 by

the first Raisbeck-modified Sabre Mk 5 60A. The Sabre 65 is powered by two 1678-kg (3700-lb) thrust Garrett-AiResearch TFE731-3 turbofans. Its cabin can be configured for four to ten passengers, and it has a cruising speed of 849 km/h (528 mph) with a maximum range with IFR reserves of 4595 km (2855 miles). In June 1979 the first production Sabreliner 65 made the longest flight of any Sabreliner in history when it flew from St Louis to Le Bourget Airport for the Paris Air Show. By December 1979, Rockwell held 70 orders for the latest model Sabreliner.

A proposed supercritical-winged model of the Sabreliner 75A has been abandoned by Rockwell, but the Raisbeck Corporation are offering Mk 5 wing retrofits to existing Model 75A operators. The modified aircraft is designated Sabreliner 80A.

Above: The Saberliner 60 was generally similar to the Series 40 and had accommodation for up to ten passengers
Below: A Series 60 takes off from a suburban airport in the USA

Sabreliner 75A

Type: business and corporate transport
Maker: Rockwell International Corporation
Span: 13.61 m (44 ft 8 in)
Length: 14.38 m (47 ft 2 in)
Height: 5.26 m (17 ft 3 in)
Wing area: 31.8 m² (342 sq ft)
Weight: maximum 10 432 kg (23 000 lb); empty 5987 kg (13 200 lb)

Powerplant: two 2041-kg (4500-lb) st General Electric CF700-2D-2 turbofans
Performance: maximum cruising speed 906 km/h (563 mph); range 3149 km (1957 miles) with 4 passengers and IFR reserves
Payload: seats for 10 passengers
Crew: 2
Production: 610 (all types) by 1980

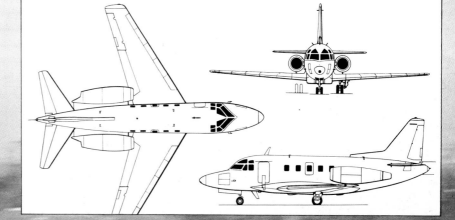

Turbo Commander, Rockwell

FIRST FLIGHT 1964

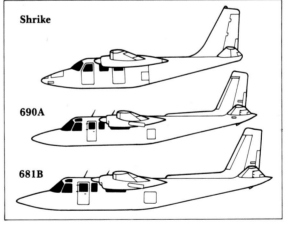

Shrike

690A

681B

THE lineage of the Rockwell Turbo Commander can be traced back 30 years to the Aero
Commander Model 520 light twin-engine business
aircraft. It was designed by ex-Douglas Aircraft
project engineer Ted Smith and went into production at Bethany, Oklahoma in 1951. A succession of piston-engined models followed, including
the Model 560 (260-hp Lycoming GO-480 engines), Model 680 Super (340-hp supercharged
Lycomings), Model 500 (260-hp Continental IO-
470-M or 250-hp Lycoming O-540-A2Bs), and the
Model 720 Alti Cruiser introduced in 1959 which
was the first light business aircraft to have a
pressurized passenger cabin.

In the early 1960s the line was refined and a
stretched Aero Commander 680FL Grand Commander introduced. It was the airframe of a
pressurized 680FLP Grand Commander which
formed the basis of the first Model 680T Turbo
Commander which first flew from Bethany on
December 31, 1964. Apart from its Garrett-
AiResearch turboprop engines the Turbo Commander was externally similar to its piston-powered stablemate. Production deliveries commenced
in April 1965 and after Aero Commander merged
with North American Rockwell, the improved
Models 680V (increased gross weight) and 680W
(lengthened nose, uprated engines) Turbo Commanders were introduced, followed by a further
refined Model 681 Hawk Commander. The original name Turbo Commander was restored when
the Model 681B, featuring 605-shp Garrett-
AiResearch turboprops and with accommodation

for up to nine passengers, was marketed in 1971.

The 1977 Turbo Commander 690B established
seven world records for its class, including five
which were set publically during the 1978 Hanover
Air Show when Rockwell's famous test and demonstration pilot Bob Hoover climbed a 690B to
3000 m (9842 ft) in 2 min 21 sec from take-off brake
release, to 6000 m (19 685 ft) in 5 min 11 sec, and
to 9000 m (29 527 ft) in 9 min 23 sec. German
Commander dealer Jo Blumschein flew the same
aircraft to a zoom altitude record of 12 725 m
(41 750 ft) and a sustained altitude of 12 444 m
(40 830 ft). In 1979 the Turbo Commander 690B
was offered in a specially commissioned grey
pinstripe colour scheme to appeal to the business-
executive market.

Top left: The Jetprop
Commander 840 (top) and
the 980 (bottom) in flight in
August 1979. Both aircraft
have wingletted wings which
give improved performance
Above left: The flight-deck of
the Commander 980; it has
been designed for easy
maintenance with an
emphasis on crew comfort
Left: Side elevations showing
the variants of the
Commander series
Above: A West German
Turbo Commander; it was a
great success at the Hanover
Air Show in 1978 where it set
up five world records for its
class

Sales of all Hawk/Turbo Commanders had been less than satisfactory when another model, the Turbo Commander 690 (first flown on March 3, 1969) was certificated by the US Federal Aviation Administration in July 1971. This model had longer wings, engines uprated to 700 shp each, higher gross weight and many performance improvements. It was followed a year later by the further improved Turbo Commander 690A which had increased cabin pressure differential and still better performance, offering a cruising speed of 465 to 518 km/h (289 to 322 mph) and a range of 2223 km (1381 miles) at high-speed cruise. The 690A's Garrett-AiResearch TPE331-5-251 turboprop engines were flat-rated to 725 shp each.

At the US National Business Aircraft Association Convention held in October, 1979 at Atlanta, Georgia, Rockwell announced two new Turbo Commander models for the 1980s which will replace the 690B – the Jetprop Commanders 840 and 980. Both aircraft feature new high-efficiency wingletted wings which the manufacturers claim contribute an additional 7.5 km/h (4.6 mph) in cruise speed and improve climb performance by up to 11%. The two Jetprop Commanders are externally similar except for their 840-shp and 980-shp Garrett-AiResearch TPE331 engines, which drive lightweight supercritical propellers developed by Dowty-Rotol in England. The Jetprop 840 cruises at 547 km/h (340 mph) while the more powerful 980 cruises at 583 km/h (362 mph). Deliveries of the 840 began in October 1979 and the 980 in January 1980. Two more Turbo Commander derivatives are under development.

690A

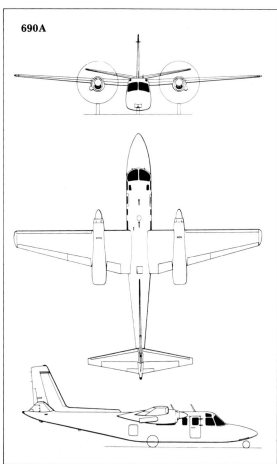

Turbo Commander 690B

Type: business and corporate transport
Maker: Rockwell International General Aviation Division
Span: 14.22 m (46 ft 8 in)
Length: 13.52 m (44 ft 4 in)
Height: 4.56 m (14 ft 11½ in)
Wing area: 24.7 m² (266 sq ft)
Weight: maximum 4683 kg (10 325 lb); empty 2810 kg (6195 lb)
Powerplant: two 700-shp Garrett-AiResearch TPE331-5-251K turboprops
Performance: maximum cruising speed 526 km/h (327 mph); range (full fuel) 2379 km (1478 miles)
Payload: seats for 6 passengers
Crew: 2
Production: 280 (all types)

BAe 125, British Aerospace

FIRST FLIGHT 1962

THE BAe 125 is one of the most successful of all European business jets. It dates back to a design originally known as the Jet Dragon. This was a 6- to 8-passenger aircraft designated the DH.125, for two crew and powered by two 1360-kg (3000-lb) Bristol Siddeley Viper 20 turbojets. A production batch of 30 aircraft was planned for the Chester factory and two prototypes were built at Hatfield. Design had begun in 1961 and a prototype first flew in July 1962, followed by the maiden flight of the other in December. The first production aircraft was fitted with Viper 520 engines, which were to power the first batch of production aircraft. The first two customer deliveries went to Germany and Switzerland.

Nine Series 1 production aircraft were built,

after which the cabin windows were decreased from six to five. A change of engines to Viper 521s and 522s was also made, thus enabling an increase of gross weight to 9525 kg (21 000 lb). As with subsequent aircraft, the Series 1A denoted aircraft for the American market, and 1B aircraft for the rest of the world.

The first American delivery was made in late 1964. By then, de Havilland had been absorbed into the Hawker Siddeley group, but in the United States it was decided to continue selling the aircraft as the DH.125 and not HS.125.

It was sold in Britain and Europe as the HS.125, as well as attracting custom as a VIP transport from foreign air forces. One British-registered aircraft was in fact hijacked while carrying a

Left: A BAe 125 in manufacturer's livery during a test flight
Below left: A line-up of BAe 125s await delivery. They are painted in customer colours which include the RAF and JCB (JC Barford, civil engineers). Optional extras include an interior leather trim, stereo cassette player, slide-out bar and luxury lavatory

BAe 125-700

1 Radome
2 Radar scanner
3 Nose equipment bay
4 VOR localizer aerial
5 Nose undercarriage bay
6 Nosewheel doors
7 Windscreen
8 Instrument panel shroud
9 Back of instrument panel
10 Rudder pedals
11 Nosewheel steering jack
12 Twin nosewheels
13 Control column
14 Second pilot's seat
15 First pilot's seat
16 Safety harness
17 Electrical distribution panel
18 Baggage compartment
19 Avionics racks
20 Vestibule
21 External doorhandle
22 Entry steps
23 Handrail
24 Galley
25 Galley storage locker
26 ADF aerial
27 HF aerial
28 Wardrobe
29 Fuselage stringer construction
30 Rearward facing passenger seats
31 Cabin windows
32 Folding table
33 Emergency exit window
34 Fuselage main frame
35 Right wing fuel tank
36 Wing fence
37 Right navigation light
38 Static dischargers
39 Right aileron
40 Trim tab
41 Geared tab
42 Aileron fence
43 Airbrake
44 Right flap
45 Window blind
46 Rear cabin seats
47 Ram air intake
48 Passenger service unit
49 Cabin window panel
50 Three-seat settee
51 Magazine rack

52 Right engine cowling
53 Intake duct to heat exchangers
54 Water tank
55 Air-conditioning supply
56 Wash basin
57 Toilet compartment
58 Pressure bulkhead frame
59 Dorsal fuel tank
60 Heat exchanger
61 Air-conditioning plant
62 Auxiliary power unit
63 APU intake
64 Rear equipment compartment
65 Fin spar attachment
66 Fin root fairing
67 Fin construction
68 Control cable ducting
69 Aerial attachment
70 Right tailplane
71 Right elevator
72 Static dischargers
73 Elevator tab
74 Overfin
75 Anti-collision light
76 VHF aerial
77 Fin bullet fairing
78 Tail navigation light
79 Left elevator
80 Tailplane construction
81 Leading-edge de-icing
82 Elevator hinge control
83 Rudder construction
84 Rudder tab
85 Tailcone
86 Ventral fin
87 Rudder hinge control
88 Oxygen bottles
89 Batteries
90 Engine pylon fairing
91 Fire extinguisher
92 Garrett-AiResearch TFE731 turbofan
93 Detachable cowling
94 Engine intake
95 Ventral fuel tank
96 Main undercarriage well
97 Flap hinge control
98 Undercarriage leg pivot fixing
99 Flap screwjack
100 Double-slotted flap construction
101 Airbrake jack
102 Left airbrake
103 Aileron fence

104 Aileron hinge control
105 Geared tab
106 Trim tab
107 Aileron construction
108 Static dischargers
109 Aileron horn balance
110 Fuel filler cap
111 Integral wing fuel tank
112 Wing fence
113 Leading-edge construction
114 Main undercarriage leg
115 Twin mainwheels
116 Landing and taxi lamp
117 Wing construction
118 Leading-edge de-icing
119 Rear spar attachment links
120 Centre wing box construction
121 Front spar attachment links
122 Ventral strake
123 Wing root fillet

former Congolese prime minister, and was impounded in Algeria for almost a year.

An order for 20 was placed by the RAF in 1963. Designated Series 2, these became known as the Dominie T Mk 1 and serve as navigation trainers and VIP transports. Series III crew trainers, with Boeing 707-style cockpit layouts, were built for Qantas. Series IIIA and IIIB versions had Viper 522 engines. Improvements followed to give an increase in take-off weight, allowing additional fuel capacity in a large tank faired to the fuselage underside, and a ventral fin had to be added. From mid 1967 all HS.125s were built to this standard, as the Series IIIA-RA and IIIB-RA. The Series 400 followed, with seven luxury seats, an integral airstair door, new flight-deck and further weight increase to 10 570 kg (23 300 lb).

In 1969 HS.125 marketing in the US was transferred to Beechcraft, the aircraft was termed the BH-125 and the Beechcraft Hawker Aircraft Corporation was created. By early 1972 over 270 125 aircraft of all kinds had been built, most of them being exported. The Series 600 was faster and larger with more powerful Viper 600 turbojets, but even more performance was produced by the Series 700, introduced in 1976. This was fitted with Garrett-AiResearch TFE731-3-1H turbofan engines of better specific fuel consumption than the earlier Viper turbojets, which met all international noise requirements. The prototype was produced from a Series 600 airframe, first flying June 1976.

Airframe improvements in Series 700 aircraft for less drag and more attractive appearance include a re-shaped wing keel skid, use of countersunk, instead of mushroom-headed, rivets in the inner tank doors, aileron trailing edges and flap-botton skins, a new ventral fin and fairings, and countersunk rivets for the fuselage and tail.

There were also interior refinements such as leather trim, stereo cassette player, luxury lavatory, slide-out bar box and a range of new interior colour schemes.

The first Series 700 aircraft flew in November 1976 and was certificated a year later. By late 1979 over 100 Series 700s had been sold, including 60 for the US. The Irish Air Corps was just one of several military customers. From 1978 the designation has been BAe 125, reflecting the manufacturer's absorption in British Aerospace.

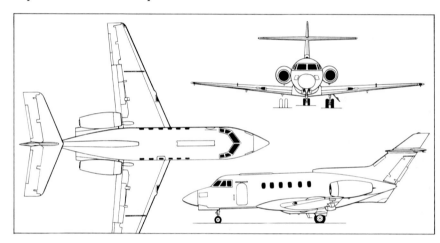

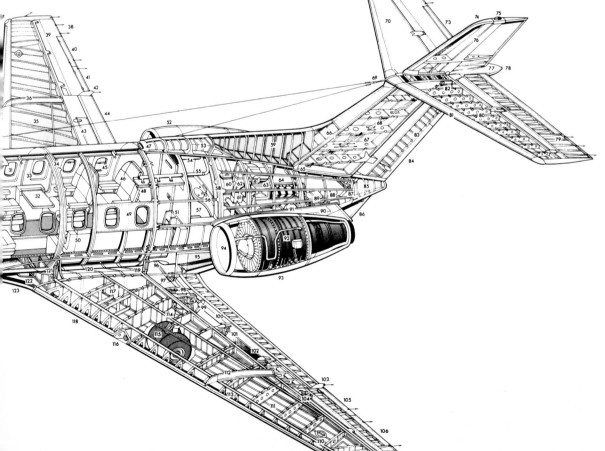

BAe 125 Series 700

Type: executive transport
Maker: British Aerospace
Span: 14.33 m (47 ft)
Length: 15.46 m (50 ft 8½ in)
Height: 5.36 m (17 ft 7 in)
Wing area: 32.8 m² (353 sq ft)
Weight: maximum 11 249 kg (24 800 lb); empty 5826 kg (12 845 lb)
Powerplant: two 1678-kg (3700-lb) st Garrett-AiResearch TFE 731-3-1H turbofans
Performance: maximum cruising speed 808 km/h (502 mph) at 8380 m (27 500 ft); range 4318 km (2683 miles)
Payload: seats for 8 passengers
Crew: 2
Production: 480 (of all models)

P.166, Piaggio

FIRST FLIGHT 1957

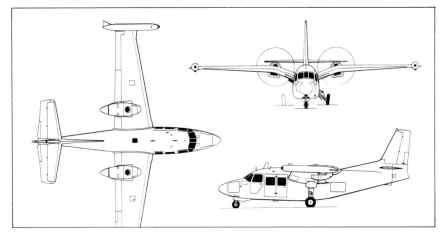

THE history of this Italian executive light-transport aircraft, which is still in production today, can be traced back almost to World War II. The type is based upon and carries some of the design characteristics of the earlier Piaggio P.136, a five-seat amphibian flying boat, which first flew in 1948. The most obvious family resemblance is in the use of the P.136's high wing, retaining the cranked 'gull' shape, and also in using the same Lycoming GSO-480 pusher engines.

Initial flight by the first P.166 prototype took place in November 1957 and first deliveries less than 18 months later. More than 30 were built for feederline use in Germany, Greece and Australasia, carrying ten passengers, and as executive aircraft, with layouts for six to eight people. The P.166 was also available in different versions for aerial-survey, ambulance and freight duties. The P.166B (named *Portofino*) flew in March 1962. This model, of which only five were built, featured more powerful Lycoming IGSO-540-A1A engines, a longer nose and a new cabin layout, revised to accommodate between six and ten passengers. As many as 12 people could be seated in the two P.166Cs which had new housing for the main undercarriage to provide greater cabin volume. A variant designed for search and surveillance duties was developed, known as the P.166S, of which 26 were built. First flown in 1975 – almost 20 years after the prototype – the P166-DL2 features a number of significant changes: internal fuel capacity was substantially increased by the adoption of integral wingtip tanks, while maximum take-off weight of the variant was increased by 300 kg (662 lb). The DL2 is powered by 380-hp Lycoming engines.

The latest addition to the Piaggio family is the P.166-DL3, which introduces turbine power: two 587-shp Avco Lycoming LTP101-600 turboprops are fitted, driving three-blade Hartzell propellers. Only the changes necessary to accommodate the new engines provide any detail difference between the DL2 and DL3 models. The large cabin door has been maintained and the DL3 has been promoted for use in geophysical-survey and aerial-photography work. A military version with a left-hand side cargo-loading door and stronger floor was built for the Italian and South African air forces; more than 50 P.166Ms were produced.

P.166-DL3

Type: light transport
Maker: Rinaldo Piaggio SpA, Industrie Aeronautiche e Meccaniche
Span: 13.51 m (44 ft 4 in)
Length: 11.9 m (39 ft 3 in)
Height: 5 m (16 ft 5 in)
Wing area: 26.56 m² (286 sq ft)
Weight: maximum 4300 kg (9480 lb); empty 2126 kg (4688 lb)
Powerplant: two 587-shp Lycoming LTP101-600 turboprops
Performance: maximum speed 417 km/h (259 mph) at 3050 m (10 000 ft); range with maximum payload and 30 min reserves 741 km (460 miles)
Payload: seats for up to 10
Crew: 1
Production: minimum 150 (of all models)

Left: A P.166-DL3
Below: The main landing gear, hinged to a tubular frame. Brakes and retraction mechanism are both hydraulically operated
Far left below: A P.166 of Charrington United Breweries
Below left: A P.136 amphibian taxies ashore

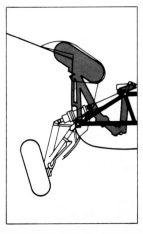

Falcon 20, Dassault-

FIRST FLIGHT 1963

DASSAULT'S Falcon 20, otherwise known as the Fan Jet Falcon or Mystère 20, is in widespread use as an executive jet. Its original name was the Mystère 20, and development was undertaken jointly with Sud-Aviation. The prototype first flew in May 1963 and was powered by two 1497-kg (3300-lb) thrust Pratt & Whitney JT12A-8 turbojets with SNECMA thrust reversers. It was later fitted with General Electric CF700-2B turbofans and these became standard for production aircraft.

Other modifications on production versions included a 1-m (3ft 3-in) increase in wing span for a lower approach speed, a longer cabin, and twin instead of single wheels on the three undercarriage legs. The first production aircraft flew in January 1965 and French certification and US type approval were granted in June of that year.

The Business Jets division of Pan American placed a first order for 54 soon after early flights in 1963, and the Mystère 20 was marketed in the USA as the Fan Jet Falcon. By late 1977 orders had reached 427, including 239 for the United States. Some have seen airline use, particularly with Pacific-based Air Nauru.

The production version in 1979 was the Falcon 20F, with more powerful turbofans in place of the original engines, bigger fuel capacity and more high-lift devices for take-off and landing. These consist of slotted slats outboard of the wing fences, and simple slats inboard of them.

Other Falcon 20 roles have included navigational aid calibration, aerial survey and photography.

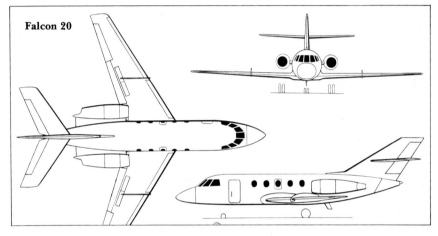

Falcon 20

Four aircraft, designated Falcon STs, have had Mirage combat radar and navigation installations for the French air force. A cargo version was developed by Little Rock Airmotive, the prototype flying in May 1972. The Federal Express Corporation ordered 33 of these, which became known as Falcon D Cargo Jets. They have an upward-opening cargo door in the left side and a strengthened freight floor, and fly frequent night services delivering freight and mail.

Another prolific version is the Falcon 20G Guardian for maritime surveillance, 41 of which have been ordered by the US Coast Guard. These have 2290-kg (5050-lb) Garrett-AiResearch ATF3-6 turbofans which can be retrofitted to existing aircraft.

Falcon 20F

Type: executive transport
Maker: Avions Marcel Dassault-Breguet Aviation
Span: 16.3 m (53 ft 6 in)
Length: 17.15 m (56 ft 3 in)
Height: 5.32 m (17 ft 5 in)
Wing area: 41 m² (440 sq ft)
Weight: maximum 13 000 kg (28 660 lb); empty 7530 kg (16 600 lb)
Powerplant: two 2041-kg (4500-lb) General Electric CF700-2D-2 turbofans
Performance: maximum cruising speed 862 km/h (536 mph) at 7620 m (25 000 ft); range 3350 km (2080 miles)
Payload: 1180 kg (2600 lb); seats for up to 14 passengers
Crew: 2
Production: 413 by January 1980 (plus 41 Guardian)

Top: A Dassault-Breguet Falcon 20DC, which in Federal Express service – Little Rock, Arkansas – bears the name Theresa
Left: Bearing the PanAm logo on their engine pods, but carrying a French registration, two Falcons make a test flight over water

Falcon 10, Dassault-Breguet

FIRST FLIGHT 1970

THE Falcon 10 'Mini Falcon' is the smallest in the range of business jets manufactured by France's Avions Marcel Dassault-Breguet Aviation and first flew on December 1, 1970 – seven years after the first flight of its larger brother the Mystère/Falcon 20.

The aircraft was first announced in June 1969 and was conceived as a scaled-down version of the Falcon 20 of about three-quarters the power and two-thirds the weight, providing accommodation for two crew and four to seven passengers. The prototype was powered by a pair of 1340-kg (2954-lb) thrust General Electric CJ610-6 turbojet engines pending delivery of the Garrett-AiResearch TFE731-2 turbofans which powered production versions. These engines were installed in the second prototype which flew on October 15, 1971, and which was subsequently used to test the French-designed Larzac turbofan at that time also being considered as a potential Falcon 10 powerplant.

Like its stablemates from AMD's Bordeaux factory, the Falcon 10 gained ready acceptance among business operators in the United States. The Falcon Jet Corporation, which markets Falcons in North America, placed an initial order for 54 aircraft with options on a further 106 and deliveries began in November 1973. The Falcon 10 is the only business jet certificated by the United States Federal Aviation Administration with no life-limitation on major components; other types are restricted to a given number of hours, after which certain structural components must be replaced. The Falcon 10's airframe is manufactured from high-strength non-zinc aluminium alloy and designed on a fail-safe principle, all loads having multiple stress paths to avoid catastrophic failure in the event that one component should fail.

Production of the Falcon 10 is approaching 200 aircraft. Though primarily a business and corporate transport, the Falcon 10 is also employed as an air ambulance and serves as a navigation trainer and communications aircraft with the French navy. Three machines designated Mystère-Falcon 10MER are used as intruders for training Super Etendard pilots and for calibrating shipborne radars. The navy has an option on a further two.

Production at the Istres plant is running at a rate of two aircraft per month with parts coming from factories in Italy, Spain and France.

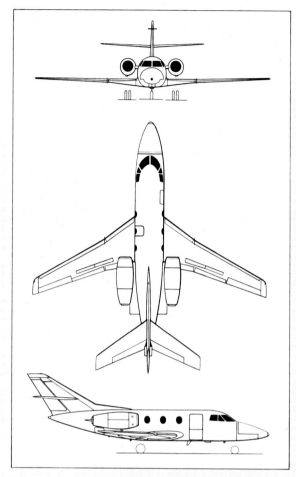

Falcon 10

Type: business and corporate transport
Maker: Avions Marcel Dassault-Breguet Aviation
Span: 13.08 m (42 ft 11 in)
Length: 13.85 m (45 ft 5 in)
Height: 4.61 m (15 ft 1½ in)
Wing area: 24.1 m² (259 sq ft)
Weight: maximum 8500 kg (18 740 lb); empty 4880 kg (10 760 lb)
Powerplant: two 1466-kg (3230-lb) st Garrett-AiResearch TFE731-2 turbofans
Performance: maximum cruising speed 915 km/h (568 mph) at 9145 m (30 000 ft); range 3555 km (2209 miles) with 4 passengers and IFR reserves
Payload: 1060 kg (2337 lb); seats for up to 7 passengers
Crew: 2
Production: 151 delivered, (194 ordered), by 1980

Below: A Falcon 10 at Harlingen, Texas in October 1978. The aircraft is a scaled-down version of the successful Falcon 20
Bottom: An American-registered Falcon 10. To ease the problems of selling in the US, it is marketed by the Falcon Jet Corporation

Falcon 50, Dassault-Breguet

FIRST FLIGHT 1976

Left and below: The trijet Falcon 50, like its smaller namesakes, has been widely sold in the United States. Even before the prototype made its maiden flight, 50 options had been taken, the bulk from the US. It offers operators an intercontinental business jet which uses many Falcon 20 components

Dassault-Breguet's search for an intercontinental-range business jet to add to their existing Falcon 10/20 line produced a series of design studies in the early 1970s based on the Falcon 20 airframe. In 1974 plans for a larger twin-jet aircraft, the Falcon 30, were dropped in favour of the Falcon 50 which was to use many basic Falcon 20 components coupled to a three-engine layout and improved wing design. The same basic fuselage cross-section was to be used, but lengthened to offer more space for fuel and baggage. Passenger accommodation would be similar to the earlier aircraft, but range and operating economics of the aircraft were to be improved by a substantial amount.

The Falcon 50 was announced in May 1974 and the first prototype flew on November 7, 1976. After initial flight testing, Falcon 50 No 01 returned to the factory for the installation of a production-standard supercritical-airfoil wing based on the advanced aerodynamics of the Dassault Mercure jet airliner, and the modified prototype Falcon 50 was flown again on May 6, 1977, making its public debut at the Paris Air Show during the following month.

On October 9, 1977 the first prototype appeared at the US National Business Aircraft Association's convention in the United States and set two world records for non-stop straight-line distance and speed in its class, on the return transatlantic flight from Teterboro, New Jersey to Le Bourget, Paris. The Falcon 50 is powered by three Garrett-AiResearch turbofans, two of them pod-mounted on either side of the rear fuselage and the third fed by an S-duct ahead of the fin. A second prototype joined the test programme on February 16, 1978, followed by the first pre-production aircraft on June 13, 1978. The third aircraft established a further record in September 1978 with a Chicago-Paris flight in 8 hours 30 min.

Fifty options had been taken by customers by the time the prototype Falcon 50 flew, most of the orders coming from the United States.

The tri-jet Falcon 50 was certificated in France and the United States in the spring of 1979 and the first production aircraft was delivered across the Atlantic to the American distributors, Falcon Jet, who had placed 70 of the 100-plus Falcon 50 orders held by Avions Marcel Dassault-Breguet Aviation by the end of 1979.

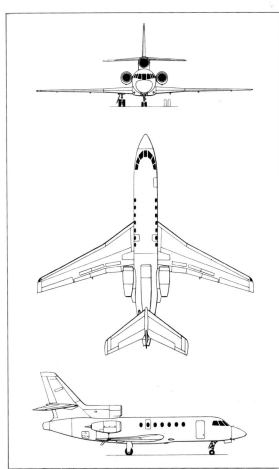

Falcon 50

Type: business and corporate transport
Maker: Avions Marcel Dassault-Breguet Aviation
Span: 18.86 m (61 ft 10½ in)
Length: 18.3 m (60 ft 0½ in)
Height: 6.9 m (22 ft 7½ in)
Wing area: 46.83 m² (504 sq ft)
Weight: maximum 17 000 kg (37 480 lb); empty 9000 kg (19 840 lb)
Powerplant: three 1680-kg (3700-lb) st Garrett-AiResearch TFE731-3-1C turbofans
Performance: maximum cruising speed 870 km/h (540 mph); range 6950 km (4318 miles)
Payload: seats for 8 passengers
Crew: 2
Production: 117 ordered by 1980

Learjets

FIRST FLIGHT 1963

IN their several versions, Learjets are probably the most familiar of all business jets. The design was conceived at the end of the 1950s by William Powell Lear Snr, soon known to aviation simply as Bill Lear, one of the most renowned figures in American aviation. He invested about $10 million in the new project. Earliest design studies were done in Switzerland, because the Learjet was to be styled after the P-16 Swiss fighter-bomber. Then in 1963 Lear opened a factory at Wichita. Late that year the prototype Learjet 23 made its first flight. It went through its FAA-certification trials in just nine months, and only a year had gone by when the first production aircraft was delivered to a customer. This was the first of 73 orders existing then – a fitting reply to the sceptics who had claimed there was no market for such an aircraft. The T-tailed Learjet looked simple but elegant, could fly six passengers at a height of 12 500 m (41 000 ft) and at up to 870 km/h (540 mph), and could operate at about 50 cents a mile using relatively small airports. It soon became a familiar sight in general aviation circles, gained some world transcontinental speed records, and achieved a timed climb distinction of 12 300 m (40 000 ft) in 7 min 21 sec.

While the aircraft itself was successful, Learjet Industries was less so, and a welcome transaction took place in 1967 when industrialist and business aircraft operator Charles C Gates bought Bill Lear's share of the business, eventually turning it into the Gates Learjet Corporation.

The Learjet airframe is a strong one, and structural tests on the first aircraft set new standards. With eight wing spars instead of the usual two or three, and many other similar 'strong-points', it is very much a 'fail-safe' design. The Model 23 was soon developed into the 24, with several improvements, including an extra permissible 227 kg (500 lb) take-off weight. In 1966 a Learjet 24 flew round the world in 50 hours 20 min, establishing 18 world records. Refinements to the production Learjet 24 included an even thicker bird-proof windshield, engine-fire protection, and new cabin pressurisation.

In the light of the success with Learjet 23s and 24s, the company saw prospects for bigger and better developments of the basic airframe. A fuselage stretch led to the Model 25. Originally this was just 0.6 m (2 ft) longer than the 24, and with bigger wingtip fuel tanks holding 860 litres (190 Imp gal).

Above left: A Swissair Learjet ambulance; the early design studies were done in Switzerland
Above: A Model 25 at the Midland-Odessa Regional Air Terminal, Texas, in September 1973
Left: A Model 24; a similar machine established 18 world records when it flew round the world in 50 hours 20 min in 1966
Above right: A Learjet Longhorn with its upturned wingtips (winglets) which reduce drag and increase range

Learjet 50 Longhorn

1 Radome
2 Weather radar scanner
3 Radar tracking mounting
4 Nose compartment construction
5 Baggage bay fire extinguisher
6 Windscreen emergency de-icing alcohol tank
7 Nose compartment access doors
8 Radio and electronics compartment
9 Nose undercarriage wheel well
10 Forward baggage compartment
11 Underfloor emergency oxygen bottle
12 nosewheel doors
13 Nosewheel
14 Incidence vane
15 Pitot tube
16 Forward pressure bulkhead
17 Windscreen de-icing air ducts
18 Curved windscreen panels
19 Instrument panel shroud
20 Instrument panel
21 Rudder pedals
22 Control linkages
23 Cockpit floor level
24 Seat adjusting handle
25 Pilot's seat
26 Control column handwheel
27 Centre radio and instrument console
28 Engine throttles
29 Co-pilot's seat
30 Cockpit roof constrution
31 Cabin bulkhead
32 Cabin roof frames
33 Seat mounting frames
34 Folding table
35 Handrail
36 Entry doorway
37 Upper door segment
38 Lower door segment/integral steps
39 Door latches
40 Fuselage frame and stringer construction
41 Cabin window panel
42 Door hinge torque tube
43 Passenger seating, 8-seat layout
44 Cabin wall trim panels
45 Three-seat settee
46 Cabin sidewall heater duct

47 Drinks cabinet
48 Wash basin
49 Toilet compartment, optional rear cabin position
50 Toilet compartment folding doors
51 Cabin roof air-conditioning duct
52 Baggage door/emergency exit
53 VHF/UHF aerial
54 Baggage door open position
55 Right wing fence
56 Wing integral fuel tank
57 Fuel system piping
58 Wing skin panel joint strap
59 Fuel filler cap
60 Right navigation light, green
61 Right winglet
62 Winglet honeycomb construction
63 Static dischargers
64 Fixed portion of trailing edge
65 Right aileron
66 Aileron servo tab
67 Cable control linkage
68 Right single-slotted flap
69 Flap guide rail
70 Spoiler/speedbrake
71 Fuselage skin plating
72 Air-conditioning system evaporator
73 Wing attachment fuselage double frames
74 Baggage compartment
75 Pressurization valve
76 Cabin air blower
77 Area ruled fuselage centre section
78 Rear pressure bulkhead
79 Fuselage fuel tank
80 Fuel filler cap
81 Engine pylon construction
82 Right engine intake
83 Garrett-AiResearch TFE731-3A turbofan
84 Engine fire extinguisher bottle
85 Bleed air ducting
86 Engine mounting beam
87 Fan air exhaust duct
88 Core engine 'hot-stream' exhaust
89 Pylon tail fairing
90 Ram air intake
91 Hydraulic reservoir
92 Batteries
93 Air-conditioning plant
94 Fin root fillet
95 Five-spar tailfin construction
96 VOR/ILS aerial

97 Elevator hinge control links
98 ADF sense aerial cable
99 VHF aerial
100 Tailplane trim jack
101 Anti-collision light
102 Right tailplane
103 Leading-edge electrical de-icing
104 Elevator horn balance
105 Right elevator
106 Tail navigation light
107 Tailplane pivot mounting
108 Elevator torque tube
109 Left elevator construction
110 Static dischargers
111 Elevator horn balance
112 Tailplane construction
113 Balance tab
114 Rudder construction
115 Rudder trim tab
116 Tailcone
117 Ventral fin
118 Rudder hinge control
119 Venting air louvres
120 Tailcone access door
121 Rear baggage bay
122 Pylon engine mountings
123 Detachable engine cowlings
124 Rear baggage door, open position
125 Left engine intake duct
126 Intake lip bleed air de-icing
127 Wing root trailing-edge fillet
128 Wing spar/fuselage attachment joints
129 Undercarriage hydraulic retraction jack
130 Main undercarriage mounting rib
131 Flap hydraulic jack linkage
132 Spoiler/speedbrake
133 Left single-slotted flap construction
134 Aileron trim tab
135 Servo tab
136 Aileron cable control
137 Left aileron construction
138 Fixed portion of trailing edge
139 Left winglet
140 Static dischargers
141 Wingtip strobe light, white
142 Winglet rib construction
143 Left navigation light, red
144 Fuel filler cap
145 Eight-spar wing construction
146 Wing skin panel joint strap
147 Left wing integral fuel tank

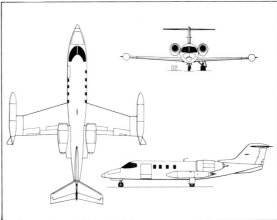

Learjet 35A

Type: light executive transport
Maker: Gates Learjet Corporation
Span: 12.04 m (39 ft 6 in)
Length: 14.83 m (48 ft 8 in)
Height: 3.73 m (12 ft 3 in)
Wing area: 23.53 m^2 (253.3 sq ft)
Weight: maximum 7711 kg (17 000 lb); empty 4132 kg (9110 lb)
Powerplant: two 1587-kg (3500-lb) st AiResearch TFE 731-2-2B turbofans
Performance: maximum cruising speed 859 km/h (534 mph) at 12 190 m (40 000 ft); range 4234 km (2631 miles)
Payload: 1810 kg (3990 lb); seats for up to 8 passengers
Crew: 1 to 2
Production: 1000 (all Learjet variants)

But the aircraft proved to have poor handling, and was soon modified to be 1.25 m (4¼ ft) longer than the Model 24, and to have rectangular instead of oval windows. First flown in 1966, the Learjet 25 was certificated in 1967 and the first delivery made the same year. The 2317-km (1440-mile) route from Wichita to a customer in Boston was flown in 2 hours 45 min.

In 1970 the first 25F, longer-range version, entered service with optional conversion from a four- or six-seat arrangement to a two-bed sleeper compartment.

A Learjet was soon fitted with a Garrett-AiResearch turbofan engine to prove the latter's suitability for future aircraft. This was a long and expensive test programme, but it led to the certification in 1974 of the Gates Learjet 35 and 36 intercontinental aircraft, with AiResearch fan-jet engines. The 35 and 36 are almost identical except in fuel capacity and accommodation.

Another major change was the re-shaped Learjet leading edge, reducing approach speeds by up to 33 km/h (21 mph). From mid 1976 Century III series Learjets (24, 25, 35, and 36 Models) had the new wing leading edge.

The latest Learjet Longhorn 28/29s have up-turned wingtip shapes, termed winglets, which reduce induced drag and lead to more range. Larger Longhorns, called the 54/55/56 series, were scheduled for delivery in 1980. Externally the same, they have different fuel capacities giving ranges up to 5745 km (3570 miles). The first Longhorn 55 flew on April 19, 1979.

148 Left wing fence
149 Twin mainwheels
150 Main undercarriage leg strut
151 Landing/taxiing lamp
152 Leading-edge stall strip
153 Leading-edge de-icing air duct

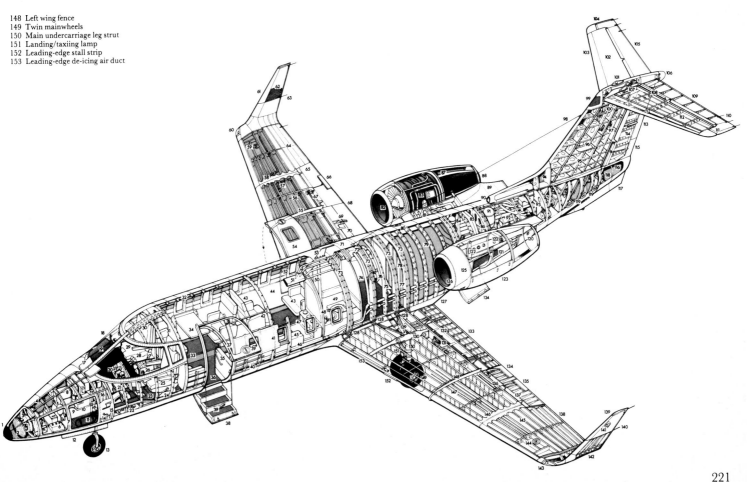

Gulfstream I, Gulfstream American

FIRST FLIGHT 1958

IN the mid 1950s the bulk of the fleet of corporate transport aircraft in the United States was made up of converted surplus military aircraft and ex-airline DC-3s. In 1956 Grumman Aircraft commenced design studies for a long-range business aircraft which would be powered by the turboprop engines then coming into airline use. Business operators were then highly sceptical of the turboprop, which was still an unknown quantity, and contemporary piston engines were considered more efficient and reliable than the usual contemporary turbines.

Undeterred, Grumman went ahead with a design for an aircraft based on the TF-1 Trader US Navy transport aircraft, with British-made Rolls-Royce Dart engines. Market and design studies showed that an entirely new design was needed and thus evolved the Grumman G-159 Gulfstream, which first flew on August 14, 1958 and was at the time the largest aircraft purpose-designed for business and corporate use. The Gulfstream (subsequently known as Gulfstream I when the jet Gulfstream II appeared in 1966) was certificated in 1959 and gained ready acceptance among major US corporations, to whom it offered an opportunity to operate worldwide entirely independently of external airfield services. The aircraft was available with any desired interior configuration from four to 19 passengers; typical executive interiors catered for ten passengers.

When production ended in 1969, 200 Gulfstream Is had been delivered to companies and heads of state worldwide. The US Navy and Coast Guard also bought Gulfstreams. Although no major changes in configuration or specification were made during the ten-year production run, in 1979 the Gulfstream American Corporation, which acquired rights and tooling for Gulfstreams I, II, and III from Grumman Aerospace Corporation, announced plans for a stretched 32 to 38-seat commuter airliner version of the aircraft. A prototype conversion designated Gulfstream IC flew for the first time on October 25, 1979.

In January 1980 no plans had been finalized for series production, but Gulfstream American will be offering the 3.2-m (10 ft 7-in) fuselage extension as a retrofit for existing Gulfstream Is following certification of the prototype in May 1980 at a cost of $1.25 million.

Gulfstream I

Type: business, corporate and third-level airline transport
Maker: Grumman Aerospace Corporation (type certificate now owned by Gulfstream American Corporation)
Span: 23.88 m (78 ft 4 in)
Length: 19.43 m (63 ft 9 in)
Height: 6.99 m (22 ft 11 in)
Wing area: 56.7 m² (610 sq ft)
Weight: maximum 16 330 kg (36 000 lb); empty 9934 kg (21 900 lb)
Powerplant: two 2210-shp Rolls-Royce Dart 529-8X turboprops
Performance: maximum cruising speed 572 km/h (356 mph); range with full tanks 4058 km (2540 miles)
Payload: seats for up to 19 passengers (38 passengers in Gulfstream IC Commuter version)
Crew: 2
Production: 200

Top: A Gulfstream I at Reykjavik, Iceland, in March 1979. When production ended in 1969 Grumman had delivered 200 Gulfstream Is. The type can carry 19 passengers, or ten in full executive furnishing

Wilga, PZL

FIRST FLIGHT 1962

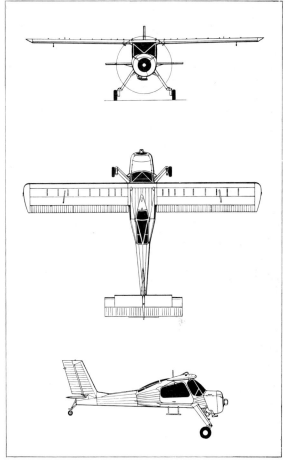

DESIGN of the PZL-104 Wilga (Thrush) was undertaken at the Centrum Naukowo Produkayjne Samolotow Lekkich PZL-Warszawa (Polish Light Aircraft Science and Production Centre, Warsaw) as a replacement for the Czechoslovakian L-60 Brigadyr general-purpose aircraft. The first prototype Wilga 1 was powered by a 180-hp Narkiewicz WN-6B radial engine and made its maiden flight on April 24, 1962. A complete redesign of the fuselage and tail surfaces followed and the Wilga 2 flew on August 1, 1963 with a 195-hp WN-6RB engine. On December 30 that year, the definitive Wilga C with a 225-hp Continental O-470 engine flew and subsequently was produced in Indonesia as the Lipnur Gelatnik, 39 examples of which were manufactured.

The first series production Wilgas from Poland were Wilga 3As (four-seat utility aircraft for club flying) and Wilga 3Ss (ambulance aircraft) which both had 260-hp Ivchenko AI-14R radial engines. In 1967 the cabin area and undercarriage of the aircraft were extensively redesigned and the aircraft was redesignated Wilga 35 (260-hp AI-14R engine) and Wilga 32 (230-hp Continental O-470K), the first examples making their maiden flights on July 28, 1967 and September 12, 1967 respectively.

The current production versions of the Wilga are: Wilga 35A (aeroclub use), 35P (passenger-carrying light transport and liaison aircraft), 35R (agricultural aircraft which can carry 270 kg [595 lb] of chemicals in an under-fuselage hopper), and the 35S air ambulance. The Wilga's excellent handling characteristics make it an ideal aircraft for use in the agricultural role, particularly when small areas have to be sprayed. The 35R is also ideal for agricultural pilot training in that its dual controls can give trainee pilots first hand experience under working conditions. Production of this unusual, insect-like STOL aircraft exceeds 400 machines, which are currently operating in Austria, Bulgaria, Czechoslovakia, Egypt, East Germany, West Germany, Hungary, Poland, Romania, United States, Spain, Switzerland, United Kingdom, USSR, and Venezuela. In addition to its specialist roles the Wilga can also be operated on skis or floats and is popular both in eastern and western countries in its role as a glider tug.

Wilga 35A

Type: light utility and agricultural aircraft
Maker: Centrum Naukowo Produkayjne Samolotow Lekkich PZL-Warszawa; Lipnur, Indonesia
Span: 11.12 m (36 ft 5¾ in)
Length: 8.1 m (26 ft 6¾ in)
Height: 2.94 m (9 ft 7¾ in)
Wing area: 15.5 m^2 (167 sq ft)
Weight: maximum 1300 kg (2866 lb); empty 850 kg (1874 lb)
Powerplant: one 260-hp Ivchenko AI-14RA radial engine
Performance: maximum speed 201 km/h (125 mph); range 680 km (422 miles)
Payload: chemical spraying equipment, capacity 270 kg (595 lb); seats for up to 4 passengers
Crew: 1
Production: minimum 400 by 1980

Top and above left: US-registered PZL Wilga 35P. The long-legged undercarriage gives a good STOL performance, which makes the Wilga an excellent agricultural aircraft

Turbo-Porter, Pilatus

FIRST FLIGHT 1961

THE first flight of the Turbo-Porter on May 2, 1961, was almost two years after the prototype Pilatus PC-6 Porter appeared. The type was to become one of the most versatile of all light STOL (short take-off and landing) transports. Design work began in 1957, leading to five prototypes followed by 20 pre-series aircraft.

The PC-G/340 basic version was powered by the 340-hp Lycoming GSO-480 engine. In December 1961, the prototype PC-6/350 flew under the power of a 350-hp fuel-injected Lycoming IGO-540 at the same gross weight of 1950 kg (4321 lb). Both the 340 and 350 models were followed by H1 and H2 versions of greater weight. In mid-1966, forward opening doors on each side of the cockpit were introduced, as were a double door on the left side of the cabin and a large rearward-moving sliding door on the right side.

The powerplant chosen for the PC-6/A Turbo-Porter was the French Turboméca Astazou II which was fitted with a reversible-pitch propeller. Again H1 and H2 versions of the PC-6/A had increased gross weight. A 523-shp version of the 630-shp Astazou X, and the 700-ehp Astazou XII equipped some PC-6/AX-H2s and similar models. In 1964 an American-engined Turbo-Porter known as the PC-6/B flew with a Pratt & Whitney PT6A-6 turboprop. This model was built in the US by Fairchild Hiller and was called at first the Heli Porter. (All models are now called Porter.) The year 1965 saw the first flight of a Porter with a third turbine engine, this time the Garrett-AiResearch TPE331, flown by Fairchild as the PC-6/C-H2.

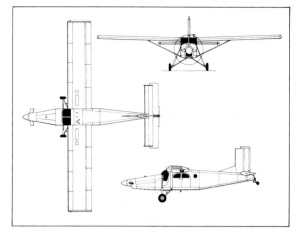

The basic form of the Porter features a conventional-wheeled undercarriage (oversize wheels and tyres are available) but the type can be flown with floats or skis. Examples have been used in agriculture for crop-spraying and water bombing, for aerial-survey and photography work, for supply dropping or conventional cargo duties, for ambulance flights (there is accommodation for two stretchers), parachuting and target towing.

The Turbo-Porter can be fitted with two underwing tanks of 190 litres (42 Imp gal) capacity. The type is in airline service in remote regions and has been used in undercover operations in Laos. AU-23A Peacemaker is the designation of an armed counter-insurgency variant supplied to the USAF for use by the Royal Thai Air Force.

PC-6/B2-H2

Type: light STOL transport
Maker: Pilatus Flugzeugwerke AG; Fairchild Industries
Span: 15.13 m (49 ft 8 in)
Length: 11 m (36 ft 1 in)
Height: 3.2 m (10 ft 6 in)
Wing area: 28.8 m² (310 sq ft)
Weight: maximum 2200 kg (4850 lb); empty 1215 kg (2678 lb)
Powerplant: one 550-hp Pratt & Whitney PT6A-27 turboprop
Performance: maximum cruising speed 259 km/h (161 mph) at 3050 m (10 000 ft); range 1400 km (644 miles)
Payload: seats for up to 7 passengers
Crew: 1
Production: minimum 500 (of all models)

Left: A French Turbo-Porter used by the Centre National de Parachutisme. The wing struts give free-fall parachutists a convenient hand-hold before their exit
Above: A Swiss Turbo-Porter climbs steeply away from its mountain airstrip

Navajo, Piper

FIRST FLIGHT 1964

THE Piper PA-31-300 Navajo prototype was described as the first of a new family series of large twin-engined executive aircraft available also for commuter airlines and corporate use. The range, which grew to spawn the similar but turboprop-powered Cheyenne series, began with the first flight in September 1964. Power came from two 300-hp Lycoming IO-540 engines which could normally be aspirated or turbocharged.

The Navajo family includes the Turbo Navajo, Navajo C/R, Pressurized Navajo and Navajo Chieftain. The basic model is the Navajo C. Each model in the series comes in Standard, Commuter or Executive versions with differences in seating arrangements and interior cabin layouts. A choice of four electronics and communications packages is available, together with co-pilot's instruments and de-icing equipment options.

The Navajo C has four passenger-seats with a fifth and sixth optional. Six seats are available in the commuter model. Standard equipment includes an aft cabin-division bulkhead and luggage shelf. Four individual seats facing one another across foldaway tables identify the executive version, in which the toilet and refreshment units may be replaced by seventh and eighth seats. Although not announced until 1970, the Pressurized Navajo began as a company project in January 1966 and flew in March 1968. Some 4000 hours of flight and ground testing went into the model, including 850 hours at altitudes up to 8840 m (29 000 ft), the type's certificated maximum operating height. Pressurization comes from turbocharger bleed air, and two engine-driven pneumatic pumps. An environmental control system regulates cabin temperature, purification and dehumidification. The Navajo C/R designation refers to counter-rotating engines as introduced in the Chieftain, a lengthened version, stretched by some 0.61 m (2 ft), and powered by 350-hp counter-rotating engines. The powerplant is one 325-hp Lycoming LTIO-540-F2BD and one 325-hp Lycoming TIO-540-F2BD flat-six turbocharged engines.

Pressures of up to 976 kg/m² (200 lb/sq ft) can be accepted by a stronger Piper cabin floor. Main cabin cargo capacity of more than 6 m³ (210 cu ft) is available, while some 91 kg (200 lb) of baggage or other cargo can be accommodated in a nose freight compartment. Almost 68 kg (150 lb) can be put in the rear area of each engine nacelle.

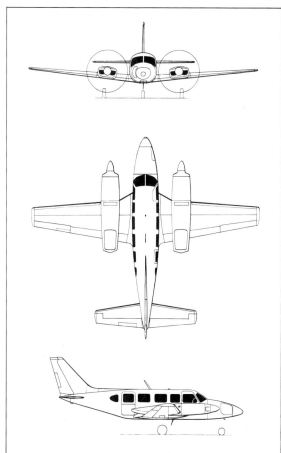

PA-31P

Type: corporate transport and commuter airliner
Maker: Piper Aircraft Corporation
Span: 12.4 m (40 ft 8 in)
Length: 10.52 m (34 ft 6 in)
Height: 3.99 m (13 ft 1 in)
Wing area: 21.3 m² (229 sq ft)
Weight: maximum 3538 kg (7800 lb); empty 2222 kg (4900 lb)
Powerplant: two 425-hp Lycoming TIGO-541-E1A 6-cylinder horizontally opposed engines
Performance: maximum speed 451 km/h (280 mph) at 5475 m (18 000 ft); range 2065 km (1285 miles)
Payload: seats for up to 8 passengers
Crew: 1
Production: current

Top: A Piper PA-31-350 Navajo Chieftain of Air Anglia. This aircraft, formerly registered N608HR, is one of 25 which link 15 British cities with Europe
Above: N7XB, an American-registered Navajo fitted with four-blade propellers

225

Super King Air, Beech

FIRST FLIGHT 1972

THE Beech Super King Air, top of the company's executive twin range, is a development of the King Air 100, but bears only a superficial resemblance. One major difference is the Super King Air's T-tail, keeping the tailplane well up out of the wing downwash or propeller slipstream. Other changes include a 2.4-m (8-ft) longer wing span, increased cabin pressurization (and consequently tougher fuselage), as well as a higher gross weight mainly taken up in extra fuel capacity to give a longer range.

Design began in late 1970, the first prototype flying in October 1972 and the second flying in December of that year. Construction of the first production aircraft began in the summer of 1973 and FAA certification followed in December. As well as winning keen interest from business users, the Super King Air soon captured military attention, and in 1974 Beech signed a contract with the US Army to supply 34 modified versions – 20 for the Army and 14 for the US Air Force. These were designated C-12As. Three aircraft designated RU-21Js were also supplied to the US Army's fleet of special-mission aircraft, carrying antennae and specially approved to operate at a high weight of 6804 kg (15 000 lb).

In 1975 both the US Army and USAF ordered more C-12As, the Air Force taking another 20 and the Army 16. The total value of the contract was $45 million. The C-12As are essentially standard Super King Airs equipped for two-pilot operation, with accommodation for eight passengers and the capacity to be converted easily for cargo carrying. Survival gear can be stored in a large baggage area.

In 1975 Beech was awarded an FAA contract to modify an aircraft for airborne evaluation of radio navigation aids and approach facilities. Two Super King Airs, specially equipped with camera installations, were also ordered by the French Institut Géographique National and delivered in February 1977. These have auxiliary wingtip fuel tanks giving another hour's endurance, and different landing gear allowing a higher take-off weight of 6350 kg (14 000 lb). Designated Beech Model 200T, these aircraft can be used in high-altitude photographic and weather observation roles.

The Maritime Monitor 200T is equipped with advanced surveillance and monitoring systems. It is intended for use as an offshore patrol and search and rescue aircraft.

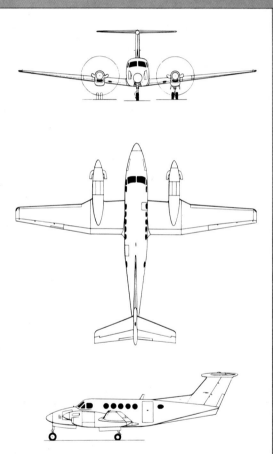

Super King Air 200

Type: passenger or executive light transport
Maker: Beech Aircraft Corporation
Span: 16.61 m (54 ft 6 in)
Length: 13.34 m (43 ft 9 in)
Height: 4.57 m (15 ft)
Wing area: 28.15 m² (303 sq ft)
Weight: maximum 5670 kg (12 500 lb); empty 3373 kg (7437 lb)
Powerplant: two 850-shp Pratt & Whitney of Canada PT6A-41 turboprops
Performance: maximum speed 536 km/h (333 mph) at 4570 m (15 000 ft); range 2752 km (1710 miles)
Payload: seats for up to 13 passengers
Crew: 1 to 2
Production: 527 ordered by 1979 (433 by commercial and private operators and 94 military C-12s)

Top: The Super King Air in service in the UK
Below: A US-registered machine. The Super King Air has proved not only to be a very popular executive transport, but has also been used by government and military organizations throughout the world

AL.60 Conestoga, Aermacchi/Lockheed

FIRST FLIGHT 1959

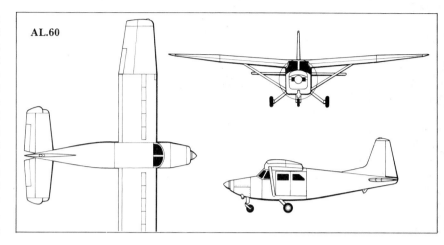

AL.60

DURING the late 1950s the Lockheed Georgia Company, Marietta, Georgia made a rare venture into the general aviation market with a design for a four to six-seat light utility transport aircraft aimed specifically at South American operators. The one and only American-built prototype Lockheed AL.60 made its maiden flight on September 15, 1959. It was a boxy, robust, all-metal high-wing monoplane with a wide square cabin which could quickly be changed from passenger to all-cargo configuration, and tricycle landing gear which could be replaced with skis or floats for bush flying. The standard seating arrangement is for four to six passengers but these can be replaced by seats without backrests for use by parachutists. The ambulance version could carry two stretchers, one seated patient and one attendant.

It was never Lockheed's intention to manufacture the aircraft in the United States. Instead a subsidiary company – Lockheed/Azcarate SA – was established in Mexico. This plant produced only 18 LASA 60s before all manufacturing and sales rights were sold to Aeronautica Macchi.

The first Italian-built LASA 60 was flown on April 19, 1961, and was subsequently developed and produced in several models which included the AL.60B1 with a 250-hp Continental IO-470-R engine, the B2 variant with a 260-hp supercharged Continental TSIO-470-B powerplant, and the C4 with a conventional tailwheel undercarriage replacing the standard tricycle landing gear. A 340-hp Piaggio-built Lycoming-engined version known as the AL.60C was developed to meet an Italian

army requirement for a liaison/utility transport. The final civil versions of the Aermacchi aircraft were the 400-hp AL.60F5 Conestoga, and a tailwheel version of the same aircraft for Canadian operators. Some 100 examples of all models were built in Italy before production terminated in 1972.

The basic AL.60C5 design, with a 340-hp engine, has been produced by the Atlas Corporation in South Africa as the Atlas C4M Kudu which first flew in 1974 and serves with units of the South African air force. A three/four-seat forward air-control aircraft known as the Aermacchi AM-3C was also developed from the basic AL.60 airframe, though modified substantially, and is serving with the air forces of Rwanda and South Africa, under the name of Bosbok.

AL.60F5

Type: utility transport aircraft
Maker: Aeronautica Macchi; Lockheed Georgia Co
Span: 11.99 m (39 ft 4 in)
Length: 8.8 m (28 ft 10½ in)
Height: 3.2 m (10 ft 6 in)
Wing area: 19.55 m² (210.4 sq ft)
Weight: maximum 2041 kg (4500 lb); empty 1043 kg (2300 lb)
Powerplant: one 400-hp Avco Lycoming IO-720-A1A piston engine
Performance: maximum speed 254 km/h (158 mph); range 1037 km (645 miles)
Payload: 653 kg (1440 lb); seats for 6 passengers
Crew: 1
Production: minimum 100

Left: An AL.60 of the German firm Aero Photo; the type has been produced in Mexico, Italy and South Africa. It was designed by Lockheed in partnership with Aermacchi for South American operators and can carry four to six passengers or cargo

MU-2, Mitsubishi

FIRST FLIGHT 1963

THE MU-2 turboprop business aircraft was the first original postwar design by the famous wartime manufacturer of the Japanese Zero fighter. The Mitsubishi company began design studies for the MU-2 in September 1959. The construction of a prototype began in 1962 and this aircraft, powered by French-built Turboméca Astazou turboprop engines, made its first flight on September 14, 1963. Two further Astazou-engined MU-2A prototypes were flown before the decision was taken to switch to American-built Garrett-AiResearch TPE331 engines, and the first such MU-2B prototype flew on March 11, 1965.

The early models all had accommodation for up to seven passengers with a two-man crew and, although designed with military applications in mind, the aircraft was marketed principally among business operators, although the Japanese Self Defence Forces use MU-2s in liaison and search-and-rescue roles. The aircraft is of unusual configuration, having a short stubby fuselage into which the main undercarriage retracts and a high, tip-tanked wing which employs spoilers rather than conventional ailerons for roll control. Thirty-four MU-2Bs were built, mostly for American customers who were attracted by its high cruising speeds and its ability to operate happily from short, rough airfields – a rare attribute in sophisticated business aircraft. The basic short-bodied MU-2 airframe has been successively developed through MU-2C, D, F, K, M and P models incorporating engineering and systems improvements, increased fuel tankage, higher gross weights and uprated Garrett engines. One baggage compartment in the MU-2F is situated over the main wheel bays with a capacity of 100 kg (220 lb). The other baggage compartment is situated aft of the main wheel bays and has a capacity of 70 kg (154 lb). There is also additional space allocated for hand luggage at the rear of the cabin.

From the beginning of production the aircraft have been manufactured in Japan and shipped to the United States where Mitsubishi Aircraft International (formerly Mooney Aircraft Inc) assemble and complete them at a San Angelo, Texas, factory.

On January 10, 1969 a stretched version, the MU-2G, was flown for the first time. It is distinguished from the short-body models by an additional 1.9 m (6 ft 3 in) of fuselage length and external bulged fuselage fairings to enclose the main undercarriage legs. Depending on internal layout, up to 12 passengers can be carried in this version, which has also been refined through MU-2J, L, and N models. The MU-2N has a cruising speed of 480 km/h (298 mph).

Total production of MU-2s exceeds 500 aircraft of all models. Responding to comments on cabin noise levels, Mitsubishi installed slow-turning four-bladed propellers on the latest MU-2N (long-body) and MU-2P (short body) models, which are now named Marquise and Solitaire. The 6 to 9-seat Marquise cruises at 571 km/h (355 mph), has a range of 2584 km (1606 miles) and can operate out of 660-m (2165-ft) airstrips, while the smaller Solitaire cruises at 576 km/h (358 mph) over 2945 km (1830 miles) and can operate from fields as short as 550 m (1800 ft).

Right: A privately-owned US MU-2. The type is popular in the US because of its ability to operate from short rough airfields – a rare characteristic in business aircraft
Below right: A Mitsubishi MU-2F of the Scandinavian operator Swedair. Though the company is a civilian operator, it includes in its activities target-towing and ground services such as aircraft maintenance and airport operation. It has eight MU-2Fs, all of which are ex-American aircraft

MU-2J

1. Nose cone
2. Hinged nose doors (left and right)
3. Hinged landing and taxi lamps (left and right)
4. Nosewheel doors
5. Forward-retracting twin nosewheels
6. Nosewheel leg
7. Landing-gear access panel
8. Forward electronics compartment
9. Forward battery
10. Bulkhead
11. Control column
12. Rudder pedals
13. Windshield wiper
14. Instrument console shroud
15. Windshield de-icing installation
16. Two-piece curved windshield
17. Control yoke
18. Second pilot's seat
19. First pilot's seat
20. Seat adjustment mechanism
21. Circuit breaker panel
22. Floor support structure
23. Main undercarriage fairing
24. Underfloor control runs
25. Main passenger cabin floor
26. Three-a-side cabin windows
27. Strengthened anti-ice panel
28. Frame and longeron fuselage construction
29. Fuselage skinning
30. Aerial mast
31. Wingroot fairings
32. Leading-edge relay panel
33. Fuselage/front spar attachment points
34. Emergency escape window (right-hand rear)
35. Wing carry-through surface
36. Centre-section fuel tank
37. No 1 right-hand fuel tank
38. Fuel lines
39. Garrett-AiResearch TPE331-6-251M turboprop
40. Intake
41. Airscrew spinner
42. Three-blade Hartzell propeller
43. Pneumatic leading-edge de-icer
44. Leading-edge ribs
45. No 2 right-hand fuel tank

46. Auxiliary tip tank
47. Tip tank fin
48. Spoilers (extended)
49. Trim aileron section
50. Flap track fairing
51. Aerial
52. Inner section double-slotted flap
53. Centre-section anti-collision beacon
54. Spoiler mechanism
55. Fuselage/rear spar attachment points
56. Flap actuator mechanism
57. Wingroot fillet
58. Cabin entry door
59. Air-conditioning ducts
60. Dorsal fillet
61. Pneumatic fin leading-edge de-icer
62. Aerial (to right-hand tailplane)
63. Fin main spar
64. Rudder tab mechanism
65. Antenna
66. Anti-collision beacon
67. Static-dischargers
68. Rudder hinge fairing
69. Rudder construction
70. Rudder tab control
71. Rudder post main beam
72. Rudder tab
73. Tail cone
74. Rear navigation light
75. Elevator tab
76. Tab mechanism
77. Left elevator
78. Tailplane construction
79. Pneumatic leading-edge de-icer
80. Tailplane fillet
81. Control runs
82. Ventral strake (left and right)
83. Electronics access panel
84. Air-conditioning and pressurization installation

85. Aft electronics compartment (main junction box and batteries)
86. Aft cabin coat closet space
87. Door handle
88. Door hinges
89. Fuel dump line (left and right)
90. Undercarriage retraction mechanism
91. Mainwheel door
92. Mainwheel leg
93. Axle
94. Left mainwheel
95. Wing ribs
96. Outer-section flap profile
97. Left auxiliary tip tank
98. Wingtip lights (navigation and strobe)
99. Tip tank fin
100. Tip tank strake

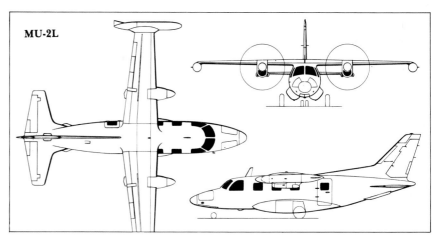

MU-2L

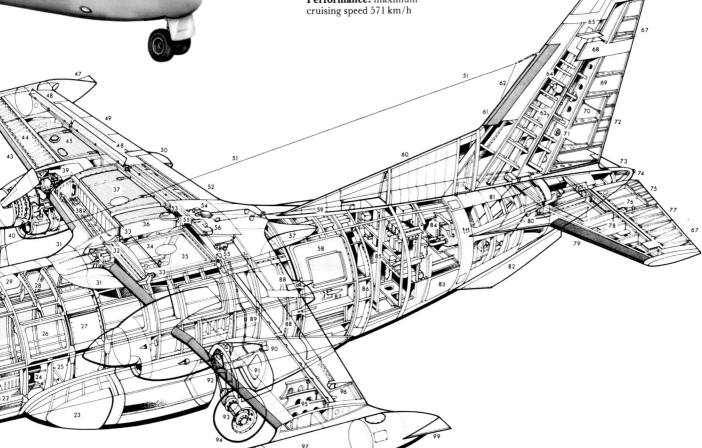

MU-2N Marquise

Type: business and corporate transport
Maker: Mitsubishi Aircraft International Inc
Span: 11.94 m (39 ft 2 in)
Length: 12.02 m (39 ft 5 in)
Height: 4.17 m (13 ft 8 in)
Wing area: 16.55 m² (178 sq ft)
Weight: maximum 5250 kg (11 575 lb); empty 3470 kg (7650 lb)
Powerplant: two 715-shp Garrett-AiResearch TPE331-10-501M turboprops
Performance: maximum cruising speed 571 km/h

(355 mph); range with 45 min IFR reserves 2584 km (1606 miles)
Payload: seats for up to 9 passengers
Crew: 2
Production: 570 ordered by March 1979 (of all types)

HFB 320 Hansa, MBB

FIRST FLIGHT 1964

IN 1961 the wartime Blohm und Voss company of Hamburg's aviation subsidiary Hamburger Flugzeugbau GmbH, began design studies on their first postwar aircraft project – a twin-jet light transport aircraft designated HFB 320. Heading the design team was Ing Richard Vogt who had been responsible for the wartime Junkers Ju 287 jet bomber project. His design for the HFB 320 was reminiscent of the Ju 287, having the same distinctive sharply forward-swept wings.

The first HFB 320 Hansa Jet made its maiden flight on April 21, 1964. Certification trials of three pre-production prototypes were conducted in Spain where the climate could guarantee uninterrupted testing, and it was during this time that the first aircraft was lost in a crash during spin testing.

The aircraft was certificated in 1967 and customer deliveries began in September of that year. Despite its bizarre appearance in a conservative market, the HFB 320 won prestigious orders, not least from the Rijksluchtvaartschool (Dutch national pilot training school) at Eelde in Holland, and from the Luftwaffe, with whom Hansas serve in VIP-transport, navigation training and experimental roles.

The Hansa Jet was one of the most unusual general aviation aircraft to reach production, principally because of its extraordinary wing arrangement, so designed to keep the main cabin area ahead of the wing roots and thus free of carry-through structure.

The passenger version could accommodate up to 12 seats with a flight crew of two. There is also a freighter version with a maximum payload of 1814 kg (4000 lb) and both versions have quick-change facilities for conversion from one form to the other.

The first 15 aircraft manufactured by Hamburger Flugzeugbau (now part of Messerschmitt-Bölkow-Blohm) were powered by General Electric CJ610-1 turbojets; later models had -5 and -9 variants of this engine. In all, 54 Hansa Jets were manufactured; apart from the Luftwaffe and Dutch orders much of the production went to United States operators as business aircraft.

In late 1977, the German Federal Defence Technology and Procurement Office ordered four Hansa Jet ECMs. The first of these (D-CANO) flew for the first time on August 22, 1979.

HFB 320 Hansa

Type: business and corporate transport
Maker: Hamburger Flugzeugbau GmbH division of Messerschmitt-Bölkow-Blohm
Span: 14.49 m (47 ft 6 in)
Length: 16.61 m (54 ft 6 in)
Height: 4.9 m (16 ft 1 in)
Wing area: 30.1 m² (324 sq ft)
Weight: maximum 9199 kg (20 280 lb); empty 5425 kg (11 960 lb)
Powerplant: two 1406-kg (3100-lb) st General Electric CJ610-9 turbojets
Performance: maximum cruising speed 825 km/h (513 mph); range 2526 km (1570 miles) with IFR reserves
Payload: 1814 kg (4000 lb); seats for up to 12 passengers
Crew: 2
Production: 54

Top and below: The HFB 320 with its distinctive, sharply swept-forward, wings. This feature was previously seen only on the wartime Junkers Ju 287 bomber. The design keeps the main fuselage free of spars and wing root bracing, to give a long unobstructed cabin

Skyvan, Shorts
FIRST FLIGHT 1963

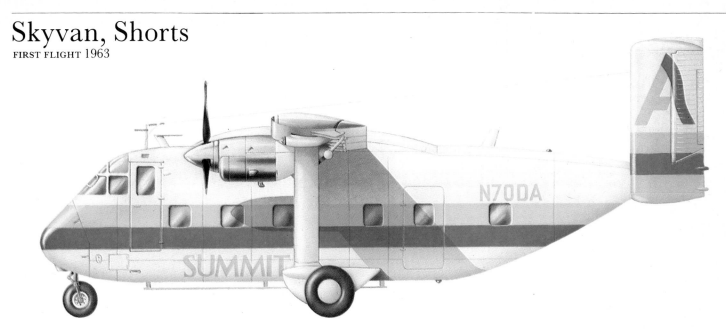

THE Skyvan project was based on F G Miles' experience with the HDM.105, an Aerovan IV fitted experimentally with an all-metal high-aspect-ratio Hurel Dubois wing of 23 m (75 ft 4 in) span. Shorts acquired the design and trials data but did not pursue the project.

However, Shorts did recognize the concept of a flying boxcar and designed a utility aircraft to carry 15 passengers or 1360 kg (3000 lb) of freight, powered by two 390-hp Continental GS10-520 turbo-supercharged piston engines. The cross-section of the fuselage interior was 1.98 m (6 ft 6 in) square and 5 m (16 ft 6 in) long, and its large rear loading door could be opened in flight. The first flight was in January 1963, but very soon the engines were replaced by two 520-ehp Turboméca Astazou II turboprops, this version first flying in October 1963. Eighteen months later saw the fitting of more powerful Astazou Xs.

The introduction of the Mk 2 led to a number of changes: 730-ehp Astazou XIIs (to be replaced in the Mk 3 by Garrett-AiResearch TPE331s), more streamlined nose, single nosewheel, and larger, square cabin windows. From the ninth Mk 2 fuel capacity was increased from 795 to 1022 litres (175 to 225 Imp gal) and cabin length extended to 5.6 m (18 ft 7 in).

The Mk 3 flew in late 1967, having further increased fuel capacity, a reduced empty weight, and other detail changes. Twenty-two passengers could be accommodated (or up to 12 stretcher cases with two attendants), or 2086 kg (4600 lb) freight, including a small vehicle. A QC (quick change) version was developed to take up to 2000 kg (4400 lb) freight on four pallets, while lightweight passengers' seats fold against the cabin sidewall. Examples of the Mk 3 are in service as airborne workshops, survey aircraft, executive transports and in oil rig-related operations. A luxury version known as the Shorts Skyliner has been developed for commuter operators by third-level airlines, featuring 22 seats in a new interior which has individual passenger-service panels and a washroom. Weather radar and area navigation systems are fitted and a new, quiet version is fitted with low-speed engines driving four-bladed propellers. A military variant – the Skyvan 3M – has accommodation for up to 22 troops or 16 paratroops, or a conveyor system for paratrooping supplies.

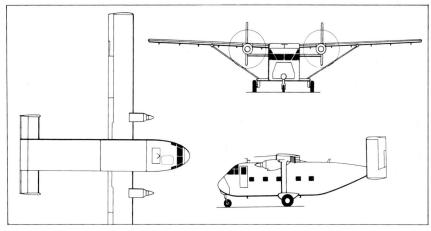

Skyvan Srs 3

Type: light civil or military STOL utility transport
Maker: Short Brothers Ltd
Span: 19.79 m (64 ft 11 in)
Length: 12.21 m (40 ft 1 in)
Height: 4.6 m (15 ft 1 in)
Wing area: 34.65 m² (373 sq ft)
Weight: maximum 5670 kg (12 500 lb); empty 3331 kg (7344 lb)
Powerplant: two 715-hp Garrett-AiResearch TPE331-201 turboprops
Performance: maximum cruising speed 327 km/h (203 mph) at 3050 m (10 000 ft); range 1115 km (694 miles)
Payload: 2086 kg (4600 lb); seats for up to 19 passengers
Crew: 1 to 2
Production: minimum 100 by 1980

Top: A Short Skyvan of Summit Airlines. Summit operates seven Skyvans on all-cargo services in the eastern US
Above left: A Skyvan in the colours of Ansett-MAL during a demonstration flight before delivery in September 1966
Left: A Ferguson tractor in the hold of a Skyvan

An-14, Antonov

FIRST FLIGHT 1958

THE Antonov An-14 Pchelka (Little Bee) was originally designed to meet a requirement for a small utility aircraft for Aeroflot, the Soviet air transport organization. Although somewhat larger than the lighter, lower-powered Britten-Norman Islander, the An-14 has a much shorter range and accommodates fewer passengers. The specification called for higher-standard seating than the widely used An-2, but for a similar STOL (short take-off and landing) performance. The initial flight by the prototype took place on March 15, 1958, the first two aircraft being powered by 260-hp Ivchenko AI-14R radial engines. Development of the type saw the introduction of dihedral on the tailplane, while the leading edge of each tailfin was modified to provide greater surface area from new rectangular fins. Two 300-hp AI-14RF nine-cylinder radials were substituted for the original powerplants, thus allowing the payload to be increased by one passenger. Performance was still not satisfactory, however, and the wing was subsequently redesigned with a span increased from just under 19.8 m (65 ft) to more than 22 m (72 ft). The original parallel chord was modified to produce a tapered section outboard of each engine. Full-span leading-edge slats and double-slotted flaps are now featured, and the fuselage has also been modified. All these changes delayed the type's entry into service, which did not occur until 1965.

The first production examples were delivered to Aeroflot as Antonov An-14As, identified in the West by the NATO codename Clod. Like the earlier An-2, the Little Bee was intended for several uses: cargo carrier, air ambulance (carrying six stretcher units and a medical attendant), aerial photography and geological surveying. The agricultural variant has a 1000-litre (220-Imp gal) chemical tank within the fuselage, and spraying bars fitted beneath the wings and along each bracing strut; skis and floats may also be fitted. Passengers enter the cabin through a pair of clamshell doors which form the underside of the upswept rear fuselage. A military version was first revealed at the Domodedovo Air Show in July 1967. This version serves with the Soviet air force, and the armed forces of Bulgaria, the German Democratic Republic and Guinea. Production of the An-14 has been centred at the Progress Plant at Arsenyev which is situated in the far east of the Soviet Union.

An-14

Type: light general-purpose aircraft
Maker: Antonov Design Bureau
Span: 21.99 m (72 ft 2 in)
Length: 11.44 m (37 ft 6½ in)
Height: 4.63 m (15 ft 2½ in)
Wing area: 39.72 m² (427.5 sq ft)
Weight: maximum 3600 kg (7935 lb); empty 2000 kg (4409 lb)
Powerplant: two Ivchenko AI-14RF 9-cylinder air-cooled radial engines
Performance: maximum speed 222 km/h (138 mph) at 1000 m (3280 ft); range 800 km (497 miles)
Payload: 720 kg (1590 lb); seats for up to 8 passengers
Crew: 1
Production: minimum 300

Top: An Antonov An-14. Though it is in Aeroflot livery, there are military-style markings on the tail
Below: The An-14 is known as the Pchelka (Little Bee). Passengers enter through clamshell doors in the rear and the high tailplane allows quick loading – essential in the ambulance version

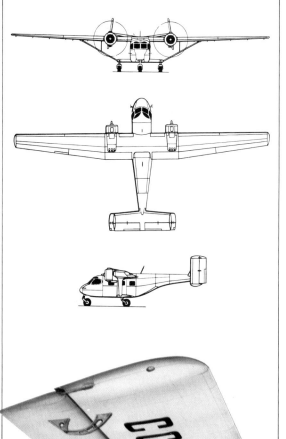

CL-215, Canadair

FIRST FLIGHT 1967

THE Canadair CL-215 is almost unique in having been designed to do a job which traditionally was only done by aged examples of older military and civil types, specially adopted and modified for the role.

The primary duty of the CL-215 is that of aerial fireman. Canadair designed this twin-engined amphibian from the outset for simplicity of operation and maintenance; it can operate from very small airstrips, from lakes, open bays, and can also be adapted for other roles. First flight was made in October 1967, with the first take-off from water occurring on May 2, 1968.

The governments of France, Canada, Spain and Greece all operate the aircraft in the fire-fighting role. Three different methods of fighting grass, bush or forest fire are offered by the CL-215: plain water lifted from any 1.2-km (¾-mile) stretch of water, or short-term fire retardants mixed with water during the scooping operation, or a load of long-term retardant, pre-mixed and loaded on the ground at a land base. A maximum load of 5455 litres (1200 Imp gal) may be carried, and the two tanks (in the fuselage) can be filled in 90 sec or, while skimming the water at 111 km/h (69 mph), in 16 to 20 sec. The original scooping system was improved to reduce this time to ten sec. Wave heights of up to 2 m (6 ft) have been successfully overcome in French operations in the Mediterranean, and on many occasions CL-215s have performed more than 100 pickups in a single day's fire-fighting. This amounts to a total lift in excess of 550 000 litres (120 000 Imp gal) of water.

A system for onboard mixing of long-term retardants has been developed, which can produce 21 000 litres (4600 Imp gal) in one flight. Tests have shown that a foam mixture can be used to fight oil fires, while in Canada, the province of Quebec converted a number of aircraft, in a huge campaign begun in 1973, for use as crop-sprayers in an effort to protect large areas of woodland and forest against the budworm.

In other operations the CL-215 can accommodate 15 passengers, (19 if header tanks are removed) or nine stretchers in the casualty evacuation role. As a search-and-rescue aircraft the CL-215 has stations for navigator, flight-engineer and two observers, with room for four seats or six stretchers as well.

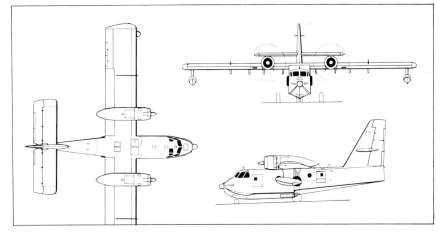

CL-215

Type: multi-role amphibian
Maker: Canadair Ltd
Span: 28.6 m (93 ft 10 in)
Length: 19.82 m (65 ft 0½ in)
Height: 8.92 m (29 ft 3 in)
Wing area: 100.33 m² (1080 sq ft)
Weight: maximum 19 731 kg (43 500 lb); empty 12 065 kg (26 600 lb)
Powerplant: two 2100-hp Pratt & Whitney R-2800-83AM2AH 18-cylinder radial engines
Performance: maximum cruising speed 291 km/h (181 mph) at 3050 m (10 000 ft); range with 1587 kg (3500 lb) payload 1853 km (1151 miles)
Payload: 2805 kg (6185 lb) as utility aircraft and 5443 kg (12 000 lb) as water bomber; seats for up to 19 passengers
Crew: 2
Production: 80 by 1980

Top: A French Canadair CL-215; the type has proved highly successful fighting fires in Southern France, where some aircraft have made more than 100 water pickups in one day's work
Left: A Canadian CL-215 dumps its 5443-kg (12 000-lb) payload over a forest fire

Westwind, IAI

FIRST FLIGHT 1963

Left: A Canadian-registered Jet Commander which was the basis for the Westwind Below: The Westwind II showing its wingtip tanks with their characteristic Whitcomb winglets which improve cruise performance. The Westwind has been widely sold as both a maritime-surveillance aircraft and business jet

ISRAEL Aircraft Industries' Westwind business jet may be traced back to the American Aero Commander Model 1121 Jet Commander which was designed by Ted Smith and first flew in January 1963. When Aero Commander merged with North American Rockwell they were obliged to sell off the Jet Commander to avoid conflict with US antitrust laws (the parent company was already marketing the Sabreliner business jet).

Israel Aircraft Industries bought the entire Jet Commander programme and all production tooling and sales rights, and after refining the design returned it to the market as the 1123 Commodore Jet, later renamed the 1123 Westwind. The Westwind had a lengthened fuselage, more powerful engines and tiptanks. The longer fuselage could accommodate up to ten passengers. The first Israel-built Westwind 1123 flew on September 28, 1970 and 36 had been delivered when production ceased in mid 1976 in favour of the Model 1124 which was re-engined with fuel-efficient Garrett-AiResearch TFE731 turbofans in place of the pure turbojets used in all previous models.

The first Model 1124 Westwind flew on July 21, 1975 since when production of the aircraft, known as Westwind I, has been running at three to four per month to meet heavy demand from United States business operators. The pressurized cabin can accommodate up to ten passengers with a flight crew of two. The interior arrangement can be altered to suit customer requirements. The cabin is heated, ventilated and air-conditioned. More than 90 have been delivered.

Three Model 1123 Westwinds were modified for maritime surveillance roles for the Israeli navy in 1977 and a maritime aircraft called the Westwind Sea Scan is today based on the 1124 airframe. It incorporates Litton LASR-2 search radar in a bulbous nose radome, Global Navigation's NS-500A VLF navigation system, forward-looking infrared scanner systems, low-light-level television cameras and monitors, magnetometers and sonobuoys, depth chargers or emergency-rescue equipment.

A further civil version called Westwind II is currently under development in Israel featuring drag-reducing Whitcomb winglets mounted atop the aircraft's tiptanks, which are expected to improve cruise performance by some 70 km/h (43 mph) and range by 560 km (348 miles).

Westwind II

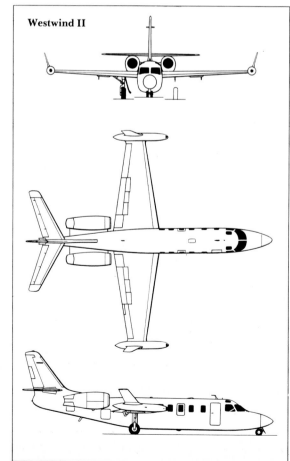

Westwind I

Type: business and corporate transport
Maker: Israel Aircraft Industries
Span: 13.65 m (44 ft 9½ in)
Length: 15.93 m (52 ft 3 in)
Height: 4.81 m (15 ft 9½ in)
Wing area: 28.64 m² (308 sq ft)
Weight: maximum 10 659 kg (23 500 lb); empty 5578 kg (12 300 lb)
Powerplant: two 1680-kg (3700-lb) st Garrett-AiResearch TFE731-3-1G turbofans
Performance: maximum speed 872 km/h (542 mph) at 5800 m (19 000 ft); range 4619 km (2870 miles)
Payload: seats for up to 10 passengers
Crew: 2
Production: minimum 170 by 1981

Gulfstream II,

FIRST FLIGHT 1966

DESPITE the fact that it shares a common name with its turboprop predecessor, the Grumman Gulfstream II was a completely new design launched in May 1965. Of similar size to the Gulfstream I, with seating for ten in a typical executive interior and up to 19 in high-density layouts, the Gulfstream II was planned as an up-market business jet offering the performance and range of (and greater comfort than) intercontinental airline jet transports.

Unusually, no prototype was built, the first aircraft, which flew on October 2, 1966 from Grumman's Bethpage, Long Island, factory, having been manufactured from production tooling. It was certificated by the US Federal Aviation Administration on October 19, 1967 and the first customer deliveries began that December. With the Gulfstream II, non-stop transcontinental and intercontinental flights became possible, and significantly about 97% of all G-IIs have been sold to major international companies.

The first 82 Gulfstream IIs built had a lower gross weight (26 080 kg [57 500 lb]) than current models, and after 166 had been built the Rolls-Royce Spey turbofan engines were fitted with acoustic hush-kits to meet more stringent environmental regulations. In 1975 Grumman began a protracted test and certification programme for the installation of wingtip tanks which increased fuel capacity by 1415 kg (3120 lb) and improved the range by 14%.

In 1977 Grumman announced plans for a stretched Gulfstream III which would incorporate

Gulfstream III

a number of aerodynamic improvements including an entirely new wing of supercritical airfoil. Forty customer deposits were received when, six months later, Grumman announced that the project had been cancelled as too expensive to develop. However, following the acquisition of production rights and tooling by the Gulfstream American Corporation, the Gulfstream III has been revived. The fuselage has been stretched and although an entirely new wing has not been developed, the existing surface has been greatly modified and incorporates drag-reducing Whitcomb winglets at the tips. The first Gulfstream III flew on December 2, 1979 and during 1980 this aircraft will replace the Gulfstream II on the Savannah, Georgia, production line. Forty aircraft had been sold by 1980.

Gulfstream II
Type: business and corporate transport
Maker: Gulfstream American Corporation
Span: 21.87 m (71 ft 9 in) with tiptanks
Length: 24.36 m (79 ft 11 in)
Height: 7.47 m (24 ft 6 in)
Wing area: 75.2 m² (810 sq ft)
Weight: maximum 29 711 kg (65 500 lb); empty 16 867 kg (37 186 lb)
Powerplant: two 5175-kg (11 400-lb) st Rolls-Royce Spey Mk 511-8 turbofans
Performance: maximum cruising speed 936 km/h (581 mph) at 7620 m (25 000 ft); range with reserves and tiptanks 6880 km (4275 miles)
Payload: seats for up to 19 passengers
Crew: 2
Production: 256 (II only)

Top left: The Rolls-Royce Spey turbofans of the Gulfstream II. Aircraft after number 166 have been fitted with acoustic hush-kits to conform with noise regulations to be introduced in the mid 1980s
Above: The Gulfstream II was designed to give the performance of intercontinental airline jets but with the comfort of an executive interior

Bandeirante, Embraer

FIRST FLIGHT 1968

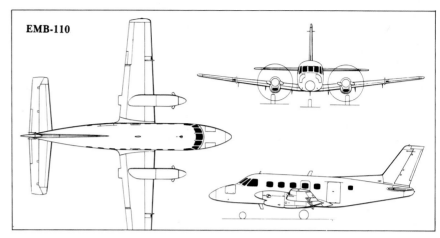

EMB-110

EMBRAER, formed to promote the development of the Brazilian aircraft industry, came into being in late 1969, but the Bandeirante (Pioneer) had been conceived before then. The Brazilian Ministry of Aeronautics' specification had called for a general-purpose twin-turboprop light transport capable of carrying out missions such as navigation training, general transport and aeromedical evacuation.

There are nine versions of the Bandeirante, with two fuselage lengths and two engine sizes. The standard 15-passenger commercial transport version is the EMB-110C, operated by Transbrasil, the Chilean navy and Uruguayan air force. The EMB-110B is a special version operated by the Brazilian air force for aerial photography with an electrically-operated ventral sliding door, Doppler navigation system and crew of three equipment operators.

The executive transport version is the EMB-110E(J), with accommodation for seven passengers, four in individual seats and three on a sideways-facing sofa. Other luxuries include a galley, wardrobe, and stereo radio and tape-deck facilities. The EMB-110K1 is an all-cargo version, lengthened by a 0.85-m (2 ft 9½-in) plug between the flight-deck and centre fuselage. This is available as a quick-change version for passenger or cargo work and is designated EMB-110P1. Twenty of the cargo version are in service with the Brazilian air force under the designation C-95.

The EMB-110P is a commercial third-level commuter version for 18 passengers. A further passenger development of the long-fuselage Bandeirante is the EMB-110P2, which carries up to 21 passengers. It is powered by two 750-shp Pratt & Whitney Aircraft of Canada PT6A-34 turboprop engines and is fitted with four integral fuel tanks in the wings. These are in service by, or destined for, Air Littoral, Talair (Niugini), Masling Commuter Air Services (Australia), Air Wales, Brittany Air International, Fairflight Charters and Air Sudan.

Other Bandeirantes are the EMB-110S1 for geophysical survey work, and the EMB-111 maritime patrol version, which first flew on August 15, 1977. It is in service with the Brazilian air force and the Chilean navy. Those supplied to the Chilean navy are equipped with a full de-icing system and passive ECM antennae.

EMB-110P2

Type: general-purpose transport
Maker: Empresa Brasileira de Aeronáutica
Span: 15.32 m (50 ft 3¼ in)
Length: 15.1 m (49 ft 6½ in)
Height: 4.92 m (16 ft 1¾ in)
Wing area: 29.1 m² (313.23 sq ft)
Weight: maximum 5670 kg (12 500 lb); empty 3516 kg (7751 lb)
Powerplant: two 750-hp Pratt & Whitney PT6A-34 turboprops
Performance: maximum speed 460 km/h (286 mph) at 2440 m (8000 ft); range 1900 km (1180 miles)
Payload: 1681 kg (3706 lb); seats for up to 21 passengers
Crew: 2
Production: 270 (all versions) by early 1980

Left: The Bandeirante (Pioneer) with Brazilian registration and Mountain West livery. This is a popular third-level airline machine which comes in two lengths and with two sizes of engine. Like many general aviation aircraft it is also used by the armed forces of some smaller nations

Arava, IAI

FIRST FLIGHT 1969

DESIGN work on a light STOL (short take-off and landing) civil and military transport aircraft began at Israel Aircraft Industries in 1966. The aircraft was to have full rough-field performance capabilities, and for ease of loading a twin-boom layout with rear cargo doors was chosen. The first prototype IAI 101 Arava flew for the first time on November 27, 1969; a second aircraft followed on May 8, 1971 and the production civil version, IAI 101, was type certificated in April 1972.

A military derivative designated IAI 201 flew in prototype form on March 7, 1972. The commercial Arava can carry up to 20 passengers, while the IAI 201 can accommodate 24 fully equipped military personnel, or 17 paratroops, or 12 stretcher cases together with two medical attendants. The rear fuselage swings open to make loading easier. The military Arava can be armed with two side-mounted rocket pods which contain seven 68-mm (2.67-in) rockets each and a forward firing 12.7-mm (0.50-in) Browning machine-gun either side of the fuselage in addition to a rear-firing machine-gun.

Three Aravas were leased to the Israeli air force for operational trials during the Yom Kippur war, but principal customer interest has come from Third World air forces. Aravas are currently in service with the air arms of Bolivia, Ecuador, Guatemala, Honduras, Mexico, Nicaragua, and El Salvador, in addition to the Israeli air force which has taken 14 of the 60-plus Aravas built for liaison duties.

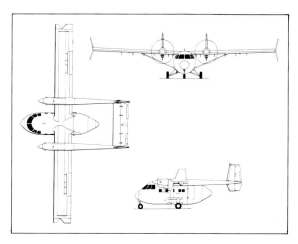

The latest development of the Arava is the IAI-202, distinguished from previous models by its increased length, the drag-reducing Whitcomb winglets which were mounted at the wingtips and a boundary layer fence just inboard of each tip. This modification is available as a retrofit on other Arava aircraft. It is powered by a pair of 750-shp Pratt & Whitney Aircraft of Canada PT6A-36 turboprops and fuel is accommodated in two integral tanks in each wing with optional cabin-mounted fuel tanks.

The interior accommodation can be adapted to suit the intended specialist role of the aircraft. The tail unit is a cantilever light alloy structure with twin fins and rudders attached to twin booms which extend aft from the engine nacelles.

IAI 201 Arava

Type: STOL utility aircraft
Maker: Israel Aircraft Industries
Span: 20.96 m (68 ft 9 in)
Length: 13.03 m (42 ft 9 in)
Height: 5.21 m (17 ft 1 in)
Wing area: 43.68 m² (470 sq ft)
Weight: maximum 6803 kg (15 000 lb); empty 3998 kg (8816 lb)
Powerplant: two 750-shp Pratt & Whitney of Canada PT6A-34 turboprops
Performance: maximum speed 326 km/h (203 mph) at 3048 m (10 000 ft); range with maximum fuel and 45 min reserves 1306 km (812 miles)
Payload: 2351 kg (5184 lb); seats for up to 24 passengers
Crew: 1 to 2
Production: 129 by 1980

Below: The IAI Arava 202 which is recognizable by its Whitcomb winglets and boundary-layer fence inboard of each tip. Military types carry a variety of loads including paratroops, cargo and even external weapons pods

Pawnee, Piper

FIRST FLIGHT 1959

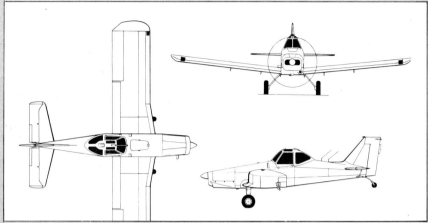

THE PA-25 Pawnee agricultural aircraft was designed for Piper Aircraft Corporation in the late 1950s by consultant designer engineer Fred Weick, who had previously designed the Erco 415 Ercoupe light plane, and the Transland agricultural aircraft at Texas A & M University. Weick's intention was to produce an aircraft which would dramatically reduce pilot fatalities from the low-speed crashes which are common in crop-dusting operations. He designed a hump-backed fuselage in which the pilot sat high up, giving good all-round vision and providing a deep under-cockpit floor to absorb vertical impact. The forward structure was designed to collapse progressively while the cockpit layout was designed so as to minimize injury in a crash and not collapse if the aircraft turned over. The Pawnee's wings came from the Piper Super Cub and were braced by overhead struts. When the Pawnee entered production at Lock Haven, Pennsylvania in 1959, it revolutionized the agricultural aviation business, which hitherto had been served largely by converted military Stearman biplanes and Piper Cubs.

The first Pawnees were powered by 150-hp Lycoming O-320 engines, since replaced with a 235-hp Lycoming O-540-E engine. This model remains in production as the Pawnee D; a 260-hp variant with a payload of 544 kg (1200 lb) of chemicals and an optional second seat for mechanic/loader/trainee pilot is also available.

In 1972 a new Pawnee designated PA-36 and named Brave was introduced. It was an almost entirely different airframe, with metal skinning replacing the fabric covering of the earlier models, a new cantilever wing, new tail surfaces and a choice of 285-hp Continental Tiara or 375-hp Lycoming IO-720-D1CD engines. The Tiara-engined variant proved troublesome in operation and has since been dropped in favour of a conventional 300-hp Lycoming engine. From 1978 the Pawnee was called Brave 300 or 375.

Some 5000 Pawnees of all models have been built by Piper and under licence in Argentina. Among claims made by the manufacturer for the aircraft is the doubling of Ghana's cocoa crop, the creation of the first ever corn crop on the Florida peninsula by effective pest-suppression, and the saving of over $3½ billion in crop losses per year in the United States alone. The Pawnee has been exported to more than 90 countries worldwide.

PA-36 Brave 375

Type: single-seat agricultural aircraft
Maker: Piper Aircraft Corporation; Chincul SA, Argentina
Span: 11.82 m (38 ft 9 in)
Length: 8.38 m (27 ft 6 in)
Height: 2.29 m (7 ft 6 in)
Wing area: 20.96 m² (225.65 sq ft)
Weight: maximum 2177 kg (4800 lb); empty 1104 kg (2434 lb)
Powerplant: one 375-hp Avco Lycoming IO-720-D1CD 8-cylinder piston engine
Performance: maximum speed 257 km/h (160 mph); range with reserves 861 km (535 miles)
Payload: dry chemical spraying equipment, maximum capacity 862 kg (1900 lb)
Crew: 1
Production: minimum 5000 up to 1980

Above left: A haze of spray hangs behind a Piper Pawnee
Left: The simple cockpit with a minimum of instruments, which include an airspeed indicator, rev counter, compass and fuel gauge
Below: A Pawnee skims a crude landing strip

Thrush Commander, Ayres

FIRST FLIGHT 1968

THE Snow S-2A, designed by Leland Snow in 1958, was offered with 220-hp Continental (S-2A), 450-hp Pratt & Whitney (S-2B), and 600-hp Pratt & Whitney (S-2D) radials.

In 1965 Snow sold the manufacturing rights to Aero Commander Inc of Bethany, Oklahoma, who renamed it Ag Commander S-2D. Two years later when Aero Commander became part of North American Rockwell, the design was further developed with a fully-enclosed cockpit, electric flaps and an enlarged 1818-litre (400-Imp gal) chemical hopper and marketed as the S-2R Thrush Commander from a production line at Albany, Georgia.

The Thrush Commander proved popular with crop-dusting and spraying operators, and also for aerial seeding, fertilizing and even water-bombing. Its robust structure was carefully designed to absorb energy on impact and thus protect the pilot from serious injury in a crash, and the ease of access to its corrosion-proofed tubular fuselage structure via quick-release side panels greatly facilitated cleaning chemical deposits from the airframe.

In 1977 Rockwell International disposed of the Thrush Commander type certificate and all production facilities to Frederick Ayres of Ayres Corporation, who continued production at Albany while working on a number of improvements to the basic design. Among these was a trial installation of a 750-shp Pratt & Whitney of Canada PT6A turboprop engine which was aimed both at reducing operating costs and solving the increasingly difficult problem of obtaining spares for the radial piston engines powering all previous Snow/Commander/Thrush models. The PT6-powered Turbo Thrush (known in the business as the 'Hush Thrush' because of its quietness compared to the radials) is now in full production at Albany alongside the standard S-2R Thrush 600 and 800 which are offered with either Pratt & Whitney or Polish Pezetel 3S 600-hp powerplants or an 800-hp Wright Cyclone. The Turbo Thrush also incorporates a larger 2273-litre (500-Imp gal) chemical hopper, and for pilot comfort all current production models offer optional air conditioning and even stereo cassette decks. A two-seat Thrush has been developed to enable a mechanic/flagman to be ferried to working sites or to permit dual instruction for trainee Ag pilots. Parts of the cabin and the outer wings of the Thrush were used for the PZL M-18 Dromader.

Above: The Turbo Thrush, known as the 'Hush Thrush' because of its quiet engine, is powered by a Pratt & Whitney PT6A. The aircraft shown here is operated by AG Aviation (UK) Ltd
Left: The earlier radial-engined thrush: powerplants included 220-hp, 450-hp and 600-hp, but now it is becoming harder to find spares for these engines and the turboprop version is more popular

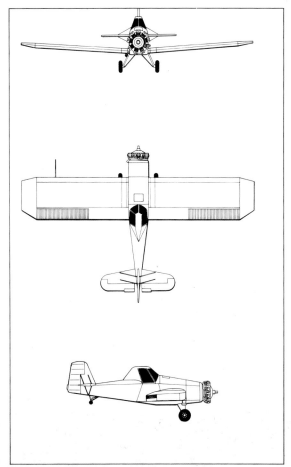

Thrush 600

Type: single-seat agricultural aircraft
Maker: Snow Aeronautical Corporation; Rockwell International; Ayres Corporation
Span: 13.51 m (44 ft 4 in)
Length: 8.95 m (29 ft 4½ in)
Height: 2.79 m (9 ft 2 in)
Wing area: 30.34 m² (327 sq ft)
Weight: maximum 3130 kg (6900 lb); empty 1678 kg (3700 lb)
Powerplant: one 600-hp Pratt & Whitney R-1340 Wasp 9-cylinder radial engine
Performance: maximum cruising speed 200 km/h (124 mph); range 648 km (403 miles)
Payload: chemical spraying equipment, capacity 1514 litres (333 Imp gal) or 1487 kg (3280 lb)
Crew: 1
Production: not available

Airtruk, Transavia

FIRST FLIGHT 1965

ONE of the world's strangest looking aircraft, the Transavia Airtruk was designed by Luigi Pellarini specifically to meet the special needs of agricultural operators in Australasia. He opted for a most unorthodox configuration, choosing to place the main fuselage containing the engine and chemical hoppers below the pilot's position, and to facilitate loading, mounted two separate fins and tailplane halves on twin booms with a wide gap between, so that a truck might be backed right up to the loading area. The tail units are mounted on twin cantilever tubular Alclad booms extending backwards from the upper wing. The smaller stub wings, situated below the fuselage, are braced to the cabin by a single strut and to the upper wings by a V strut on each side.

The first Airtruk flew on April 22, 1965, powered by a 300-hp Continental IO-520-D engine, and was put into production by Transavia at Bankstown, New South Wales, Australia, in 1966 as the Model PL-12. In December 1970 a utility passenger/cargo model designated PL-12U was first flown. This model is externally similar to the agricultural Airtruk, except for accommodation. By removing the central chemical hopper from the fuselage, space has been created for a single passenger sitting back-to-back with the pilot and four more passengers on the lower fuselage deck. It is powered by a 300-hp Rolls-Royce Continental IO-520-D flat-six engine which drives a McCauley D2A34C58/90AT-2 two-blade constant-speed metal propeller with spinner. The PL-12U is also available in cargo, air ambulance and aerial-survey layouts.

A 300-hp Lycoming IO-540-K1AS-engined version of the Airtruk has also been developed and is known as the Model T-300 Skyfarmer. In January 1976 the T-320 was certificated with a 325-hp Continental Tiara 6-320-2B engine in place of the standard Rolls-Royce-built Continental powerplant. The Tiara-engined Airtruk cruises some 32 km/h (20 mph) faster than the PL-12 model, and entered production in October 1976.

All models of the Airtruk are also assembled in New Zealand by Flight Engineers Limited from Transavia-manufactured components. Nearly 100 Airtruks of all models have been built, of which 18 are operating in Australia and 22 in New Zealand. The rest were exported to Denmark, India, Malaysia, East and South Africa and Thailand.

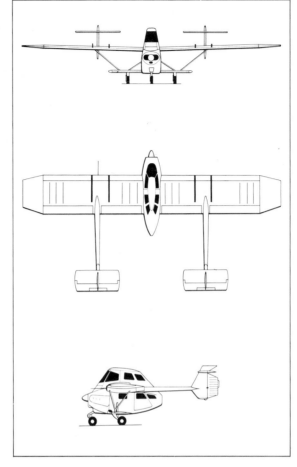

PL-12 Airtruk

Type: agricultural and utility aircraft
Maker: Transavia Corporation Pty Ltd; Flight Engineers Ltd
Span: 11.98 m (39 ft 3½ in)
Length: 6.35 m (20 ft 10 in)
Height: 2.79 m (9 ft 2 in)
Wing area: 23.8 m² (256 sq ft)
Weight: maximum 1855 kg (4090 lb); empty 839 kg (1850 lb)
Powerplant: one 300-hp Rolls-Royce Continental IO-520-D flat-six engine
Performance: maximum cruising speed 175 km/h (109 mph); range 531 km (330 miles)
Payload: seats for 2 passengers
Crew: 1
Production: minimum 100 (of all models by 1980)

Above: The experimental PL-7; the designer Luigi Pellarini developed the unusual tailplane to facilitate quick loading for chemical hoppers
Left: The PL-12 Airtruk; despite its looks, it has proved to be a popular and efficient aircraft and has been exported to Africa, the Far East and Denmark

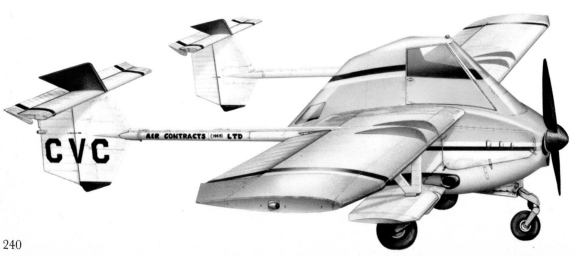

240

Air Tractor AT-301

FIRST FLIGHT 1973

Left: The prototype Air Tractor at Rio Hondo, Texas, in 1974. Leland Snow included overlapped sealed joints in the wings to prevent chemical seapage, and a sealed air-conditioned cockpit
Below: An Air Tractor at an aviation display at Harlingen, Texas, in October 1979

THE Air Tractor design dates from Texas crop-duster pilot and aeronautical engineer Leland Snow's 1958 Snow S-2A agplane. The latter series of aircraft became known as the Rockwell S-2R Thrush. Having disposed of the manufacturing rights to the Snow, the designer began work in January 1971 on a new aircraft designated Air Tractor AT-301. Construction of the prototype began in August 1972, first flight was from Olney, Texas in September 1973, and it was certificated by the US FAA within two months.

Like its predecessor the Air Tractor is a single-engine low-wing agricultural aircraft. The fuselage is constructed of welded steel tube and covered with quick-release skinning to provide easy access to the internal structure for maintenance and cleaning. The metal wing skins are sealed at joints and overlap to prevent chemical seepage, and the single-place cockpit is sealed and air-conditioned against noxious fumes. Chemicals are carried in a 1211-litre (266-Imp gal) glassfibre hopper forward of the raised cockpit area. The AT-301 is powered by one 600-hp Pratt & Whitney R-1340 air-cooled radial piston engine, which drives a Hamilton Standard two-blade metal constant-speed propeller type 12D40. Fuel is carried in two integral wing tanks which have a combined capacity of 288 litres (63.4 Imp gal). Some 200 Air Tractor AT-301s have been ordered and production at the Olney plant is running at about six aircraft per month.

Leland Snow began design studies on a turboprop-powered Air Tractor in September 1976, and the first production example, designated Model AT-302, flew in November of the following year. The basic airframe is similar to that of the radial-engined AT-301. The powerplant is a 600-shp Avco Lycoming LTP 101-600A turboprop which drives a Hartzell three-blade metal constant-speed propeller. This engine offers greater economy and longer times-between-overhaul than the piston engine and is relatively maintenance-free in field operations. An interesting point is the use of two large dry paper automobile-type air filters on the air intake to prevent chemicals being sucked in. The AT-302 is also in current production and 30 had been ordered by the beginning of 1979.

The AT-302A is similar to the AT-302 and first appeared in 1979. It is fitted with a 1457-litre (320-Imp gal) hopper with a 0.97-m (3 ft 2-in) wide gatebox for high application rates of dry chemicals.

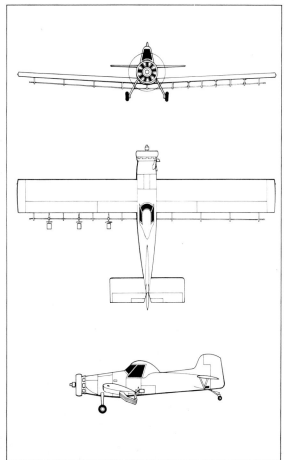

AT-301

Type: agricultural aircraft
Maker: Air Tractor Inc
Span: 13.72 m (45 ft)
Length: 8.23 m (27 ft)
Height: 2.59 m (8 ft 6 in)
Wing area: 25.08 m² (270 sq ft)
Weight: maximum 3130 kg (6900 lb); empty 1633 kg (3600 lb)
Powerplant: one 600-hp Pratt & Whitney R-1340 Wasp radial piston engine
Performance: maximum cruising speed 241 km/h (150 mph); range 650 km (403 miles)
Payload: 1497 kg (3300 lb)
Crew: 1
Production: 244 ordered by 1979

Citation, Cessna

FIRST FLIGHT 1968

THE Cessna Citation has its origin in the Fanjet 500, an eight-seat executive jet that made its first flight in October 1968. Cessna subsequently changed the name to Citation, increased the gross weight and made several other changes which included a lengthened fuselage, a repositioning of the engine nacelles, larger fin and re-sited tailplane. The first production aircraft made its first flight in July 1971 and was granted FAA certification in September that year.

The early Series 500 Citation was designed to fly from relatively short runways only 762 m (2500 ft) long, and to use unpaved surfaces. It was also a fairly quiet aircraft for its type and size.

In 1972 it was certificated at a maximum weight (for take-off) of 4922 kg (10 850 lb) and later that year this weight was increased to 5216 kg (11 500 lb). New certification at that weight was granted early in 1973, and it was possible to modify earlier existing aircraft in order to operate at the increased weight.

A further increase in take-off weight was allowed by the FAA in 1976, together with optional thrust reversers. Later that year the Citation I was announced, with an increased span and JT15D-1A turbofans. This was certificated in December 1976, and subsequent aircraft were of this configuration. Basic passenger layout of the Citation I was for six seats (plus two pilots) although there were other special versions available.

The Citation II was announced in 1976, with new features that included a fuselage lengthened by 1.14 m (3 ft 9 in), a wing with increased aspect

242

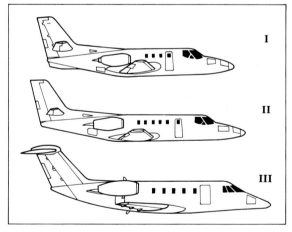

ratio, and more fuel and baggage capacity. Pratt & Whitney JT15D-4s were the new choice of engine. The prototype was flown in early 1977 and certification was granted in 1978. The basic Citation II is a two-crew aircraft, but the Citation II/SP can be operated by one pilot at a weight of 5670 kg (12 500 lb).

The Citation III has some superficial resemblance to the earlier designs, but is really a completely new aircraft. Cessna wanted a larger passenger cabin and substantially faster cruise than the Citation II, and opted for one of the new supercritical aerofoil shapes for a good high-speed cruise at high altitude. As a result Citation III cruises at some 185 km/h (115 mph) faster than the straight-wing Citation II, but also handles well at

Above: A Cessna Citation 500 of Euralair. This aircraft was formerly registered N136CC and is one of two Citations operated by this Paris-based airline. Euralair flies to destinations in Europe and the North African coast
Left: Side elevations showing Citation variants

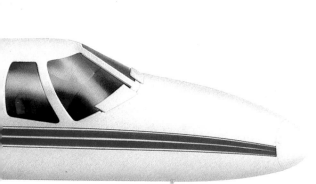

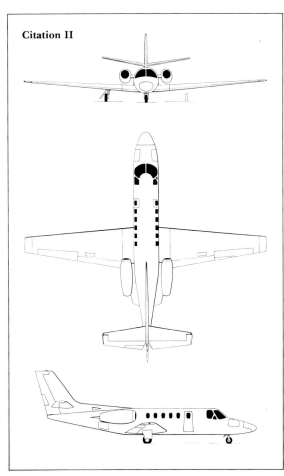

slow speeds, partly because of the small angle of sweepback and trailing-edge flaps.

The fuselage has a circular section similar to earlier Citations, but aisle height is up from 145 cm (57 in) to 178 cm (70 in) and the cabin is longer. Pressurization gives a cabin altitude of 2438 m (8000 ft) up to the operating ceiling of just over 15 548 m (51 000 ft). Although a conventional tail-plane was part of the original design, this was later changed to a T-tail, giving less drag at high speeds. The new engines are Garrett-AiResearch TFE731-3 turbofans, and an APU (auxiliary power unit) function is available on the right-hand engine to provide electrical power on the ground.

Citation III is designed for two-crew operation and will carry up to 13 passengers, although seating layouts for smaller numbers will probably be more common in service. Maximum take-off weight is 8830 kg (19 500 lb). A long-range version has a similar weight but about a third more fuel capacity, so that it will have a practical range of about 5550 km (3450 miles) and thus have a trans-atlantic capability. Extra fuel is stored in a tank between the rear pressure bulkhead and the aft baggage compartment, which is made smaller.

Typical Citation III flights will probably average 925 km (575 miles) with four passengers and a total of 600 hours utilization annually. By the end of 1979 sales were approaching 150, accounting for most production into the mid 1980s. With the Citation III and its popular predecessors Cessna was aiming to capture half the business jet market by 1985.

Citation II

Citation I

Type: executive transport
Maker: Cessna Aircraft Co
Span: 14.35 m (47 ft 1 in)
Length: 13.26 m (43 ft 6 in)
Height: 4.36 m (14 ft 3¾ in)
Wing area: 24.2 m² (260 sq ft)
Weight: maximum 5375 kg (11 850 lb); empty 2935 kg (6470 lb)
Powerplant: two 2200-lb (998-kg) st Pratt & Whitney JT15D-1A turbofans
Performance: maximum cruising speed 649 km/h (403 mph) at 7620 m (25 000 ft); range 2474 km (1537 miles)
Payload: seats for 6 passengers
Crew: 2
Production: 150 (1000 of all models)

Corvette, Aérospatiale

FIRST FLIGHT 1970

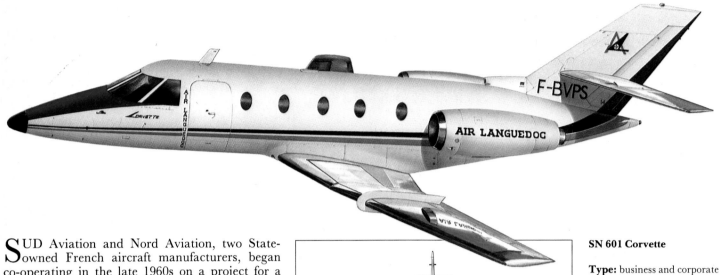

SUD Aviation and Nord Aviation, two State-owned French aircraft manufacturers, began co-operating in the late 1960s on a project for a light jet business aircraft/commuter airliner designed primarily for the North American market.

Development of the aircraft – designated SN600 – proceeded when the two companies merged into Aérospatiale and the first prototype flew on July 16, 1970, but was destroyed during test flying in March 1971. Two development SN601 prototypes followed, making their maiden flights on December 20, 1972 and March 7, 1973, followed by the first production standard Corvette 100 on November 9, 1973. The all-metal wings are of conventional two-spar fail-safe structure of aluminium alloy. The aluminium alloy ailerons are manually-operated and the double-slotted, long-travel, trailing-edge flaps are electrically-operated. The two Pratt & Whitney Aircraft of Canada JT15D-4 turbofans each generate a static thrust of 1134 kg (2500 lb) and are mounted in pods on either side of the rear fuselage. Standard seating arrangement is for 6 to 14 passengers in single seats on either side of a centre aisle.

Certification of the aircraft was long delayed by a protracted strike at Pratt & Whitney Aircraft of Canada, who supplied the JT15D-4 turbofan engines. The Corvette was finally certificated by the French authorities on May 28, 1974. Most initial customer interest came not from America but from domestic airlines in France. The first customer delivery was made in September 1974 to Air Alpes, who operated the Corvette out of Paris and in Air France colours on the Lyons-Brussels route. In airline service the Corvette had a 12-seat interior and could be equipped with wingtip tanks for extended range.

A planned 18-seat version to be called Corvette 200 proceeded no further than the design stage, and in service the standard Corvette proved too small for its intended role as a commuter airliner. Forty Corvettes had been built when Aérospatiale terminated the programme in 1977; a number remain in airline service with Air Alsace and Touraine Air Transport in France and with operators in Belgium, Holland, Sweden and African states. Refurbished Corvettes for the business market are being marketed by Air National Aircraft Sales and Service Inc of San Jose, California, on behalf of Aérospatiale.

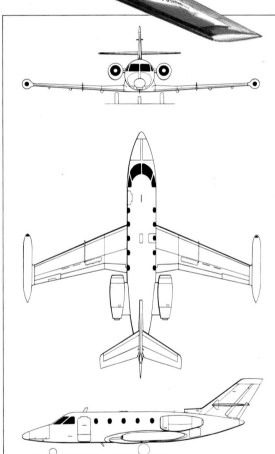

SN 601 Corvette

Type: business and corporate transport
Maker: Société Nationale Industrielle Aérospatiale
Span: 13.7 m (45 ft)
Length: 13.83 m (45 ft 4½ in)
Height: 4.23 m (13 ft 10½ in)
Wing area: 22 m² (237 sq ft)
Weight: maximum 6600 kg (14 550 lb); empty 3510 kg (7738 lb)
Powerplant: two 1134-kg (2500-lb) st Pratt & Whitney Aircraft of Canada JT15D-4 turbofans
Performance: maximum cruising speed 760 km/h (472 mph) at 9144 m (30 000 ft); range 2555 km (1588 miles)
Payload: seats for up to 14 passengers
Crew: 2
Production: 40

Top: A Corvette in the colours of Air Languedoc. This small French domestic operator uses aircraft from the Touraine Air Transport fleet and connects Paris (Le Bourget) with Béziers in Languedoc
Below: A Corvette in Aérospatiale livery takes off during a demonstration flight

244

Nomad, GAF

FIRST FLIGHT 1971

IN 1965 Government Aircraft Factories, which is operated by Australia's Department of Industry and Commerce, began studies for a small utility transport aircraft at their headquarters at Fisherman's Bend, near Melbourne. The aircraft was intended both to fulfil civil and military domestic needs for a rugged STOL aircraft and to ensure a level of continued domestic production activity.

The Government-funded prototype aircraft was known as the N2 and made its first flight on July 23, 1971, followed by a second aircraft on December 5, 1971. The aircraft followed conventional utility format in having a square, boxy fuselage and a high wing, and was powered by two Allison turboprop engines. Australian certification was granted on August 11, 1972 and production of the developed N22 Nomad model began immediately. The Nomad's ability to operate from small unprepared airstrips has made it popular with Third World air forces and civilian operators. Most of the short-bodied N22s and N22Bs (with increased gross weight) have been delivered to military operators, including the air arms of Australia, Indonesia, Papua New Guinea and the Philippines. Military Nomads have provision for armour-plating, self-sealing tanks and external armament pods if required. The aircraft can also operate on skis or floats and several Nomads have been so modified.

A stretched N24 Nomad model with seating capacity increased from 12 to 15 passengers (19 in high-density layouts) first flew in 1976 and is intended primarily for commercial operators. The

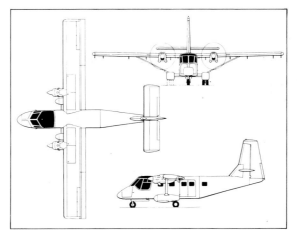

N24A has seats for up to 17 passengers and has a commuter interior and IFR avionics.

The Mission Master is the short-fuselage military version. It is used for maritime surveillance, forward area support and surveillance, and transport by the services of Australia, Papua New Guinea, the Philippines and Indonesia. The latest Nomad model is the maritime-patrol Searchmaster variant of the N22B. The Searchmaster B was introduced in 1975 while the Searchmaster L with Litton LASR-2 search radar, and a flat-plate phased array scanner in an undernose radome, in place of the former's smaller Bendix unit, began testing in 1978. More than 100 Nomads have been delivered and are now operating in Australasia, the Far East, Europe and North America.

N22B

Type: STOL utility transport
Maker: Government Aircraft Factories
Span: 16.46 m (54 ft)
Length: 12.56 m (41 ft 2⅖ in)
Height: 5.52 m (18 ft 1½ in)
Wing area: 30.1 m² (324 sq ft)
Weight: maximum 3855 kg (8500 lb); empty 2116 kg (4666 lb)
Powerplant: two 400-shp Allison 250-B17B turboprops
Performance: maximum cruising speed 311 km/h (193 mph); range with reserves 1352 km (840 miles)
Payload: seats for 15 passengers
Crew: 1
Production: 100 by mid 1979 (of all types)

Below left: The Government Aircraft Factories Nomad was designed to fulfil a civil and military requirement for a STOL machine for freight and passenger transport

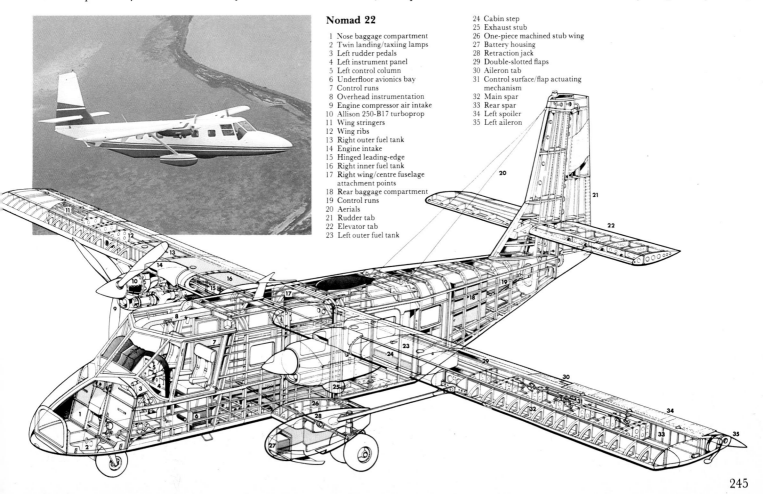

Nomad 22

1 Nose baggage compartment
2 Twin landing/taxiing lamps
3 Left rudder pedals
4 Left instrument panel
5 Left control column
6 Underfloor avionics bay
7 Control runs
8 Overhead instrumentation
9 Engine compressor air intake
10 Allison 250-B17 turboprop
11 Wing stringers
12 Wing ribs
13 Right outer fuel tank
14 Engine intake
15 Hinged leading-edge
16 Right inner fuel tank
17 Right wing/centre fuselage attachment points
18 Rear baggage compartment
19 Control runs
20 Aerials
21 Rudder tab
22 Elevator tab
23 Left outer fuel tank
24 Cabin step
25 Exhaust stub
26 One-piece machined stub wing
27 Battery housing
28 Retraction jack
29 Double-slotted flaps
30 Aileron tab
31 Control surface/flap actuating mechanism
32 Main spar
33 Rear spar
34 Left spoiler
35 Left aileron

Cheyenne, Piper

FIRST FLIGHT 1969

THREE models comprise the Cheyenne range which grew out of the Piper Navajo family of executive aircraft – the original version (now called Cheyenne II), the smaller, low-cost Cheyenne I, and the much larger Cheyenne III, which features a number of basic changes. (This model now carries the designation Piper PA-42.)

With an airframe very similar to that of the established pressurized Navajo, the Cheyenne introduced turboprop power to the Piper line for the first time. The first flight was in August 1969 with FAA certification coming in May 1972.

Following the introduction of a low-cost version (I) and the stretched model (III), the standard aircraft became the Cheyenne II in 1978. The Cheyenne I differs primarily in having less powerful Pratt & Whitney PT6A engines of 500 shp against the 628-shp units in the II. Internal fuel capacity is slightly reduced, and the wingtip tanks, fitted as standard on the II and III, are optional on this model. Late in 1977 Piper announced the introduction of the third member of the Cheyenne family, the III, which was to feature several significant changes from the two established models. The III has increased wing span – some 1.47 m (4 ft 10 in) greater than the II – a lengthened fuselage, T-tail and more powerful PT6A-41 engines, rated at 680 shp. The Cheyenne III can accommodate up to nine passengers, in addition to pilot and co-pilot, but the aircraft can be operated in a single-pilot configuration. All three Cheyenne models are available in many versions with most of Piper's 'group options' for interior fit and electronics available. The standard cabin packages comprise: individual seats, four-way adjustable crew seats, seatbelts, curtains and wall-to-wall carpets. Tinted windows, a stereo system and leather seat coverings are offered as extras. The executive interior adds reclining seats, drinks storage and dispenser, folding tables, toilet and refreshment centre, including razor socket, and the same extras. Two other packages include a de-icing system comprising pneumatic leading-edge boots for the wing and tailplane and an ice-inspection light, as well as a co-pilot panel of instruments, with alternate static pressure system, toe brakes and windscreen wiper. There is also available a total of seven different factory-installed packages of avionics equipment.

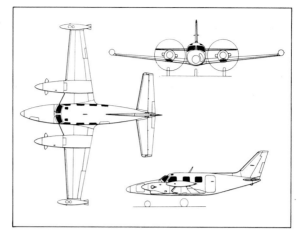

PA-31T Cheyenne II

Type: executive or corporate transport and commuter airliner
Maker: Piper Aircraft Corporation
Span: 13.01 m (42 ft 8¼ in)
Length: 10.57 m (34 ft 8 in)
Height: 3.89 m (12 ft 9 in)
Wing area: 21.3 m² (229 sq ft)
Weight: maximum 4082 kg (9000 lb); empty 2257 kg (4976 lb)
Powerplant: two 620-hp Pratt & Whitney PT6A-28 turboprops
Performance: maximum cruising speed 525 km/h (326 mph) at 3355 m (11 000 ft); range with maximum fuel and 45 min reserves 2557 km (1589 miles)
Payload: seats for up to 6 passengers
Crew: 1
Production: not available

Below: A Piper PA-31T Cheyenne operated by a private owner in California. The Cheyenne comes with a range of interior fittings designed to attract a variety of owners from the airline to the private individual who may demand the highest levels of personal comfort

Conquest, Cessna

FIRST FLIGHT 1975

THE first turboprop aircraft to come from the world's most prolific manufacturer, the Conquest was designed for a gap in the business aircraft market between twin piston-engined aircraft and turbofan-powered types. It was announced in late 1974, and the prototype first flew in 1975. Power comes from two 625-shp Garrett-AiResearch turboprop engines specially developed to meet Cessna's high-altitude high-speed requirements. High performance comes in part from the use of a new high-aspect-ratio bonded wing, like that of the Cessna Titan except for an increase in span and area by adding wingtip extensions.

The Conquest is large in comparison with other Cessna twins, weighing 1089 kg (2400 lb) heavier than the 421C Golden Eagle. The fuselage is similar to the Titan's but is strengthened for pressurization, and the Conquest also shares the Titan's high-strength trailing-link hydraulically-retractable landing gear, noted for its very forgiving ride over rough surfaces. Accommodation in the pressurized cabin is for four to ten passengers. There are a variety of seating arrangements available depending on customer requirement with optional extras including refreshment area, toilet, writing tables and stereo system.

Four Conquests had been delivered by the beginning of 1978, but then disaster struck when an elevator-tab actuator failed in flight on an aircraft in service, causing a fatal crash. Cessna grounded all aircraft in service before duplicating the actuator rods. But on a subsequent flight there was a further rod failure, which led to tailplane

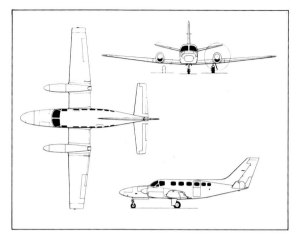

vibration in the air, but was followed by a successful landing. The FAA withdrew the Conquest's Certificate of Airworthiness pending investigations into the tailplane and elevator design.

Cessna engineers originally intended to strengthen the actuator assembly further, but felt that this would make the sub-assembly too strong in proportion to the surrounding structure. To avoid harmonic distortions the whole structure was redesigned, and the modification embodied by replacing the tailplane. Fifteen extra ribs were added, plus an extra front spar and thicker skin.

After exhaustive flight and ground tests the FAA re-instated the Certificate of Airworthiness in September 1979, subject to installation of the new tailplane on all Conquests.

C-441 Conquest

Type: pressurized executive transport
Maker: Cessna Aircraft Co
Span: 15.04 m (49 ft 4 in)
Length: 11.89 m (39 ft 0¼ in)
Height: 3.99 m (13 ft 1¼ in)
Wing area: 23.6 m²
(253.6 sq ft)
Weight: maximum 4468 kg
(9850 lb); empty 2535 kg
(5589 lb)
Powerplant: two 625-hp
Garrett-AiResearch TPE331-8-401S turboprops
Performance: maximum
speed 547 km/h (340 mph) at
4875 m (16 000 ft); range
1899 km (1180 miles)
Payload: seats for 10
passengers
Crew: 1
Production: approx 200 by
1980

Below: The aptly registered G-AUTO operated by the British Automobile Association

Skyservant, Dornier

FIRST FLIGHT 1959

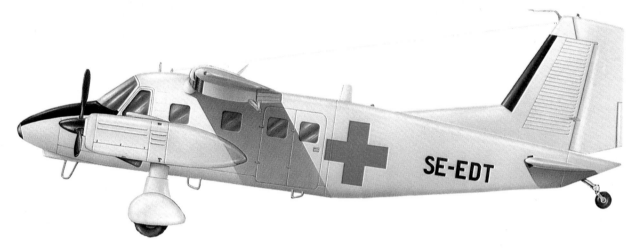

FOLLOWING World War II, the initial Dornier project was the Do 25 monoplane, from which was developed a more advanced design, the Do 27. This subsequent type came to be built in Germany, along with a twin-engined variant, designated the Do 28.

The Do 28 was a simple development with the two engines each mounted on a small stub wing alongside the cockpit. Fixed undercarriage units are suspended beneath each powerplant. Two 180-hp Lycoming IO-360s were chosen for the prototype, which first flew in 1959.

A second aircraft, powered by Lycoming IO540s of 250-hp, featured increased wing span. Initial production versions which began to appear in 1960 had seating for seven passengers. Professor Dornier achieved the type's famous STOL (short take-off and landing) characteristics by the use of fixed slats over the whole span, double-slotted flaps, and with the inner aileron portions drooped. A wheel/ski undercarriage was available, while a floatplane conversion was developed in Canada. Versions featuring increased power from turbocharged engines, increased gross weight and payload were developed, and one proposal featured pressurization and turboprop engines. A new fuselage section was introduced for the Do 28 D Skyservant seating up to 12 passengers and with a 1.48-m² (16-sq ft) door on the left side. The first flight in 1966 and type approval a year later was followed in 1968 by FAA (Federal Aviation Administration) certification. The Do 28 D-1 included increased wing span and gross weight. Records for piston-engined business aircraft in the 3000–6000 kg (6615–13 230 lb) range were established for altitude, payload and time-to-height.

Several aerodynamic and other detail design changes have been introduced in the Do 28 D-2 including another increase in gross weight, dual controls and a dual braking system. This version is powered by two Lycoming IGSO-540 engines of 380 hp. An all-flying one-piece tailplane is installed and the variant is available in float or wheel/ski undercarriage layouts. The type is in major service as a corporate or executive transport, as a commuter and third-level airliner, and as an airtaxi. It is extensively used by governments and military services all over the world. A turboprop variant, the Do 28 D-5 TurboSky, powered by two Lycoming LTP101 engines of 620-ehp, flew in April 1978.

248

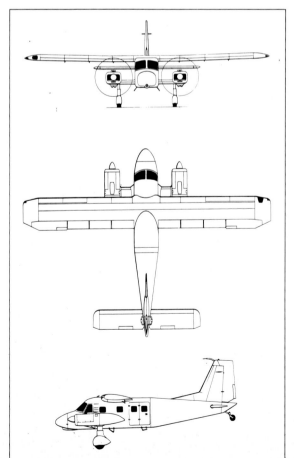

Do 28 D-2

Type: STOL transport and utility aircraft
Maker: Dornier GmbH
Span: 15.55 m (51 ft 0¼ in)
Length: 11.41 m (37 ft 5¼ in)
Height: 3.9 m (12 ft 9½ in)
Wing area: 29 m² (312 sq ft)
Weight: maximum 4015 kg (8853 lb); empty 2328 kg (5132 lb)
Powerplant: two 380-hp Lycoming IGSO-540-A1E flat-six engines
Performance: maximum speed 325 km/h (202 mph) at 3050 m (10 000 ft); range with maximum payload 1052 km (652 miles)
Payload: seats for 13 passengers (or 5 stretchers and 5 seats)
Crew: 1
Production: minimum 200

Top: A Swedish-registered Dornier Skyservant in service with the International Red Cross. This versatile aircraft is ideal for work in underdeveloped countries
Above: A Skyservant on a grass airstrip in the summer of 1969

Xingu, Embraer

FIRST FLIGHT 1976

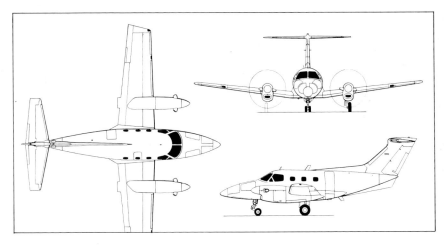

FOLLOWING the successful introduction of their EMB-110 Bandeirante light transport aircraft, Empresa Brasileira de Aeronautica of São Paulo, Brazil drew up plans in the early 1970s for a series of derivatives of the Bandeirante design. The first to appear is the Embraer EMB-121 Xingu. The Xingu is a pressurized twin-engine turboprop business aircraft which has a new, shorter fuselage of circular cross-section, clipped Bandeirante wings, more powerful Pratt & Whitney of Canada PT6A engines and a fashionable T-tail. A six-seat prototype was flown for the first time in October 1976 followed by a production standard machine on May 20, 1977.

First customers for the Xingu were the VIP transport flight of the Brazilian air force based at Brasilia, who took six early production aircraft, and the Brazilian racing driver Emmerson Fittipaldi. The Xingu was awarded type certification by the Brazilian Centro Technico Aeroespacial in the summer of 1979 and immediately South America's biggest air-taxi operators, Lider Taxi Aereo of Brazil, ordered six aircraft prior to the Xingu's official market launch.

Though less elegant externally than its American counterpart, the Beech King Air 90, Embraer's Xingu offers a roomy cabin for up to six passengers and can cruise at speeds up to 463 km/h (288 mph) at altitudes above 3048 m (10 000 ft).

Two further developments of the Xingu airframe are planned: the EMB-120 Araguaia with a stretched fuselage accommodating up to 20 passengers; and the EMB-123 Trapajos again with a lengthened cabin accommodating ten passengers, but with a new wing of supercritical airfoil section and tiptanks. Both aircraft will be powered by uprated Pratt & Whitney of Canada PT6A-45 turboprops. With the Xingu variants Embraer – already a leading world General Aviation manufacturer – hope to capture a share of the low-volume/high-value business turboprop market, which is the fastest growing General Aviation sector and is currently almost entirely US-dominated.

Notable among the Xingu's achievements in a short career to date was the first flight over the North Pole by a Brazilian-manufactured aircraft when an early demonstrator returned to the factory from Europe via the Polar route on September 28, 1977.

EMB-121 Xingu

Type: business and corporate transport
Maker: Empresa Brasileira De Aeronauta SA
Span: 14.45 m (47 ft 5 in)
Length: 12.25 m (40 ft 2¼ in)
Height: 4.74 m (15 ft 6½ in)
Wing area: 27.5 m² (296 sq ft)
Weight: maximum 5670 kg (12 500 lb); empty 3500 kg (7716 lb)
Powerplant: two 680-shp Pratt & Whitney of Canada PT6A-28 turboprops
Performance: maximum cruising speed 450 km/h (280 mph); range 2352 km (1461 miles)
Payload: seats for up to 9 passengers
Crew: 2
Production: 16 ordered by mid 1979

Left: The Embraer EMB-121 Xingu; the type has proved popular with air-taxi operators including Lider Taxi Aereo of Brazil

Challenger, Canadair

FIRST FLIGHT 1978

THE Learstar 600, was designed to carry 14 passengers over 5550 km (3450 miles) cruising at 15 240 m (50 000 ft). The fuselage was planned to be very spacious, seating three-abreast when laid out as a small airliner. Bill Lear's original objective was a low-cost, long-range aircraft which would outperform every type in its class.

Canadair accepted the project in 1976 and widened the fuselage still further, increasing the weight. The engines selected were geared turbofans by Avco Lycoming producing 3402 kg (7500 lb) thrust. The design was named Challenger in 1976, and with orders of over 50 in that first year Canadair and the Canadian Government committed large sums to the project.

The Challenger promised a remarkable performance that includes the ability to fly from short runways and cruise for long distances in airline-style speed and comfort. Take-off from a 1524-m (5000-ft) runway can be accomplished at maximum weight, and the aircraft is designed for high-altitude cruising over most commercial jet airliner routes.

Maximum cruise altitude is 14 935 m (49 000 ft), and performance claims include the ability to reach 12 497 m (41 000 ft) 17 min after take-off at maximum weight. Range has been quoted at over 7400 km (4600 miles), beating all the other top-performing business jets such as the Falcon 50, Jetstar II and Gulfstream II.

By mid 1978 orders for the executive version were over 100, and performance figures (with tolerances) had virtually been guaranteed. Minimum level speed at 10 973 m (36 000 ft) is over 925 km/h (575 mph). Take-off and landing guarantees are below 1524 m (5000 ft). The 1979 price was over $8 million, but that was for a comprehensive package deal, including personnel training and maintenance.

Construction of three pre-production Challengers began in April 1977 and the first roll-out took place in May 1978. First flight was made in November 1978, only two years after the programme got its official go-ahead.

A stretched version of the Challenger has been developed, called the Challenger E. This extends the fuselage by some 2.75 m (9 ft), to give a major weight increase to 22 226 kg (49 000 lb) and a range of 8520 km (5294 miles). The wing will be modified to include high-lift devices on the leading edges.

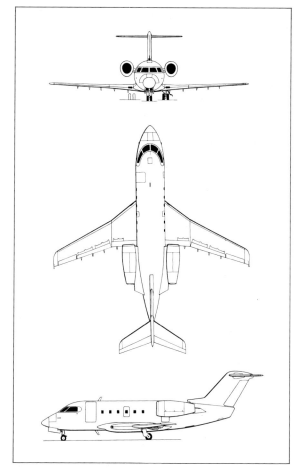

Challenger

Type: business, cargo and commuter transport
Maker: Canadair Ltd
Span: 18.85 m (61 ft 10 in)
Length: 20.85 m (68 ft 5 in)
Height: 6.3 m (20 ft 8 in)
Wing area: 41.8 m² (450 sq ft)
Weight: maximum 16 329 kg (36 000 lb); empty 7711 kg (17 000 lb)
Powerplant: two 7500-lb (3402-kg) st Avco Lycoming ALF 502L turbofans
Performance: maximum speed 925 km/h (575 mph) at 14 935 m (49 000 ft); range with IFR reserves and 426 kg (940 lb) payload 8246 km (5124 miles)
Payload: 3400 kg (7500 lb); seats for up to 14 (Challenger E, 40) passengers
Crew: 2
Production: 120 ordered by June 1979

Below: A pre-production Challenger with an instrumentation antenna in the nose and the X registration indicating an experimental model
Bottom: the Challenger can operate off short runways, but offers airline-style comfort

Dromader, PZL

FIRST FLIGHT 1976

DESIGNERS at the Wytwornia Sprzetu Komun Ikacyjnego PZL (transport equipment manufacturing centre) at Mielec, Poland, designed the PZL M-18 Dromader (Dromedary) to fill the gap in their agricultural aircraft range between the smaller 106A Kruk and the M-15 Belphegor jet biplane. To save time in development, and with an eye to the export market, PZL sought the co-operation of American manufacturers Rockwell International, and used the outer-wing panels, cabin area and other components from the Rockwell International S2R Thrush Commander.

Particular attention was paid to pilot safety in the design, the cockpit area being strengthened to withstand a 40 g impact without collapsing, and all fuel being carried in the outer-wing panels, well away from the pilot. These fuel tanks have a combined usable capacity of 400 litres (88 Imp gal). The structure, where exposed to possible contamination by chemicals, was treated with polyurethane or epoxy enamels or fabricated from stainless steel, and the welded-tube fuselage framework filled with anti-corrosive oil. The glassfibre epoxy hopper can accommodate either liquid or dry chemicals. With a payload of 2600 kg (5732 lb) and a hopper capacity of 2500 litres (550 Imp gal), the Dromader is one of the world's largest purpose-built agricultural aircraft. It is also one of the most powerful, having a 1000-hp Polish-built ASz-62IR radial engine of the type fitted to the Soviet Antonov An-2 biplane which the Dromader will hopefully replace in some Eastern bloc countries. This supercharged engine drives a PZL Warszawa AW-2-30 four-blade constant-speed aluminium propeller.

The first prototype Dromader made its maiden flight on August 27, 1976, and made its western debut at the 1977 Paris Air Show. Before the type received its Polish certificate on September 27, 1978, ten pre-series aircraft were built. Two of these were employed for static and fatigue testing and five for operating trials. In the summer of 1978 two were used for spraying and dusting Egyptian cotton. Apart from its prime role as a crop-duster/sprayer, the aircraft can also be equipped with Rockwell-developed water bombing/fire-fighting equipment. Indeed, a fire-fighting version of the Dromader was flown for the first time on November 29, 1978.

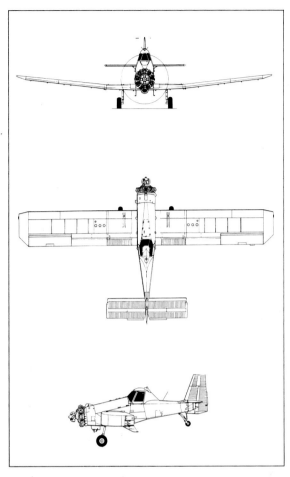

Left: A Dromader buzzes the crowd at the Paris exhibition of 1977
Below: The Dromader is one of the world's largest purpose-built agricultural aircraft, capable of lifting 2500 litres (550 Imp gal) or a payload of 2600 kg (5732 lb). Besides crop-dusting the Dromader can be used for fire-fighting using equipment designed by the American manufacturers Rockwell International

M-18 Dromader

Type: agricultural aircraft
Maker: Wytwornia Sprzetu Ikacyjnego PZL-Mielec
Span: 17.7 m (58 ft 0¾ in)
Length: 9.48 m (31 ft 1¼ in)
Height: 3.1 m (10 ft 2 in)
Wing area: 40 m² (430.56 sq ft)
Weight: maximum 4200 kg (9259 lb); empty 2560 kg (5644 lb)
Powerplant: one 1000-hp PZL Kalisz ASz-62IR 9-cylinder supercharged radial air-cooled engine
Performance: maximum cruising speed 190 km/h (118 mph); range 520 km (323 miles)
Payload: chemical spraying equipment, capacity 2500 litres (550 Imp gal) or 1500 kg (3307 lb)
Crew: 1
Production: 60 ordered by the end of 1979

Kruk, PZL

FIRST FLIGHT 1973

STUDIES for a replacement for the Polish PZL-101A Gawron agricultural and utility aircraft began at WSK-Okecie in the early 1960s under the leadership of Andrzej Frydrychewicz. Initially an extensive redesign of the high-wing Gawron was planned and a 260-hp AI-14R radial-engined prototype designated PZL-101M Kruk (Raven) was flown. By 1972 the design team elected instead to produce a more powerful version in the braced low-wing configuration favoured by agricultural operators in the West, and the first such prototype, designated PZL-106, flew on April 17, 1973 in the hands of test pilot Jerzy Jedrzejewski. This and a second prototype were powered by 400-hp Lycoming IO-720 engines; four more prototypes were tested with 600-hp PZL-3S seven-cylinder radial engines and this powerplant was chosen for the PZL-106A production model, manufactured at Centrum Naukowo Produkayjne Samolotow Lekkich PZL-Warszawa (Light Aircraft Science and Production Centre, Warsaw).

The Kruk has distinctive, slightly swept wings, set far forward to counteract the weight of the engine and features an advanced, corrosion-proofed structure whose fuselage is skinned with quick-release glass-reinforced plastic panels for ease of access for maintenance and cleaning. The hopper can release 1000 kg (2205 lb) of chemicals in less than 5 sec. Liquid chemicals are distributed by means of a fan-driven centrifugal pump. Fuel is carried in two wing tanks with a total capacity of 310 litres (68 Imp gal). The cockpit is air-conditioned and stressed to withstand a 40 g impact. A rearward-facing seat behind the pilot's enables a mechanic/loader to be ferried to work sites, making the Kruk largely independent of ground support.

Production started in 1976, with the first export aircraft going to Hungary in 1977. The total requirement for Kruks from the Council for Mutual Economic Aid (CMEA) countries is expected to exceed 600 aircraft. A two-seat trainer version and an uncowled tropical model of the Kruk have been developed. The two-seat version has dual controls and a 400-litre (88-Imp gal) hopper and this facility is available on any production PZL-106A. The latest version, the PZL-106AR, was flown for the first time on November 15, 1978 and is equipped with a geared PZL-3SR engine.

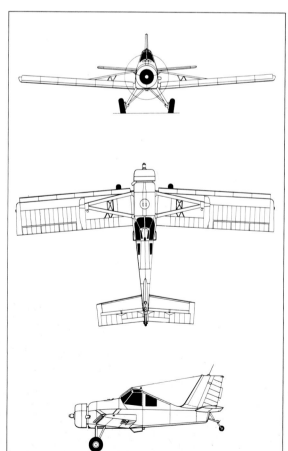

PZL-106A Kruk

Type: single-engine agricultural aircraft
Maker: Centrum Naukowo Produkayjne Samolotow Lekkich PZL-Warszawa
Span: 14.8 m (48 ft 6½ in)
Length: 9.10 m (29 ft 10 in)
Height: 3.32 m (10 ft 10¾ in)
Wing area: 28.4 m² (306 sq ft)
Weight: maximum 3000 kg (6614 lb); empty 1575 kg (3472 lb)
Powerplant: one 600-hp Pezetel PZL-3S radial engine
Performance: maximum speed 211 km/h (131 mph); range 400 km (248 miles)
Crew: 1
Production: 600 anticipated

Top: The PZL-106 showing its underwing spray boom. Like most modern crop-sprayers it has a skin designed to resist penetration or contamination by chemicals
Above: A PZL Kruk (Raven) flies low over the runway at Farnborough in September 1976

252

IAR-827

FIRST FLIGHT 1970

THE IAR-827 is the latest in a line of agricultural aircraft produced by the Intreprinderea de Constructii Aeronautice at Brasov in Romania. The first, IAR-821, was designed at the former Industrial Aeronautica Romana works and flew for the first time in 1967, with series production commencing at IRMA (Aircraft Repair Factory) the following year. The IAR-821 was powered by a 300-hp Ivchenko radial engine.

In October 1968 design started on the improved IAR-822 which first flew in March 1970 with a 290-hp Avco Lycoming IO-540-G1D5 engine. Five pre-production aircraft and 200 series production examples were manufactured before the wood/ metal IAR-822 and two-seat IAR-822B were superseded by the all-metal IAR-826 in 1973. Produced both for domestic and export markets, the IAR-826 serves as an agricultural aircraft, glider tug, (up to three sailplanes can be towed simultaneously) aerial-survey aircraft, fire-fighter, pipeline patroller, highway de-icer, trainer and light cargo or mail carrier (in which role the agricultural hopper can be replaced with a 700-kg 1543-lb cargo container).

The IAR-827 is a developed version of the all-metal IAR-826 designed in 1973 by Dipl Ing Radu Manicatide. His aim was to produce an agricultural aircraft with an airframe life of 4000 hours or 22 000 flights which could carry 2 kg per hp of payload, with an airframe expressly designed to minimize damage from chemical corrosion in the field.

The first IAR-827 was powered by a 400-hp Avco Lycoming IO-720 engine which drove a

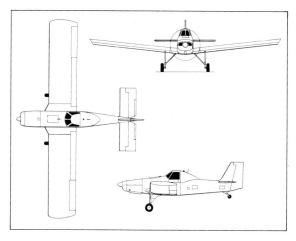

Hartzell two-blade constant-speed metal propeller with spinner. The fuel is carried in tanks in each leading edge with a capacity of 100 litres (22 Imp gal) each. It featured increased payload and improved operating and handling characteristics over earlier models. Accommodation was for pilot and mechanic in side-by-side seats in a fully-enclosed, heated and ventilated cockpit. It made its first flight on July 22, 1976 but trials revealed that more power was needed and production was delayed while the prototype aircraft were re-engined with 600-hp PZL-3S radial engines. Thus powered the IAR-827 will be able to carry 800 kg (1763 lb) of dry chemicals or 1200 litres (264 Imp gal) of liquids. A two-seat version for training or ferrying is flying in Romania.

IAR-827

Type: agricultural aircraft
Maker: Intreprinderea de Constructii Aeronautice, Brasov
Span: 14 m (45 ft 11¼ in)
Length: 9.6 m (31 ft 6 in)
Height: 2.6 m (8 ft 6½ in)
Wing area: 29 m² (312 sq ft)
Weight: maximum 2350 kg (5180 lb); empty 1280 kg (2822 lb)
Powerplant: one 400-hp Avco Lycoming IO-720-DA1B flat-eight engine
Performance: maximum cruising speed 175 km/h (109 mph)
Payload: 1070 kg (2358 lb)
Crew: 1 to 2
Production: not available

Below: The IAR-822 at an air display in May 1972. This aircraft built in wood and metal was followed by the all-metal IAR-827. They are used for a vast variety of work which includes mail carrying and highway de-icing

Commander 700, Rockwell

FIRST FLIGHT 1975

FUJI Heavy Industries of Japan began design of this pressurized wide-body twin engine business aircraft in 1971 as part of a diversification programme for their general aviation aircraft line. Three years later the company entered into an agreement with Rockwell International's General Aviation Division whereby the American company would share development, and would assume responsibility for marketing the aircraft in the US.

Six development and certification prototypes were planned, three in each country. The prototype Fuji FA-300 flew for the first time on November 13, 1975; the first Rockwell-assembled Model 700 made its first flight on February 25, 1976, and following US FAA (Federal Aviation Administration) certification in 1977, the aircraft replaced the heavier Commander 685 on the Rockwell production line.

With its capacious fuselage the Rockwell 700 offers an uncommonly roomy cabin for 6 to 7 passengers, with comfort rivalling that of larger aircraft. The pressurization system maintains sea level altitude conditions to 3810 m (12 500 ft) and provides an 1830 m (6000 ft) cabin environment to 6100 m (20 000 ft). Customer deliveries began behind schedule late in 1978, but the well engineered airframe proved heavy and underpowered with the 340-hp Lycoming piston engines, and, with a full load of passengers, range was severely compromised for all but short-haul journeys. The fuselage is constructed mainly from aluminium alloy and the tail unit has swept-back vertical surfaces and shallow dorsal fin. There is a built-in airstair in the left side of the fuselage. In Japan an uprated 450-hp version known as the Fuji FA-300 Kai (Rockwell 710) made its first flight on December 22, 1976 and has since appeared with a number of modifications, including Whitcomb winglets. Rockwell have not taken up their option to produce this aircraft.

By early 1980 deliveries of Rockwell 700s had totalled only 29 aircraft, and the American company announced the termination of its joint development and marketing agreement. Rockwell have continued to support Model 700 operators and have continued to assemble from existing shipsets of Japanese components during 1980, but any future production will be concentrated in Japan.

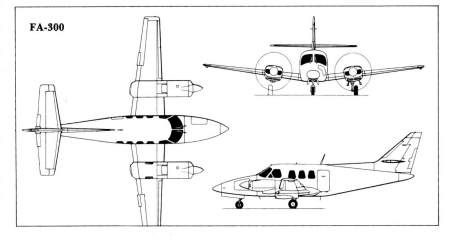

FA-300

Commander 700

Type: business and corporate transport
Maker: Rockwell International General Aviation Division; Fuji Heavy Industries
Span: 12.94 m (42 ft 5½ in)
Length: 12.03 m (39 ft 5¾ in)
Height: 4.05 m (13 ft 3½ in)
Wing area: 18.6 m² (200 sq ft)
Weight: maximum 3151 kg (6947 lb); empty 2134 kg (4704 lb)
Powerplant: two 340-hp Avco Lycoming TIO-540-R2AD turbocharged flat-six engines
Performance: maximum speed 409 km/h (254 mph) at 5180 m (17 000 ft); range with full tanks and 45 min reserves 2226 km (1384 miles)
Payload: seats for 6 passengers
Crew: 1
Production: 29 ordered by 1980

Left: A Rockwell 700 at an air display in May 1978. Originally designed in Japan the aircraft is assembled at Rockwell's Bethany factory in Oklahoma, and in Japan as the Fuji FA-300

ST-600, Foxjet

ESTIMATED FIRST FLIGHT MID 1980s

ST-600-S/8

Type: business transport
Maker: Foxjet International Inc
Span: 9.64 m (31 ft 7½ in)
Length: 9.7 m (31 ft 10 in)
Height: 3.12 m (10 ft 2¾ in)
Wing area: 11.61 m² (125 sq ft)
Weight: maximum 2064 kg (4550 lb); empty 1092 kg (2408 lb)
Powerplant: two 800-lb (363-kg) st Williams Research WR44-800 turbofans
Performance: maximum cruising speed 659 km/h (410 mph) at 11 000 m (36 000 ft); range 1768 km (1099 miles)
Payload: seats for 6 passengers
Crew: 1
Production: 140 ordered by mid 1980

BUSINESS jets, which are the fastest and probably most glamorous way for the executive to travel, usually seat at least eight people. The Foxjet therefore raised a lot of eyebrows when it was announced in the spring of 1977, since it was designed to seat only four to six people.

It was conceived by Tony Fox of Tony Team Industries (later Fox Industries) who set up a subsidiary company, Foxjet International, to develop and market the project. One of his original aims was to provide a high-speed answer to the fuel shortage, since he claimed a fuel cost of 6 cents per km (9 cents per mile), or a range of about 2.5 km per litre (7 miles per Imp gal). Early performance claims included a cruising speed of 531 km/h (330 mph) at 11 890 m (39 000 ft) for up to 2253 km (1400 miles). Power was to have been provided by two Williams Research WR19-3 turbofans, each of 258 kg (570 lb) thrust and weighing only 30 kg (67 lb), but these were later developed to give 40% more thrust and the original dimensions were scaled up to seat up to six rather than four people. Together with these changes went a new wing, with reduced sweepback and higher aspect ratio, designed by the Branson Aircraft Corporation. This was based on supercritical aerodynamic principles and should improve low-speed control, stability and all-round performance.

The Foxjet is of conventional all-metal construction, and has a traditional business jet appearance with rear-mounted engines and swept-back tail surfaces. Cabin pressurization gives a 'cabin altitude' equivalent to 3048 m (10 000 ft) at 12 190 m

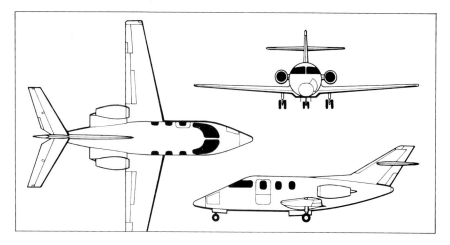

(40 000 ft). A two-piece clamshell door also acts as a step, and gives access to a luxuriously appointed cabin with individual bucket seats trimmed in tufted velour.

Standard features include two wheels for each undercarriage leg and a one-man 'power towbar' for easy ground handling. Firm orders for some 100 aircraft, backed up by deposits, had been received by the end of 1978, and further engine developments were envisaged. By the end of 1979, however, the prototype still had not flown, although full-size gleaming Foxjet mock-ups had received plenty of exposure at American trade airshows, along with publicity for Fox Industries' several other very successful products in the fields of refuse control and power tools.

Top left: Designer Tony Fox (on the right) watches as an ST-600 is refuelled. The aircraft has been designed with an emphasis on fuel conservation and operates at 6 cents per km (9 cents per mile)

M-15 Belphegor, PZL

ESTIMATED FIRST FLIGHT 1973

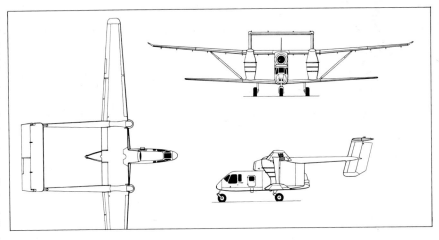

IN 1971 an agreement was concluded between Poland and the Soviet Union whereby Poland would develop and manufacture new agricultural aircraft for use in Soviet-bloc countries. A joint Soviet/Polish design team headed by R A Ismailov and K Gocyla began work at Wytwornia Sprzetu Komun Ikacyjnego PZL (the transport and equipment manufacturing centre) at Mielec, Poland on a revolutionary and unique design – a jet-powered biplane.

An aerodynamic prototype or 'flying laboratory' designated LLP-M15 was first flown on May 20, 1973 and was followed on January 9, 1974 by the first representative M-15 airframe. By any standards it was an odd-looking machine, its outdated biplane configuration having been dictated by the need for the low wing-loading demanded by a slow-flying aircraft with high take-off weight. As a result the M-15 is not only the world's only jet biplane to date (and likely to remain so), but is also the world's largest specialist agricultural aircraft, having a capacity for a massive 2200 kg (4850 lb) of dry chemicals or 2900 litres (640 Imp gal) of liquid insecticide carried in containers, forming struts between the wings and providing a swath width of nearly 61 m (200 ft). The wings are constructed mainly of aluminium alloys and steel with glassfibre laminates and the upper wing is fitted with five fuel tanks. The Ivchenko AI-25 turbofan is mounted in a pod on top of the fuselage.

Five pre-production aircraft from an initial batch of 20 were sent to the Soviet Union in April 1975 for evaluation trials and series production got

under way later that year. The M-15 Belphegor made its western debut at the Paris Air Show in 1977, where incredulous observers watched it fly at speeds down to 145 km/h (90 mph), and some cynics were heard to observe that with such an ugly aircraft chemicals were unnecessary – just fly it low and frighten the bugs to death!

To date all production of the M-15 at Mielec has been for a massive Russian order of some 3000 aircraft to replace the ageing Antonov An-2 biplanes in Aeroflot's agricultural fleet as support for the USSR's five-year agricultural plans. Production of the jet biplane is believed to be running at up to four aircraft a week, and fire-fighting and cargo-carrying versions are believed to be under development.

M-15 Belphegor

Type: agricultural aircraft
Maker: Wytwornia Sprzetu Ikacyjnego PZL-Mielec
Span: 22.33 m (73 ft 3 in)
Length: 13.14 m (43 ft 1 in)
Height: 5.34 m (17 ft 6¼ in)
Wing area: 67.5 m² (727 sq ft)
Weight: maximum 5750 kg (12 456 lb); empty 3230 kg (7120 lb) dusting, 3270 kg (7210 lb) spraying
Powerplant: one 1500-kg (3307-lb) st Ivchenko AI-25 turbofan
Performance: maximum cruising speed 200 km/h (124 mph); range 400 km (248 miles)
Payload: chemical spraying equipment, capacity 2900 litres (638 Imp gal) or 2200 kg (4850 lb)
Crew: 1
Production: approx 3000 ordered by 1980

Right and below: The unique PZL M-15 is not only the world's first jet biplane, but also the largest specialized agricultural aircraft. Despite its odd looks it has proved to be successful in a variety of roles besides agricultural work

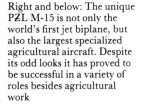

Bell 47

FIRST FLIGHT 1945

THE Bell Model 47 was ordered for the US Army and Navy towards the end of World War II and first flew in 1945. The pre-production model had a 178-hp Franklin engine and a car-type body. Only ten were built, but some were airborne as early as 1943. However, the Model 47 has the distinction of being the first helicopter to receive a CAA (Civil Aviation Administration) approval certificate, which was granted on March 8, 1946. The A and B models used the enclosed body. The 47B-3, a utility and agricultural model, had an open sports-car style body and it was from this design that the now familiar goldfish bowl moulded canopy was derived. The FAA (Federal Aviation Administration) certified the 47D with its new canopy in February 1948. A year later Bell produced the 47D-1 with an openwork tail boom.

The three-seat configuration, later combined with a 200-hp Franklin engine, produced the 47G which was granted an FAA certificate in 1953. This became one of the most successful versions remaining in production in improved forms into the 1970s. It was adopted by a wide range of civil and government operators for survey work, traffic control, coastguard work, crop-spraying (using the AgMaster chemical application system) and as an executive transport.

Not content with this success Bell have developed further models and in 1955 they installed a new powerplant. The 200-hp Lycoming VO-435 allowed the helicopter to operate at greater weights but without a fall-off in performance.

In 1952 Agusta SpA of Italy was granted a

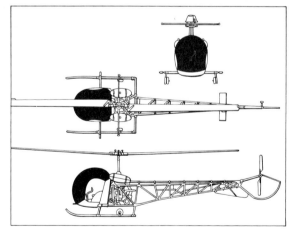

licence to build the Bell 47 and produced its first 47G in 1954. Since then Agusta has built over 1000 G and J marks. Kawasaki in Japan received a licence a year later and like Agusta developed its own versions of the Bell originals.

The Bell 47H with a fully enclosed car-type cabin and 200-hp engine was not a commercial success, but in the early 1960s the J series sold well. Seating four in an enclosed cabin, it was powered by a 220-hp Lycoming VO-435 engine. With power controls and metal rotor blades in the Model 47J-2 in 1960 it became popular as an executive transport. Agusta produced a three-seat version as the EMA 124 and though Bell have stopped production the G and J series are still being built in Italy and Japan.

Bell 47G-3

Type: utility helicopter
Maker: Bell Helicopter Co
Rotor diameter: 11.35 m (37 ft 3 in)
Length: 8.69 m (28 ft 6 in) fuselage
Height: 2.83 m (9 ft 3½ in)
Main rotor disc area: 101.24 m² (1090 sq ft)
Weight: maximum 1157 kg (2550 lb); empty 698 kg (1539 lb)
Powerplant: one 225-shp Franklin 6VS-335 6-cylinder horizontally opposed air-cooled inline engine
Performance: maximum cruising speed 169 km/h (105 mph) at sea level; range 380 km (236 miles)
Payload: seats for up to 2 passengers
Crew: 1
Production: approx 5000 (civil and military)

Above: A Bell 45 G5 equipped with an AgMaster chemical application system banks at the end of a spraying run. The G2 to G5 were similar but had various Lycoming engines varying from 200 to 280 hp and optional metal blades. The G was produced by Bell from 1953 to 1974

Hiller 360

FIRST FLIGHT 1948

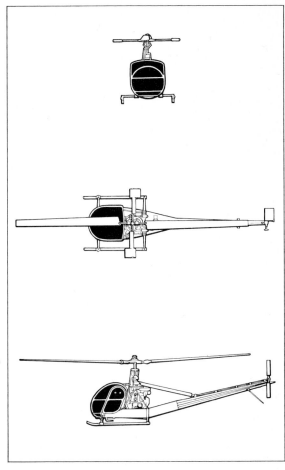

STANLEY Hiller Jnr designed the Model 360 which has enjoyed considerable commercial success since its first flight in 1948. It was derived from the UH-5 which had proved very unstable during trials and had subsequently been fitted with a new stability system patented as the Hiller 'Rotormatic'. It entailed fitting the two-blade rotor with two small paddles which acted as a control rotor and were also connected to a hanging stick. This servo 'paddle control' system tilts the rotor head and actuates the cyclic pitch control.

It received its FAA (Federal Aviation Administration) approval in October 1948 and a year later a production model designated Model 12 made the first transcontinental helicopter flight across the USA. At that time it still had an open cockpit, and the 178-hp Franklin 6V4-178-B33 was in an open engine bay.

Models 12A, B and C were powered by a 200-hp 6V4-200-C33 or a 210-hp 6V-335-B Franklin piston engine. The 12C was the first version with a goldfish bowl canopy.

The Korean War gave an added impetus to improvements and when the Hiller 12E appeared in 1959 it came either as the L3 with a 305-hp Lycoming VO-540-C2A or as the SL3 with a supercharged 315-hp TIVO-540-A2A engine.

The 12E has been used for the usual range of civil work, like fire-fighting, crop and forestry control, and as a private and business transport.

A Model E4 was built with a longer fuselage to take a bench for three passengers and it introduced stabilized tail surfaces. All new helicopters now have these features and they can be retrofitted on Model 12Es. A turbine-powered retrofit kit is available as the UH-12E4. This engine pack was jointly developed with Soloy Conversions of Chehalis, Washington who began work on it in 1976.

The Model 12 has the usual equipment for helicopter safety and civil work, but can also be fitted with a night-lighting kit, a 454-kg (1000-lb) capacity cargo hook, twin heavy duty cargo racks, and auxiliary fuel tanks. Equipped with extra tanks the 12E has a maximum range of 676 km (420 miles).

Production of both the 12E and 12E-4 is running at about five a month and with over 2200 helicopters built since the introduction of the Model E there is a world-wide maintenance service.

Hiller 360 (UH-12E)

Type: utility helicopter
Maker: Hiller Aviation
Rotor diameter: 10.8 m (35 ft 5 in)
Length: 8.69 m (28 ft 6 in) fuselage
Height: 3.08 m (10 ft 1¼ in)
Main rotor disc area: 91.97 m² (990 sq ft)
Weight: maximum 1270 kg (2800 lb); empty 798 kg (1759 lb)
Powerplant: one 340-shp Lycoming VO-540 6-cylinder horizontally opposed air-cooled inline engine
Performance: maximum speed 154 km/h (96 mph) at sea level; range 346 km (215 miles)
Payload: seats for up to 2 passengers
Crew: 1
Production: 2200 (civil and military)

Top left: A crop-spraying Hiller 360, or Raven, makes a low pass during agricultural work
Above left: Topping up the tanks of a British registered Hiller 360 with agricultural chemicals. In the UK the Hiller 360 was used for pilot training, agricultural work and as an executive transport

FH-1100, Fairchild Hiller

FIRST FLIGHT 1963

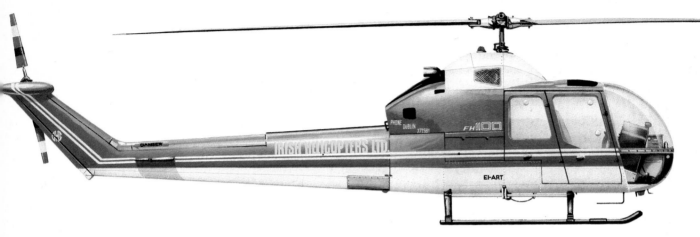

THE Hiller Model 1100 grew out of the US Army's specification for an LOH (Light Observation Helicopter). The competition was won by Hughes, so in the early 1960s Hiller had five high-speed five-seater helicopters on their hands.

One went on display at the Le Bourget Air Show in 1965 and subsequently proved a modest success. The five prototypes were powered by a 250-shp Allison T63-A-5 turboshaft engine. The first machine to fly (N81005) took to the air on January 21, 1963. These army prototypes were later reworked as civilian demonstration machines.

An FAA (Federal Aviation Administration) type certificate was awarded to the Model 1100 on July 20, 1964. The FH-1100 is powered by an Allison 250-C18 which is the civil version of the T63 engine.

The first production model was completed in June 1966. By the mid 1970s the initial production run of 250 machines was well under way.

The FH-1100 has a baggage compartment which will take 68 kg (150 lb) with seating for two or three stretchers and an attendant. It is available with a skid or float undercarriage.

When it first came onto the market its turbine engine and power controls were in advance of anything then currently available in the civil helicopter field.

It has a two-bladed semi-rigid teetering rotor with an automatic stabilizing system. This relieves the pilot of the need to attend constantly to the cyclic controls. The doors covering the stabilizer system serve, when open, as maintenance plat-

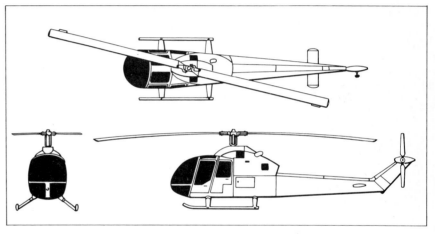

forms for access to the engine top and transmission. The glassfibre engine-cowling slides aft for routine inspection and maintenance.

Prospective buyers saw that it could have military applications, but though the Dutch were reported to be evaluating it as an antisubmarine warfare helicopter in the 1960s, it remained largely a civil machine.

The largest civil operator was Okanagan of Canada with 30 while the Royal Thai Police Department took 16. Argentina, Brazil, Chile, Cyprus, Ecuador, Panama, the Philippines and Salvador were single-figure customers.

It has been used for executive, and business work in addition to the usual range of civil and police work.

FH-1100

Type: general-purpose light helicopter
Maker: Fairchild Industries
Rotor diameter: 10.79 m (35 ft 5 in)
Length: 9.08 m (29 ft 9½ in) fuselage
Height: 2.83 m (9 ft 3½ in)
Main rotor disc area: 91.51 m² (985 sq ft)
Weight: maximum 1247 kg (2750 lb); empty 633 kg (1395 lb)
Powerplant: one 317-shp Allison 250-C18 turboshaft
Performance: maximum speed 204 km/h (127 mph); range 560 km (348 miles)
Payload: seats for up to 3 passengers
Crew: 2
Production: maximum 250

Above: An FH.1100 of Irish Helicopters, a subsidiary of Aer Lingus
Left: A Fairchild Hiller FH.1100 lifts off from the London heliport at Battersea

Bristol 171

FIRST FLIGHT 1947

THE Bristol 171 was the first postwar British commercial helicopter, and was also the first venture by the Bristol Aeroplane Company into the field of rotorcraft. Work had begun back in June 1944 when a team under Raoul Hafner designed a machine powered by a Pratt & Whitney R-985 Wasp Junior engine. It received the Ministry of Supply Specification E.20/45 and the Mk 1 prototypes were registered VL958 and VL963.

The Mk 1 flew in July 1947. The crankshaft lay horizontally, with power transmitted to the vertical driveshaft through a gearbox. The three rotor blades were made of wood with leading edges in hardwood.

The Alvis Leonides LE 21 HM engine was fitted to the Mk 2 in a horizontal position with the crankshaft running vertically. This eliminated the lower gearbox which not only saved weight but made the engine more accessible for checking and repairs, and increased the seating from two to five.

The Mk 2 had flown in 1948 and a year later the Mk 3 appeared with a smaller Alvis Leonides 73 engine. Seating was increased to six. The Mk 3A was bought by British European Airways; it had a slightly superior performance to the Mk 3 and greater baggage capacity.

In 1950 Bristol produced the 'universal' Sycamore which had extended landing gear and a larger baggage compartment at the rear of the fuselage. It had detachable clamshell doors which made loading quicker and a hydraulic winch which hung directly in front of the door opening and was powered by a pump connected to the drive on the

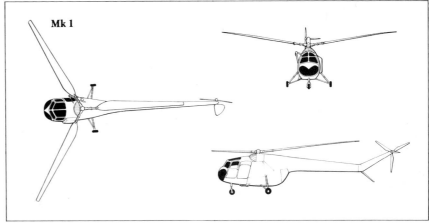

Mk 1

main gearbox. It was a machine ideally suited to search-and-rescue work, air ambulance and passenger carrying. The pilot sat American-style on the right-hand side. Production ended in 1959 with sales to British Commonwealth air forces and also to the Federal German forces and Belgium.

In August 1955 a Bristol 171 became the first helicopter to be used in an air-to-surface television transmission.

In the mid 1950s Bristol Aircraft Ltd began work on a turbine-powered helicopter using a Mk 3 with an increased fin area. Under the name Bristol 203 it was to be an 11-seat machine and parts from the incomplete 179th and 180th Sycamore airframes were used in the prototype machine, but unhappily the project was abandoned.

Sycamore Mk 4

Type: general-purpose helicopter
Maker: Bristol Aeroplane Co
Rotor diameter: 14.8 m (48 ft 6¾ in)
Length: 12.8 m (42 ft) fuselage
Height: 4.22 m (13 ft 10 in)
Main rotor disc area: 172.1 m² (1852 sq ft)
Weight: maximum 2540 kg (5600 lb); empty 1728 kg (3810 lb)
Powerplant: one 550-hp Alvis Leonides 9-cylinder air-cooled radial engine
Performance: maximum cruising speed 212 km/h (132 mph); range 531 km (330 miles)
Payload: seats for up to 3 passengers
Crew: 2
Production: 180 (all Sycamore marks)

Above: G-AMWH, *Sir Geraint*
Left: G-AMWG, *Sir Gawain*; on June 15, 1954 they inaugurated a £2.50 return service between Eastleigh and Heathrow/Northolt. The experiment lasted two years

Bristol 173

FIRST FLIGHT 1952

THE 173 was the first British two-engined helicopter to be developed. Its development and life span are spread over 19 years and though like many heavy helicopters it was a largely military machine, it was also intended as the first helicopter airliner for BEA service.

The 173 appeared on the drawing board in 1948 and ground tests started three years later. It was interesting not only because of its two three-blade counter-rotating rotors, but also because it could fly on one Alvis Leonides 73 engine and the centre of gravity could be displaced. The two rotors were synchronized by a shaft in conjunction with a gearbox. In the event of a breakdown the shaft could transmit power from the working engine. The rear rotor was carried on a pylon which was part of the vertical fin structure. Two tailplanes were set at a sharp angle to improve longitudinal and lateral stability.

Ground resonance was cured by linking the right and left oleo struts of the undercarriage with small-bore hydraulic piping. As G-ALBN the first 173 flew on August 24, 1952.

A Mk 2 followed with stub wings and an improved undercarriage. The Mk 3 however, with more powerful engines, (two Alvis Leonides Majors rated at 850 shp each) as well as four-bladed rotors, marked an even greater advance. Seating too, was up from 14 in the Mk 1 and 2 to 16 in the Mk 3. Unfortunately however, the Mk 3 suffered from cooling problems and its service trials in 1956 were not entirely successful.

In July 1958 the Bristol 192 made its maiden flight

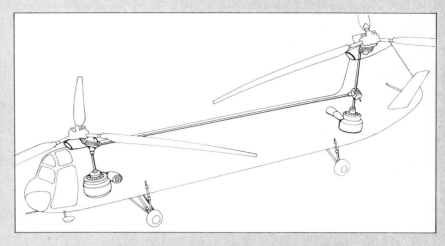

and this marked the successful climax to the development of the 173. As the Westland Belvedere this entered service with the Royal Air Force, though this was only after the 191 and 193 had been cancelled by the RAF and Royal Canadian Air Force respectively. The 192 was powered by two Napier Gazelle Series 2 engines derated to 920 shp.

As the 192C it was tested by BEA and offered its 24 passengers a unique high-speed service between London and Paris.

On May 30, 1961, C T D Hosegood flew from London to Paris in 1 hour 41 min 28 sec and on June 2, 1961, from Paris to London in 1 hour 40 min 55 sec. This is the equivalent of 202.32 km/h (125.72 mph) outwards and 203.51 km/h (126.46-mph) on the return flight.

Above: The drive for the twin rotors of the Bristol 173. One engine could operate both rotors in an emergency
Below left: XH379 in BEA and service markings during naval trials in 1954
Bottom: Re-numbered G-AMJI, XH379 was fitted with different wings when it was leased to BEA

Bristol 173 Mk 3

Type: airliner helicopter
Maker: Bristol Aircraft Ltd
Rotor diameter: 14.86 m (48 ft 9 in)
Length: 15.32 m (50 ft 3 in) fuselage
Height: 5.18 m (17 ft)
Main rotor disc area: 346.8 m² (3733 sq ft)
Weight: maximum 6124 kg (13 500 lb); empty 4463 kg (9840 lb)
Powerplant: two 850-hp Alvis Leonides Major 14-cylinder air-cooled radial engines
Performance: maximum cruising speed 183 km/h (114 mph); range 482 km (300 miles)
Payload: seats for up to 14 passengers
Crew: 2
Production: one Mk 1, one Mk 2, three Mk 3s

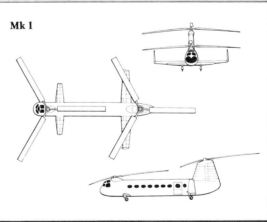

Mk 1

S-51, Sikorsky

FIRST FLIGHT 1946

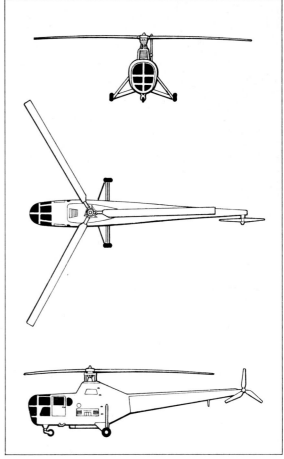

THE S-51 has the distinction of being the first helicopter in the world to fly a regular service, and it did so in the United Kingdom. It flew in British European Airways' colours between Liverpool and Cardiff in June 1950.

Work on the S-51 began in 1943 when the United States Army Air Force put out a requirement for a helicopter bigger and better than the rather crude Sikorsky R-4.

The civil version flew for the first time in February 1946. It could carry four passengers and retained the R-985-AN-5 radial engine of the military version. The Civil Aviation Administration certification was granted a month later and in August 1946 the first customer took delivery. Production lasted until 1951, by which time Sikorsky had built 285 machines.

In December 1946 Westland Aircraft of Yeovil purchased a licence to build the S-51 in Britain. When they ceased production in 1953 they had built 139 machines. The Dragonfly, as the British-built machine was known, had a 520-hp Alvis Leonides engine. Westland sold their UK-built helicopters to Belgium, Ceylon, Egypt, France, Iraq, Italy, Japan, Thailand and Yugoslavia. The bulk of these sales were for military use, but Belgium became a European pioneer in the civil field when Sabena bought three.

The S-51 had a three-blade rotor which had flapping and drag hinges and could be folded to facilitate storage. The early machines had manual control for the rotor pitch, later replaced by hydraulic servo-controls with power from a hy-

draulic pump driven by the tail transmission shaft.

In 1955 Westland produced a conversion of the S-51 which they called the Widgeon. It had a four-blade main rotor with a 520-hp Leonides 521 engine, a redesigned cabin and small clamshell nose doors. The first flight was in August 1955 with a Dragonfly converted to Widgeon standard. Westland produced 15 Widgeons and sold them to Ceylon, Jordan, Brazil and the Hong Kong police department. The Widgeon used an S-55 rotorhead which employs an offset flapping-hinge system, thus allowing more latitude in the centre of gravity and the position of cargo or passengers.

The Widgeon was the final development of the S-51 which was becoming obsolete with the rapid changes in helicopter design in the mid 1950s.

S-51

Type: general-purpose helicopter
Maker: Sikorsky Aircraft Division, United Technologies Corporation
Rotor diameter: 14.94 m (49 ft)
Length: 12.45 m (40 ft 10 in) fuselage
Height: 3.95 m (12 ft 11½ in)
Main rotor disc area: 175.2 m² (1886 sq ft)
Weight: maximum 2663 kg (5870 lb); empty 1994 kg (4397 lb)
Powerplant: one 450-hp Pratt & Whitney R-985-AN-5 Wasp Junior 9-cylinder air-cooled radial engine
Performance: maximum speed 153 km/h (95 mph); range 483 km (300 miles)
Payload: seats for up to 4 passengers
Crew: 2
Production: 300

Top left: A BEA S-51 stripp. ready for inspection; BEA inaugurated a service with S-51s in 1950
Above left: A Westland Widgeon of Bristow Helicopters; formed in 1951 Bristow operated over 150 machines in 1980 and has subsidiary firms in Africa

S-55, Sikorsky

FIRST FLIGHT 1949

Left: An S-55 of Sabena, the Belgian national airline
Below left: A BEA S-55 over the Thames in May 1955
Below centre: Engine maintenance on an S-55; the clamshell doors give easy access and the engine can be reached from ground level
Below: A BEA Westland S-55 lowers a navigation beacon on to a tower in May 1958. This was one of the earliest flying-crane operations in the UK

ONE of the most successful designs of the 1950s, the Sikorsky S-55 was built under licence in France, Britain and Japan.

The main feature of the design was the engine in the nose which could be reached easily through clamshell doors and serviced by crew standing on the ground. The pilot's position was above and forward of the cabin which gave him good visibility. Besides conventional wheeled gear, the S-55 was fitted with floats and a winch could be fitted for 'flying crane' work or as a search-and-rescue machine.

An indication of the reliability of the machine is the fact that it is still in service – with a turbine powerplant. In 1971 the FAA (Federal Aviation Administration) granted certification in the Transport Category to a version developed by Aviation Specialties. This conversion marketed in the United States by Helitec has a Garrett-AiResearch TSE331-3U-303 turboshaft engine derated from 840 shp to 650 shp. The exhaust is mounted in the nose and curves to the right to balance the weight of the tail rotor. Various mechanical and electronic components formerly located in the tail boom have been moved forward which makes them more accessible and improves the centre of gravity, which allows a wider range of loads to be carried. The conversion saves 408 kg (900 lb).

The Helitec (Sikorsky) S-55T is now in use in Alaska, Canada, Europe, South America and the USA. Piston-powered machines can be delivered to Helitec for retrofitting or a turbine package can be delivered to the operator.

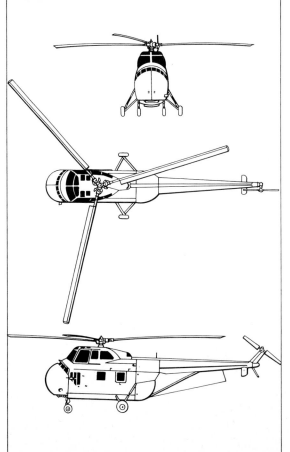

S-55

Type: transport and freight helicopter
Maker: Sikorsky Aircraft Division, United Technologies Corporation
Rotor diameter: 16.15 m (53 ft)
Length: 12.85 m (42 ft 2 in)
Height: 4.06 m (13 ft 4 in)
Main rotor disc area: 14.94 m (49 ft)
Weight: maximum 3085 kg (6800 lb); empty 1814 kg (4000 lb)
Powerplant: one 600-hp Pratt & Whitney R-1340-57 Wasp nine-cylinder radial
Performance: maximum speed 169 km/h (105 mph) at sea level; range with reserves 758 km (471 miles)
Payload: 752 kg (1658 lb) with maximum fuel; seats for up to 11 passengers
Crew: 1 to 2
Production: 1281

S-58, Sikorsky

FIRST FLIGHT 1954

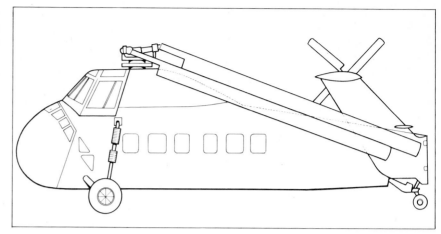

BUILDING on the success of the S-55, Sikorsky produced the S-58. It was described as a more powerful version of the S-55, but differs considerably in silhouette.

The first flight was in 1954 and production models were powered by a 1525-hp Wright R-1820-84B/D nine-cylinder radial engine. It was widely used by the US armed forces and once again Westland negotiated the licence to build in 1956. The French firm of Sud Aviation also received a licence, but the bulk of production by these two firms went to military use.

The S-58 has one main rotor with four blades with a four-bladed anti-torque rotor. The rear fuselage has a large fin and a small fixed tailplane as well as a tailwheel. Besides its crew of two it can carry 18 passengers or eight stretchers. In airline use it has seating for 12. Like the S-55 it has one door, on the right-hand side, and has provision to be fitted with a hoist.

In 1970 Sikorsky announced the S-58T, a turbine version of the S-55. Like the S-55 turbine conversion it could be retrofitted as a kit, but could also be built as a new helicopter.

Initially the powerplant was a Pratt & Whitney Aircraft of Canada Twin Pac turboshaft engine developing 1800 shp at take-off. From 1974 it was replaced by one PT6T-6 Twin Pac which developed 1875 shp on take-off.

Design of the S-58T began in January 1970 and construction started in May, with the first flight in August that year. Construction and conversion of the helicopter began in January 1971 and US

Federal Aviation Administration certification was awarded in April.

With typical American thoroughness Sikorsky offers FAA-certified kits to operators, or fits them at their works. They have also acquired used S-58s which are being re-engined and offered for sale.

The turbine version is safer and more reliable than the older piston-engined types and has the added advantage of greater lifting power, speed and improved performance in 'high and hot' conditions. However, the most attractive feature for many civil operators is that it is cheaper to run than the piston-engined model. Among the interested civil operators was British Airways who have 18 conversions for use as transports to North Sea oil rigs.

Above: The folding main rotors and tail of the S-58 reduced its length by about a quarter so that it could be stowed easily in small hangars
Below: S-58s of World Wide Helicopters caught in the sunshine of a winter evening

The licence-built version of the S-58, the Wessex, went through a wide range of marks, most of them for service use. However, in 1961 the Wessex Mk 60 appeared in conjunction with the RAF Wessex HC Mk 2. This high performance version of the HAS Mk 1 was powered by two coupled Gnome Mk 110/111 turboshaft engines. It could carry ten passengers at airline standard, 15 survivors in a rescue role or eight stretchers with an attendant. The Wessex can also be used as a flying crane with an underslung load of up to 1814 kg (4000 lb).

Two Mk 2s were converted to HCC Mk 4 VIP transports for service with the Queen's Flight, and improvements included sound-proofing. The S-58T and Wessex will remain in service with civil and military operators into the 1980s.

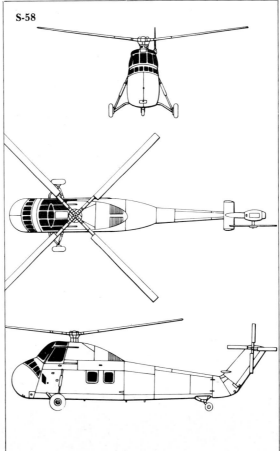

S-58

Top: A Sikorsky S-58C of Sabena Belgian World Airlines in 1959
Above: The S-58T is powered by a turboshaft engine; some machines have been built with the powerplant and some have been retrofitted with a kit supplied by Sikorsky

S-58T

Type: general-purpose helicopter
Maker: Sikorsky Aircraft Division, United Technologies Corporation
Rotor diameter: 17.07 m (56 ft)
Length: 14.40 m (47 ft 3 in) fuselage
Height: 4.85 m (15 ft 11 in)
Main rotor disc area: 228.5 m² (2460 sq ft)
Weight: maximum 5896 kg (13 000 lb); empty 3437 kg (7577 lb)
Powerplant: one 1875-shp Pratt & Whitney Aircraft of Canada PT6T-6 Twin Pac coupled turboshaft
Performance: maximum speed 222 km/h (138 mph) at sea level; range 447 km (278 miles)
Payload: seats for up to 16 passengers
Crew: 2
Production: not available

S-61N, Sikorsky

FIRST FLIGHT 1962

THE first version of the S-61 was the Sea King amphibious antisubmarine helicopter. It was ordered in 1957, first flew in 1959 and was delivered to the US Navy in 1961.

The West Germans became interested in the S-61, and in 1961 Weser Flugzeugbau received a licence to build the S-61D. This version was to be equipped with a monorail loading system, including doors and ramps, though it remained only a project.

The main commercial types are the S-61L, S-61N, and the Payloader. For commercial operations the fuselage was lengthened to 18.16 m (59 ft 7 in) with a cabin length of 9.73 m (31 ft 11 in). The powerplant comprises two 1500-shp General Electric CT58-140-1 or -2 turboshafts. The S-61N has a sealed hull with sponsons and a higher tail pylon. It first flew in August 1962.

The S-61L is a non-amphibious machine with accommodation for 30 passengers. It first flew in December 1960.

The Payloader is a stripped-down version of the S-61N which weighs 907 kg (2000 lb) less than the latter's 5675 kg (12 510 lb). It is capable of lifting a payload of more than 4990 kg (11 000 lb), and is intended for logging, powerline installation, and gas- or oil-pipeline laying. The advantage of helicopters in this type of operation is that they can combine the roles of crane and truck, moving the lengths of pipe to the site and then lowering them into position. They can also operate in areas that are difficult for normal wheeled vehicles. In the Payloader the sponsons are replaced by fixed mainwheel landing gear and the rear airstair door is sealed off.

The S-61N has comparatively luxurious accommodation contrasted to the austerity of most helicopters. The 26 to 28 passengers have an attendant who can cook meals in a galley installed in the forward luggage area. The rear seat in the passenger area can be replaced with a lavatory. If a galley is not required, the forward half of the helicopter can be provided with fold-down seats and rings for securing a cargo load. This allows operators to employ the helicopter on mixed cargo or passenger runs. Normal baggage stowage is at the front, above and below the floor.

In the late 1970s British Airways Helicopters were the largest private operators in the world using S-61s with a fleet of 26.

266

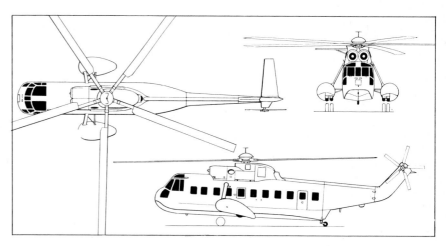

S-61N

Type: amphibious all-weather airliner helicopter
Maker: Sikorsky Aircraft Division, United Technologies Corporation
Rotor diameter: 18.9 m (62 ft)
Length: 22.2 m (72 ft 10 in)
Height: 5.63 m (18 ft 5½ in)
Main rotor disc area: 280.5 m² (3019 sq ft)
Weight: maximum 9979 kg (22 000 lb); empty 5675 kg (12 510 lb)
Powerplant: two 1500-shp General Electric CT58-140-1 or -2 turboshafts
Performance: maximum cruising speed 241 km/h (150 mph) at sea level; range 796 km (495 miles)
Payload: seats for up to 28 passengers
Crew: 2
Production: minimum 100

Top: An S-61N of KLM helicopters; this company was established in 1965
Left: After delivering an underslung load of cargo, an S-61N hovers above an oil rig
Right: British Airways Helicopters operate 2 S-61Ns and include a service to the Scilly Isles as well as oil and gas rig work

Yak-24A, Yakovlev

FIRST FLIGHT 1960

THE origins of the Yakovlev Yak-24 helicopter lie in a 1951 Soviet requirement for a 'flying boxcar' helicopter, able to carry 24 passengers or an equivalent weight of freight, to enter production within one year of design work beginning.

As conceived, the Yak-24 (NATO reporting name Horse) was powered by a pair of Shvetsov ASh-82V radial piston engines, each rated at 1700 hp for take-off and at 1430 hp for continuous running. The rear engine was located vertically at the base of the large fin, while above the fuselage was the front with a forward angle of 45°.

To ensure single-engined safety and complete synchronization of the two rotors, the transmissions were linked mechanically by a shaft mechanism running along the top of the fuselage. The two four-blade rotors were each similar in design, size and construction to that of the Mil Mi-4, whose design had been originated as a result of the same meeting as that leading to the Yak-24.

Early Yak-24s had a fuselage of steel-tube construction with fabric covering except for the fin and engine bays, though later examples were metal-covered. The interior of the aircraft, which could accommodate 40 passengers or up to 4000 kg (8818 lb) of freight, measured 10 m by 2 m by 2 m (32 ft 9½ in by 6 ft 6¾ in by 6 ft 6¾ in), and was entered by means of a ramp built into the underside of the unswept fin.

All the prototypes were prone to vibration as a result of rotor-blade flutter, and yet another prototype was lost when its tethers broke. Finally, though, the Yak-24 completed its state trials in April 1955 and entered production for the Soviet air force – some 30 months later than planned.

Various improvements followed during the initial production run, largely to improve the helicopter's handling and load-carrying capability. An indication of the type's basic ability was provided on December 17, 1955, when two records were set: a load of 2000 kg (4409 lb) lifted to 5082 m (16 673 ft), and a load of 4000 kg (8818 lb) lifted to 2902 m (9521 ft).

It was not until 1960 that a passenger model of the Yak-24 was produced: this experimental Yak-24A had seating for 30 passengers in considerable comfort, and stowage for 300 kg (661 lb) baggage. The small rectangular windows of the military Yak-24 were replaced in the Yak-24A by large continuous windows on each side. Another model developed for Aeroflot was the Yak-24K de luxe model, with seating for eight or nine passengers. The Yak-24K had a dihedralled tailplane and four large rectangular windows on each side just forward of the fin.

The Yak-24s used by the Soviet air force suffered large numbers of accidents, however, and it was judged unwise to seek to develop the type into a passenger-carrier for safety reasons. Thus the bulk of the 100 Yak-24s built were used operationally only by the military.

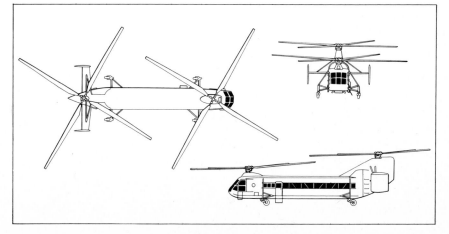

Yak-24A

Type: heavy-lift helicopter
Maker: Yakovlev Design Bureau
Rotor diameter: 21 m (68 ft 10¾ in)
Length: 21.3 m (69 ft 11 in) fuselage
Height: 6.5 m (21 ft 4 in)
Main rotor disc area: 692.72 m² (7456 sq ft)
Weight: maximum 15 830 kg (34 898 lb); empty 11 000 kg (24 250 lb)
Powerplant: two 1700-hp Shvetsov ASh-82V 14-cylinder air-cooled radial engines
Performance: maximum

cruising speed up to 1000 m (3281 ft) 155 km/h (96 mph); range 200 km (124 miles)
Payload: seats for up to 30 passengers
Crew: 2
Production: prototypes only

Above: A Yak-24A, the passenger version of the Yak-24. It first flew in 1960, five years after the military version entered service. It can carry 30 passengers in a spacious cabin with 300 kg (661 lb) of baggage. Eight or nine passengers can travel in a luxury version, designated Yak-24K, which was used by Aeroflot for senior party officials and their entourage

Whirlwind Series 3, Westland

FIRST FLIGHT 1959

WESTLAND obtained the licence to build the S-55 from Sikorsky in November 1950. The Series 1 and 2, powered respectively by a Pratt & Whitney R-1340 or Wright R-1300 engine or the 750-hp Alvis Leonides Major 755, were used for both civil and military work.

The turbine-powered S-55 made its first flight as the Whirlwind Series 3 in February 1959, powered by a General Electric T58. At the end of the year a Series 3 flew with a 1050-shp Bristol Siddeley Gnome free-turbine – the licence-built version of the T58.

Like the S-55, the Series 3 has a single door on the left side. The pilot and co-pilot sit above and behind the engine which places their cabin directly under the centreline of the main rotor. The rotor is hydraulically operated for both cyclic and collective pitch controls. Forward vision for landing was not ideal in earlier versions of the Whirlwind since the engine housing was in the nose. The turbine version was better since, though the nose was longer, it was at a more raked angle. Unlike the US turbine-powered S-55, the Whirlwind Series 3 has its engine exhaust on the left side almost immediately above the forward wheel, which can make cargo loading slightly hazardous if the engine is running or the exhaust hot. The turbine engine can be retrofitted to Series 1 and 2 machines.

The Whirlwind can carry up to ten passengers, six stretchers or a freight load. The Series 2 machines in service with BEA were fitted with floats as well as wheels for use off inland waterways. Few Whirlwinds are in civil use in the 1980s.

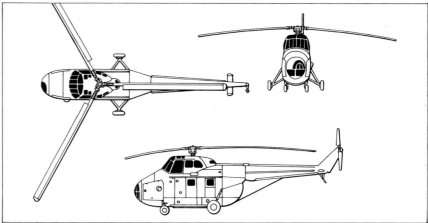

Series 3

Type: general-purpose helicopter
Maker: Westland Helicopters Ltd
Rotor diameter: 16.15 m (53 ft)
Length: 13.46 m (44 ft 2 in) fuselage
Height: 4.76 m (15 ft 7½ in)
Main rotor disc area: 204.96 m² (2206 sq ft)
Weight: maximum 3629 kg (8000 lb); empty 2129 kg (4694 lb)
Powerplant: one 1050-shp Rolls-Royce (Bristol Siddeley) Gnome H-1000 turboshaft
Performance: maximum speed 175 km/h (109 mph); range 480 km (300 miles)
Payload: seats for up to 10 passengers
Crew: 2
Production: minimum 400 (Series 1, 2 and 3)

Top: A Bristow Helicopters Whirlwind registered and operating in Bermuda. The floats allow it to work in coastal areas where landing zones may not be available ashore
Left: G-APDY, first flown in 1957 and converted to a turbine engine Series 3 in 1961

Lama, Aérospatiale
FIRST FLIGHT 1969

THE SA 315 was initially designed to an Indian Army requirement, but it bore a considerable resemblance to the successful Alouette II and III designs.

The prototype Lama flew on March 17, 1969 and received French airworthiness certification on September 30, 1970 and Federal Aviation Administration Type Approval on February 25, 1972. The Lama has the clear cabin and open-frame fuselage of the Alouette II with the power-plant and rotor system of the SA 316 Alouette III. Besides being produced by Aérospatiale in France, the Lama was also under licence production in India to Hindustan Aeronautics Limited.

The SA 315B has a three-blade main and anti-torque rotor. The tail rotor is driven through a torque shaft from the lower end of the main gearbox to a small gearbox which houses the pitch-change mechanism and supports the tail rotor.

Though the machine has a skid landing gear it can be equipped with floats. Small wheels can be fitted for ground movement.

The production Lama can transport an external load of 1135 kg (2500 lb) at an altitude of more than 2500 m (8200 ft). It can also be equipped with a hoist for loads up to 160 kg (352 lb). In an agricultural role it carries an underbelly tank developed by Aérospatiale and the Simplex Manu-facturing Company. The tank holds 1135 litres (250 Imp gal) and is connected to spray bars. It has an electrically operated emergency dump switch.

An alternative system uses two side-mounted

British registered Aérospatiale SA 315B Lama lowers a hopper of cement onto a major construction site in May 1975. The use of helicopters for this work is expensive, but can save on time and labour

glassfibre tanks made by Simplex. Up to 1000 kg (2200 lb) of liquid chemicals can be carried and when empty the tanks weigh a mere 132 kg (290 lb). The electric pump can dispense up to 455 litres (100 Imp gal) a minute.

For passenger work the Lama can accommodate a passenger in the front seat with three on a bench situated behind. Alternatively, if its role is changed to that of ambulance work, the Lama helicopter is capable of carrying two stretchers together with a medical attendant.

The first Indian-built Cheetah (as the SA 315B Lama is known) flew on October 6, 1972.

The Lama or Cheetah will certainly be in service into the 1980s since it is not only simple to produce, but is versatile.

Above: The Lama can only carry four passengers but in demonstration flights it established height records in the late 1960s and early 70s
Above right: An SA 315B hovers low over a truck to take on another load of cement
Left: Against a stormy sky an SA 315B lowers its hopper to a Unimog truck to lift off a load of cement

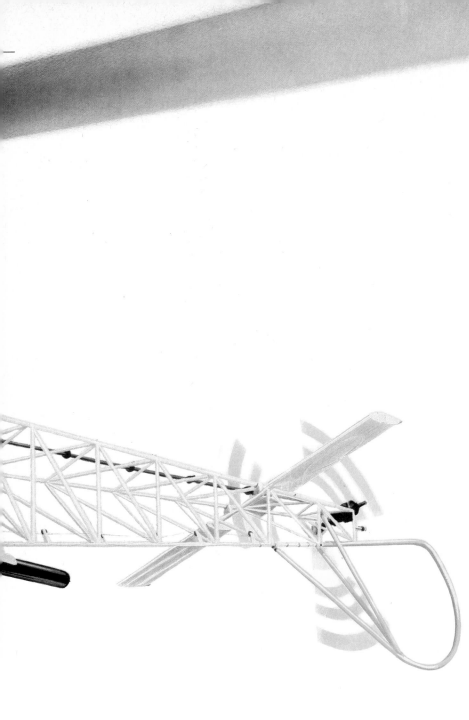

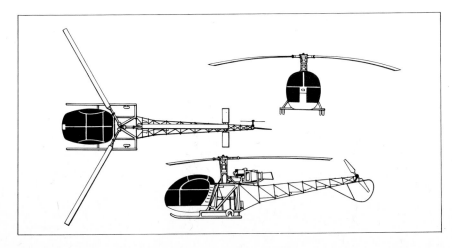

SA 315B Lama

Type: general-purpose light helicopter
Maker: Société Nationale Industrielle Aérospatiale Hindustan Aeronautics Ltd
Rotor diameter: 11.02 m (36 ft 1¾ in)
Length: 10.26 m (33 ft 8 in) fuselage
Height: 3.09 m (10 ft 1¾ in)
Main rotor disc area: 95.38 m² (1027 sq ft)
Weight: maximum 2300 kg (5070 lb); empty 1018 kg (2244 lb)
Powerplant: one 870-shp Turboméca Artouste IIIB turboshaft

Performance: maximum cruising speed 120 km/h (75 mph); endurance 3 hours 20 min
Payload: 1135 kg (2502 lb); seats for up to 4 passengers
Crew: 1
Production: minimum 230 (orders)

Alouette III, Aérospatiale

FIRST FLIGHT 1959

THE Alouette III is derived from the military Alouette II but with a larger cabin and fully streamlined fuselage with the exception of the turbine.

The accommodation is sufficient for a pilot and six passengers. Baggage can be carried in holds on either side of the centre section. The SA 316B can also carry two stretchers and two crew besides the pilot. The passenger seats can be removed for freight work and an external sling will take loads up to 750 kg (1650 lb). There are four doors, two rearward sliding and two hinged for the pilot and front passenger or co-pilot.

In 1964 an all-weather version was announced with a gyrometric compass, vertical gyro, three-axis attitude and heading indicator, radio altimeter, Doppler radar and automatic pilot.

The SA 316B is also produced under licence in Switzerland and Romania, and in India where it is called the Chetak.

In 1967 Aérospatiale produced an improved version of the Alouette III which was designated SA 319B or Astazou. It was externally very similar to the 316, but had an 870-shp Turboméca Astazou XIV turboshaft engine which was derated to 600 shp. The more powerful engine allowed the SA 319B to carry a heavier load and reach a top speed at sea level of 220 km/h (137 mph), as opposed to the 316, which could only reach 210 km/h (130 mph). Accommodation is similar to the 316. The SA 319B has an increased thermal efficiency and a 25% reduction in fuel consumption over the 316.

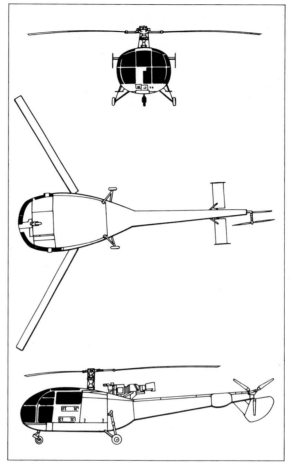

SA 316B

Type: general-purpose helicopter
Maker: Société Nationale Industrielle Aérospatiale
Rotor diameter: 11.02 m (36 ft 1¾ in)
Length: 12.84 m (42 ft 1½ in) overall
Height: 3 m (9 ft 10 in)
Main rotor disc area: 95.38 m² (1027 sq ft)
Weight: maximum 2200 kg (4850 lb); empty 1143 kg (2520 lb)
Powerplant: one 870-shp Turboméca Artouste IIIB turboshaft
Performance: maximum speed 210 km/h (130 mph) at sea level; range 540 km (335 miles)
Payload: 750 kg (1653 lb); seats for up to 6 passengers
Crew: 1
Production: minimum 1400

Below: An SE-3160 Alouette III of Air Glaciers, a Swiss firm which operates local services in the Bernese and Valaisian Alps. The helicopter has a ski and wheel landing gear

Mi-1, Mil

FIRST FLIGHT 1948

THE Mil Mi-1 (NATO reporting name Hare) was the first helicopter designed by the talented Mikhail Leontyevich Mil who was Technical Officer of the Soviet air force's First Rotorcraft Squadron for a time during World War II.

The Soviet version made its maiden flight in 1948 while a Polish version flew in 1956. It was a dramatic success for Mil who had only established his bureau a year earlier. The Mi-1 was first seen by the West at Tushino in 1951, by which time it had been in quantity production and was in service with the Soviet air force.

It consists of a cabin for three passengers with a radial seven-cylinder engine driving the rotor through an angle gearbox. A 2.5-m (8 ft 2½-in) shaft runs from the gearbox to the tail rotor. The main rotor has friction dampers and is fully articulated through hinges.

Like Soviet equipment during World War II, the Mi-1 is designed to operate at very low temperatures and has anti-freeze sprays for not only the rotors but also the windscreen.

The Mi-1 has been produced in a vast number of configurations. These include the Mi-3 a four-bladed heavy version with a wider cabin and additional flight aids. The Mi-3 appeared in 1956, but two years earlier the Mil bureau produced an ambulance version. This was interesting since the patients were carried on stretchers in streamlined pods on either side of the fuselage. Pipes connected the pods to the fuselage to allow the temperature to be controlled.

The Mi-1T carries two passengers, while the Mi-1U is a dual-control trainer. The Mi-1NKh (Narodnoye Khozyaistvo) is a utility model used for freight and mail carriage. In an agricultural role it can be fitted with spraying bars and two 250-litre (55-Imp gal) tanks.

Poland began building the Mi-1 in late 1955 at the WSK works at Swidnik where it was fitted with an AI-26V engine and designated SM-1. An SM-2 entered service in 1961 and is a larger machine with a longer nose. It can accommodate four passengers or a third stretcher inside besides the two in the external pods.

Production has probably ceased in favour of more modern turbine-powered machines, but the Mi-1 is still widely used by Soviet bloc countries and their allies in civil and military roles.

Mi-1

Type: general-purpose light helicopter
Maker: Mil Design Bureau; WSK-PZL-Swidnik
Rotor diameter: 14.35 m (47 ft 1 in)
Length: 12.1 m (39 ft 8½ in) fuselage
Height: 3.3 m (10 ft 10 in)
Main rotor disc area: 161.56 m² (1739 sq ft)
Weight: maximum 2550 kg (5622 lb); empty 1760 kg (3880 lb)
Powerplant: one 575-hp Ivchenko AI-26V 7-cylinder air-cooled radial engine
Performance: maximum speed 205 km/h (127 mph); range 590 km (367 miles)
Payload: seats for up to 3 passengers
Crew: 1
Production: not available

Top and left: A Mi-1 at an international helicopter meeting in March 1974. It is demonstrating precision hovering as the crewman lowers a marker onto the 'target'

Mi-2, Mil

FIRST FLIGHT 1962

THE Mil Mi-2, which has the NATO reporting name Hoplite, was first announced in the autumn of 1961, and is essentially the Mi-1 updated in the light of operating experience with the Mi-6. The Mi-2 thus has very distinct similarities to the Mi-1 in size and structure, but uses a twin-turboshaft powerplant giving the type about 2½ times the Mi-1's payload. Whereas the Mi-1's engine and transmission constitute about 25% of the aircraft's weight, that of the Mi-2 is only about 12.5% of the weight, but develops some 40% more power. The first Mi-2 flew in 1962, and was put through its trials fairly quickly. A measure of the type's ability was the establishment of a class speed record of 269.38 km/h (167.38 mph) on June 20, 1965, when piloted by Tatyana Russyan.

With the completion of Russian state trials, Mi-2 production began at the WSK-PZL factory at Swidnik in Poland. Construction is of the standard semi-monocoque duralumin type, with the engine and transmission assembly above the cabin. This last seats six passengers three-abreast and in two back-to-back rows, with two optional extra left-hand seats at the rear, one behind the other.

The type is produced in a variety of forms: the passenger model can be stripped of seats to provide space to carry up to 1000 kg (2204 lb) of freight; the Mi-2R is an ambulance model carrying up to four litters and an attendant; the agricultural model is fitted with two 600-litre (132-Imp gal) external tanks and their attached chemical spray spreaders; the rescue model is fitted with a winch which has a capacity of 120 kg (264 lb); the flying-crane model has 30 m (98 ft) of cable and a hook capable of lifting 1200 kg (2645 lb); and there are also pilot-training, photogrammetric survey and TV broadcast models.

Each individual rotor blade used to be of typical Mil construction, with some 20 bonded sections attached to a light alloy spar, with a light aluminium honeycomb trailing edge, the whole being covered in light alloy sheet. WSK-PZL-Swidnik have since developed a more advanced rotor blade based on an extruded duralumin spar with plastic sections and covering.

Further development of the Mi-2 has been undertaken by WSK-PZL-Swidnik with a view to selling the type to western countries. The result is the Kania or Kitty Hawk, powered by two Allison turboshafts.

276

Mi-2

Type: general-purpose, freight and passenger helicopter
Maker: WSK-PZL-Swidnik; Mil Design Bureau
Rotor diameter: 14.5 m (47 ft 6¾ in)
Length: 11.94 m (39 ft 2 in) fuselage
Height: 3.75 m (12 ft 3½ in)
Main rotor disc area: 165 m² (1776 sq ft)
Weight: maximum 3700 kg (8157 lb); empty 2365 kg (5213 lb)
Powerplant: two 436-hp Isotov GTD-350 turboshafts
Performance: maximum speed 210 km/h (130 mph) at 500 m (1640 ft); range with maximum fuel 580 km (360 miles)
Payload: 1200 kg (2645 lb); seats for up to 8 passengers
Crew: 1
Production: minimum 1000 by 1980

Top: The PZL is used for many civilian roles
Left: The PZL Mi-2 with hoppers for agricultural chemicals. This machine was displayed at the Hanover Air Show in April 1978

Mi-6, Mil

FIRST FLIGHT 1957

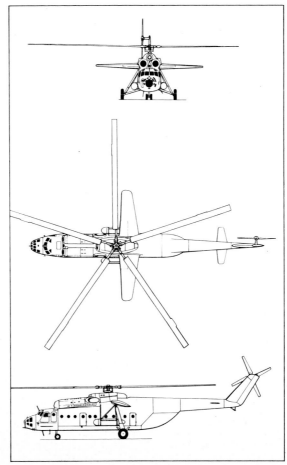

THE Mil Mi-6, which has the NATO reporting name Hook, was first announced in the autumn of 1957, and has enjoyed a number of distinctions: at one time or another the type has held 14 world records; for 12 years it was the world's largest helicopter; it was also the world's first twin-turboshaft helicopter, and the first to exceed 300 km/h (186 mph) in level flight.

The Mi-6 bears a marked similarity to its predecessors in the Mil helicopter family, but is considerably larger than its immediate antecedent, the Mi-4: rotor diameter is 66% greater, and maximum weight over four times greater.

The Mi-6 was designed to meet a joint military and civil requirement, the latter being concerned mostly with providing Aeroflot with a resources-support helicopter, able to operate in Siberia and to carry trucks, drilling rigs and so on. Design began at the end of 1954, and the first of five prototypes took to the air in the autumn of 1957. The type's record-breaking career began on October 30 of the same year, when an Mi-6 lifted 12 000 kg (26 455 lb) to 2432 m (7979 ft).

Construction is wholly conventional: the fuselage is a metal semi-monocoque pod-and-boom design, with large hydraulically operated clamshell doors at the rear of the pod. These doors, which can be removed to allow the carriage of outsize cargoes, cover an opening measuring 2.65 m by 2.7 m (8 ft 8½ in by 8 ft 10½ in) and leading into a hold with a volume of 62 m³ (2189 cu ft), measuring 12 m by 2.65 m by 2.5 m (39 ft 4½ in by 8 ft 8½ in by 8 ft 2½ in). Freight is handled with the aid of an

Mi-6

Type: general-purpose heavy helicopter
Maker: Mil Design Bureau
Rotor diameter: 35 m (114 ft 10 in)
Length: 33.18 m (108 ft 10½ in) fuselage
Height: 9.86 m (32 ft 4 in)
Main rotor disc area: 962.1 m² (10 356 sq ft)
Weight: maximum 42 500 kg (93 696 lb); empty 27 240 kg (60 053 lb)
Powerplant: two 5500-shp Soloviev D-25V (TV-2BM) turboshafts
Performance: maximum speed 300 km/h (186 mph); range with a payload of 6000 kg (13 228 lb), 650 km (404 miles)
Payload: 12 000 kg (26 455 lb); seats for up to 65 passengers
Crew: 5
Production: minimum 900 (civil and military Mi-6, Mi-10 and Mi-10K)

Above: A Mil Mi-6 operated by Aeroflot; these giant helicopters have also been exported to the Peruvian government. Roles include fire-fighting, cargo and passenger transport

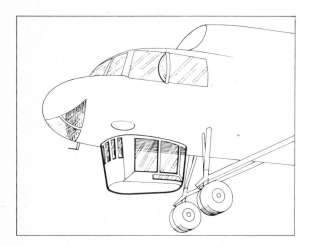

800-kg (1763-lb) winch. As an alternative to internal freight, a load of 9000 kg (19 841 lb) can be carried in a sling suspended from a cable on the aircraft's centre of gravity, dropped through a hatch in the floor. The Mi-6 also has an electric winch for use when hovering which has a capacity of 500 kg (1102 lb).

When the Mi-6 first appeared, it was claimed to have a maximum passenger capacity of 120, with normal capacity for 70 to 80, each with 20 kg (44 lb) of baggage. Such an airliner was built in 1967, but failed to proceed beyond the prototype stage. The standard capacity of 65 passengers in the convertible current model is provided with tip-up seats along the cabin walls and with removable seats on the floor.

Some 20% of the aerodynamic load is carried on stub wings measuring 15.3 m (50 ft 2½ in) in span. To save weight and increase payload, these wings are detached when the type is operated as a flying crane. For normal operations they can be fixed at either of two angles of incidence. The wings are also removed in the fire-fighting variant, which can carry 12 000 kg (26 455 lb) of water.

The prototypes were powered by two 4635-shp Soloviev TV-25VM turboshafts, but production models have the 5500-shp Soloviev D-25V developed models. Also fitted is a 100-hp AI-8 auxiliary power unit for starting the engines in the absence of any external power source. The developed engines, which keep their rating at altitudes up to 3000 m (9842 ft) and so make possible operations in 'hot and high' conditions, also allowed some notable records, the most impressive being an altitude of 2840 m (9317 ft) with a 25 105-kg (55 346-lb) payload on May 28, 1965.

From the Mi-6 was developed the Mi-10 as a specialized flying crane, which first flew in 1960. The Mi-10 is 31.8 cm (12½ in) shorter than the Mi-6, but otherwise dimensionally similar. The fuselage is much shallower, however, and the Mi-10 is fitted with a stalky quadricycle undercarriage.

In 1966 there appeared the Mi-10K, basically similar to the Mi-10 except for its shorter undercarriage legs, a chin gondola for a second pilot to control hover-loading operations, and uprated 6500-shp Soloviev D-25VF turboshafts in fully developed models. This allows a payload of 14 000 kg (30 864 lb) in the slung mode, compared with the Mi-10's 8000 kg (17 637 lb).

Above left: The ventral cockpit used for controlling the Mi-10K in its flying crane role

Above: An Mi-6 operating without stub wings. These can take up to 20% of the lift and so extend the range, but they reduce hovering performance

Left: The original Mi-10, with long landing gear, was equipped with close circuit TV for guidance in straddling its cargo, or winching it into position beneath the 'fuselage'

Mi-8P, Mil

FIRST FLIGHT 1961

THE civil Mil Mi-8 bears a similar relationship to the Mi-4 as does the Mi-2 to the Mi-1. It was designed to capitalize on the ability of turboshaft power to improve on the design of a radial-engined type without radical redesign. Designed to carry some 25 passengers over ranges of approximately 300 km (186 miles), the Mi-8 helicopter was revealed in 1961. It was allotted the NATO reporting name of Hip.

The Mi-8 was immediately notable for its similarities to the Mi-4 except for the use of a single-turboshaft powerplant above the cabin. Figures since revealed indicate that the payload of the Mi-8 is some 2½ times greater than that of the Mi-4, while operating costs were cut by half.

The original Mi-8 prototype was powered by a 2700-shp Soloviev turboshaft, but at the request of Aeroflot, who wished a twin-engined design for single-engined safety reasons, the second prototype was fitted with a pair of 1500-shp Isotov TV-2-117 turboshafts, and a five-blade rotor in place of the first prototype's four-blade unit. The twin-engined powerplant and five-blade rotor became standard on production machines.

There are three civil versions of the Mi-8. The basic Mi-8P is a passenger aircraft with seating for 28 passengers arranged four-abreast. The Mi-8T is a utility model, able to seat 24 passengers in tip-up seats along the sides of the hold, but generally intended for freight operations. The clamshell doors at the rear of the pod open to reveal a freight hold with a volume of 23 m³ (812 cu ft) and able to take a load of 4000 kg (8818 lb). The hold measures 5.34 m by 2.2 m by 1.82 m (17 ft 6 in by 7 ft 2½ in by 5 ft 11¾ in). The Mi-8T can alternatively carry a slung load of 3000 kg (6614 lb). To provide hover-loading facilities the Mi-8T is equipped with a 250-kg (551-lb) winch.

The third civil version of the Mi-8 is the Mi-8 Salon VIP transport for 11 passengers, with an eight-seat couch on the left side, and two chairs and a swivelling seat to the right; aft of the passenger accommodation is a lavatory and passenger wardrobe, and forward is the air stewardess' area with a buffet, jump-seat and wardrobe. The Mi-8 Salon has a maximum take-off weight of 10 400 kg (22 928 lb) and a range of 380 km (236 miles), but its other weights and performance are basically similar to those of the Mi-8P and Mi-8T helicopters.

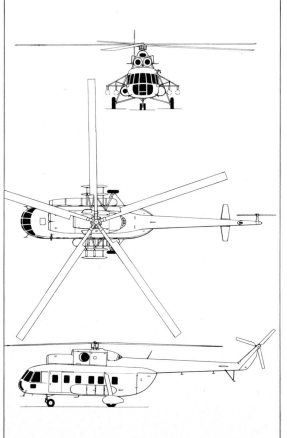

Above: The Mi-8P in Aeroflot colours at the Paris Air Show in 1965. Among its roles are patrol/survey duties in the Arctic, air ambulance work and freight and passenger carrying
Left: An Mi-8P at the Paris Air Show two summers earlier. In its civil role it can carry 28 passengers in airline accommodation or nine in executive luxury

Mi-8P

Type: transport helicopter
Maker: Mil Design Bureau
Rotor diameter: 21.29 m (69 ft 10¼ in)
Length: 18.31 m (60 ft 0¾ in) fuselage
Height: 5.65 m (18 ft 6½ in)
Main rotor disc area: 355 m² (3828 sq ft)
Weight: maximum 12 000 kg (26 455 lb); empty 7260 kg (16 005 lb)
Powerplant: two 1500-shp Isotov TV2-117A turboshafts
Performance: maximum speed 260 km/h (161 mph) at 1000 m (3281 ft); range with passengers at 1000 m (3281 ft) 425 km (264 miles)
Payload: 4000 kg (8818 lb); seats for up to 28 passengers
Crew: 2 to 3
Production: approx 5000 (civil and military)

SA 321F Super Frelon, Aérospatiale

FIRST FLIGHT 1962

THE French first experimented with three-engined four-bladed helicopters in 1959, when they developed the SE 3200 Frelon (Hornet). It was powered by Turboméca Turmo IIIBs.

In 1962 the Super Frelon made its maiden flight, and a year later a streamlined version set up a world record on a 3-km (1.86-mile), 15/25-km (9.3/15.5-mile) and 100-km (62.1-mile) closed circuit. Like most helicopters its role was first envisaged as a military machine, but the SA 321F and SA 321Ja are both used as commercial airliners. Depending on its role the SA 321F can carry 8, 14 or 23 passengers with lavatories and the rest of the cabin being used for freight. Seats can be folded against the cabin wall when they are not in use. The SA 321F can also carry 37 passengers in airline seats or 34 with a lavatory. The SA 321Ja has seating for up to 27 passengers or an internal load of 5000 kg (11 023 lb), or a similar load that can be slung.

The cabin is soundproofed and ventilated, and has a sliding door on the right with a rear loading ramp actuated hydraulically.

The second prototype of the Super Frelon flew in May 1963 and was the naval version with flotation gear. The SA 321F made its maiden flight in April 1967.

The powerplant consists of three 1550-shp Turboméca Turmo IIIC turboshaft engines with two mounted forward and one in the rear. The main gearbox is connected through mechanical drives with the six-bladed rotor and five-bladed antitorque rotor. The rotors were designed by Sikorsky

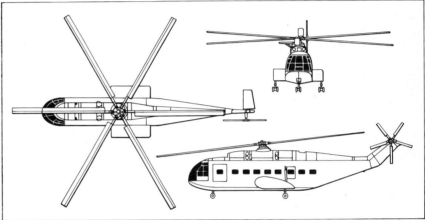

and the transmission by the Fiat company of Italy.

The rotor blades are all-metal, interchangeable and of the pretracked type. The rotor includes hydraulically assisted cyclic and collective pitch controls, hydraulic drag dampers and a centrifugal stop to reduce the blade-flapping angle.

Fuel is in flexible tanks under the floor of the main fuselage and consists of 3975 litres (874 Imp gal) or, as in the Ja version, of 3900 litres (858 Imp gal). Landing gear comprises a non-retractable tricycle designed by Messier-Hispano. Each unit has two wheels with oleo-pneumatic shock absorbers. All the wheels are fitted with hydraulic disc brakes and the nosewheel can be steered.

The bulk of Super Frelon foreign exports are for service use.

SA 321F Super Frelon

Type: commercial helicopter
Maker: Société Nationale Industrielle Aérospatiale
Rotor diameter: 18.9 m (62 ft)
Length: 19.4 m (63 ft 7¾ in)
Height: 4.94 m (16 ft 2½ in)
Main rotor disc area: 280.55 m² (3020 sq ft)
Weight: maximum 13 000 kg (28 660 lb); empty (Ja) 6868 kg (15 141 lb); 321F empty weight is greater depending on seating arrangements
Powerplant: three 1500-shp Turboméca IIIC$_3$ turboshafts
Performance: cruising speed 230 km/h (143 mph) at sea level; range 625 km (388 miles)
Payload: 5000 kg (11 023 lb); seats for up to 37 passengers
Crew: 2
Production: minimum 100 (civil and military orders)

Top: A Super Frelon leased to Olympic Airways. This civil version can carry freight and passengers
Left: An SA-321J, the utility and public transport version of the Super Frelon. This machine is in service with the Norwegian operator BAT

281

Brantly

FIRST FLIGHT 1953

THE current Brantly-Hynes Helicopters company was formed in January 1975 when Michael K Hynes took over Brantly Operators, which had itself acquired all rights in Brantly helicopter designs during 1970. Brantly, a weaving-machinery expert with the Penn Elastic Company, designed his first helicopter in 1946. The B-1 had contrarotating co-axial rotors and was in fact built by the Penn Company.

Brantly Operators continues as the main servicing and rebuild agency for Brantly helicopters, while Brantly-Hynes Helicopters has restarted the production of the B-2B and the Model 305.

The Brantly B-2, which first flew on February 21, 1953, was for its time an extremely advanced design for a side-by-side two-seater intended for the executive operator or private pilot. At a time when helicopters tended to sacrifice aerodynamic cleanliness for light steel-tube rear fuselages, the B-2 was notable for its excellent streamlining, with its almost hemispherical nose section and long conical tail section. Development of the B-2 was slow, and the type entered production only in 1959. The current B-2B is very similar to the original B-2, but incorporates modern developments where applicable. These include a new type of rotor blade with a rigid inboard end built round a steel spar blade, and a flexible outboard portion built round an extruded aluminium leading-edge spar with a polyurethane core, and an aluminium skin riveted to the spar and bonded to the core.

The Brantly-Hynes Model 305 is basically a five-seat development of the B-2B, with the rotor scaled up to a diameter of 8.74 m (28 ft 8 in) and power provided by a 305-hp Lycoming IVO-540-A1A flat-six piston engine. The prototype of the Model 305 first flew in January 1964, and the US Federal Aviation Administration's Type Approval was granted in July 1965.

The 305 keeps the same fine fuselage lines as the B-2 family, with the cylindrical section in the centre lengthened to provide space for the rear bench seat for three more passengers. The Model 305 can carry a light underslung load, and possesses the following primary performance characteristics: maximum speed at sea level 193 km/h (120 mph); range with maximum payload 354 km (220 miles); and service ceiling 3658 m (12000 ft). Maximum take-off and empty weights are 1315 kg (2900 lb) and 817 kg (1800 lb) respectively.

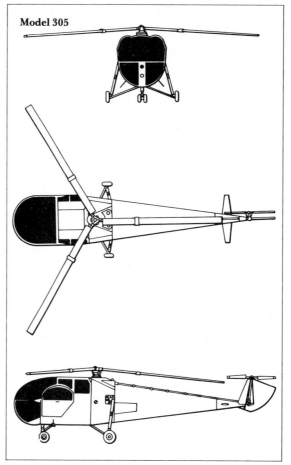

Model 305

Above: G-ATSJ, the only Brantly 305 registered in the UK by 1980, starts up its engine
Left: The Brantly-Hynes B-2 which was used in the James Bond film *The Spy Who Loved Me*. The first B-2 flew in 1953 and was notable for its attractive streamlining

B-2B

Type: light helicopter
Maker: Brantly-Hynes Helicopters Inc
Rotor diameter: 7.24 m (23 ft 9 in)
Length: 6.62 m (21 ft 9 in) fuselage
Height: 2.06 m (6 ft 9 in)
Main rotor disc area: 41.06 m² (442 sq ft)
Weight: maximum 757 kg (1670 lb); empty 463 kg (1020 lb)
Powerplant: one 180-hp Lycoming IVO-360-A1A 4-cylinder horizontally opposed air-cooled piston engine
Performance: maximum speed 161 km/h (100 mph) at sea level; range 402 km (250 miles)
Payload: 113 kg (250 lb); seat for 1 passenger
Crew: 1
Production: minimum 400

Hughes 300
FIRST FLIGHT 1956

HUGHES Helicopters began the design of its Model 269 two-seat light helicopter in September 1955. Two prototypes were built, the first flying in October 1956, but the design was thought to be too complex. Compared with the 269, the 269A had a braced tubular tail boom in place of the original structure of welded steel, and an increase in the length of the landing skids.

Five of the type were evaluated by the US Army, under the designation YHO-2HU, in the command and observation role. Main military production of the 269A was in the form of the TH-55A primary trainer for the US Army, some 792 of the type being delivered.

The Model 300 was developed for civil use as a three-seat version of the Model 269A under the engineering designation 269B. The improved type received its US Federal Aviation Administration Type Approval on December 30, 1963. By 1964 production was at the rate of one Model 300 per day, a similar rate with the 269A having been attained by September 1961. The most important development of the 300 is the Quiet Tail Rotor (QTR), fitted on production aircraft since June 1967 and also available as a retrofit kit for the owners of earlier 269A and 300 helicopters. The installation of this QTR reduces the aircraft's noise signature by some 80%, making its cruise-regime noise comparable with that of small fixed-wing aircraft.

The Model 300C is a further development of the 300, with a 45% increase in payload resulting from the use of a more powerful engine and slightly

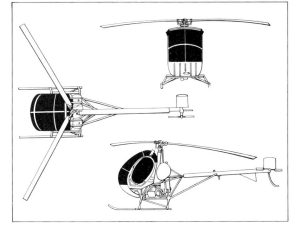

larger main rotor. These have necessitated other related alterations to the basic airframe, including a taller main rotor mast, structural strengthening, and increase in the area of the fixed fin and of the tail-rotor diameter. The 300C first flew in August 1969, with production beginning in December and certification following in May 1970.

Further development has led to the Model 300CQ, the quiet version of the 300C, and which is also the civil version of the 'Quiet One' modification of the military OH-6A Cayuse. The 300CQ is approximately 75% quieter than the 300C. Performance of the 300C is almost identical with that of the 300C, but for quiet flight both maximum take-off weight and payload have to be reduced slightly.

Model 300

Type: general-purpose light helicopter
Maker: Hughes Helicopters (Summa Corporation); Kawasaki Heavy Industries; RACA; BredaNardi
Rotor diameter: 7.71 m (25 ft 3½ in)
Length: 6.8 m (21 ft 11¾ in) fuselage
Height: 2.5 m (8 ft 2¾ in)
Main rotor disc area: 46.73 m² (503 sq ft)
Weight: maximum 757 kg (1670 lb); empty 434 kg (958 lb)
Powerplant: one 180-hp Lycoming HIO-360-A1A 4-cylinder horizontally opposed air-cooled inline engine
Performance: maximum speed 140 km/h (87 mph) at sea level; range 483 km (300 miles)
Payload: approx 136 kg (300 lb); seats for up to 2 passengers
Crew: 1
Production: minimum 650

Above: A British-registered Hughes 300C starts up its engine on a summer evening. This machine first flew in July 1972

Hughes 500

FIRST FLIGHT 1974

Left: A British-registered Hughes 500, one of five in use in the United Kingdom in 1980. This machine made its first flight in November 1969. Some machines have an executive interior, while others have a convertible freight cabin

THE Hughes 500 is basically the civil variant of the controversial OH-6 Cayuse light multirole helicopter. This compact helicopter was ideally suited for development into a civil type, the Hughes 500, which entered production in November 1968.

The original variant was the Model 500, with a four-blade main rotor powered by a single 317-shp Allison 250-C18A turboshaft, derated to 278 shp for take-off and to 243 shp for continuous running. The next variant was the Model 500C, basically similar to its predecessor except for the installation of a 400-shp Allison 250-C20 turboshaft.

The Model 500D has more radical improvements. This type was announced in February 1975, some months after the first flight of the prototype in August 1974. Power is provided by the 420-shp Allison 250-C20B, and the main rotor is a five-blade unit, of the same type of construction used in the blades of the 500 and 500C: an extruded aluminium spar bonded to a one-piece wrap-round aluminium skin, connected to the laminated strap retention system by quick-disconnect pins.

Modifications to reduce the type's noise output are similar to those pioneered in the 'Quiet One' research programme for the OH-6A, and consist mainly of the provision of a five-blade main rotor, engine exhaust silencer, soundproofing of the powerplant and air intake, and a revision of the blade tips. At the same time, the 500D was given a small T-tail assembly in place of the 500 and 500C's tailplane, ventral fin and fixed upper fin. The T-tail gives the Model 500D improved stability at high and low speeds, and improves handling.

284

Hughes 500

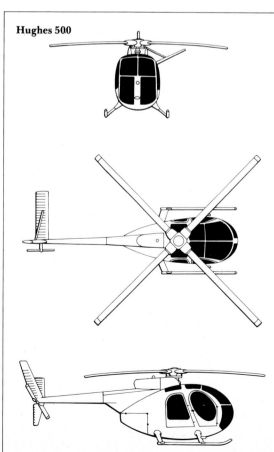

Hughes 500D

Type: general-purpose light helicopter
Maker: Hughes Helicopters (Summa Corporation)
Rotor diameter: 8.05 m (26 ft 5 in)
Length: 9.3 m (30 ft 6 in) overall
Height: 2.53 m (8 ft 3½ in)
Main rotor disc area: 50.89 m² (548 sq ft)
Weight: maximum 1361 kg (3000 lb); empty 598 kg (1320 lb)
Powerplant: one 420-shp Allison 250-C20B turboshaft
Performance: maximum cruising speed 258 km/h (160 mph) at sea level; range at 1524 m (5000 ft) 539 km (335 miles)
Payload: approx 490 kg (1080 lb); seats for up to 2 passengers
Crew: 1
Production: minimum 350 (orders)

Bell 204

FIRST FLIGHT 1956

THE Bell Model 204 and its successors have been produced in greater numbers than any other helicopter. The origins of the design lay with a June 1955 competition run by the US Army to find a new general-purpose helicopter. Bell produced its 204 to meet the requirement, and three prototypes were ordered under the initial designation XH-40.

The first of these helicopters flew on October 22, 1956, only 16 months after the start of design work. Thé first civil model was the Bell 204B powered by the 1100-shp Lycoming T5309A turboshaft, the civil counterpart of the similarly rated T53-L-11 used in later production examples of the military UH-1B, which introduced the enlarged cabin, and wider-chord rotor blades of honeycomb construction also featured on the 204B.

The 204B was also produced in Italy by Agusta under the designation AB 204B. The type was produced with a main rotor spanning either 13.41 m (44 ft) or 14.63 m (48 ft), and a variety of powerplants ranging from the T53 of the original US version, to the General Electric T58 and Rolls-Royce Gnome turboshafts.

In Japan the 204 was also built for military and civil operations by Fuji Heavy Industries, as the Fuji-Bell 204B. This variant was powered by the Kawasaki-built Lycoming T5311A turboshaft.

During 1973 Fuji developed an uprated model of the Bell 204B under the designation Fuji-Bell 204B-2. This is distinguishable from the 204B in having a 1400-shp Lycoming T5313B turboshaft, and the tractor-type anti-torque tail rotor pioneered on the Fuji-Bell UH-1H military helicopter.

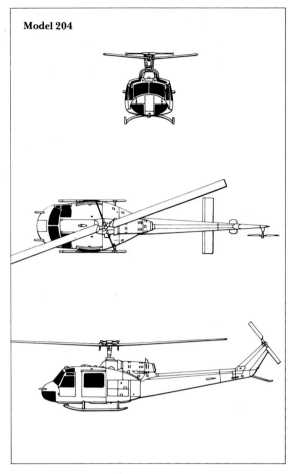

Model 204

204B-2

Type: utility helicopter
Maker: Bell Helicopter Textron; Costruzioni Aeronautiche Giovanni Agusta; Fuji Heavy Industries
Rotor diameter: 16.63 m (48 ft)
Length: 12.31 m (40 ft 4¾ in) fuselage
Height: 4.42 m (14 ft 6 in)
Main rotor disc area: 168.1 m² (1810 sq ft)
Weight: maximum 3856 kg (8500 lb); empty 2177 kg (4800 lb)
Powerplant: one 1400-shp Lycoming T5313B turboshaft
Performance: maximum cruising speed 204 km/h (127 mph); range at sea level 383 km (238 miles)
Payload: seats for up to 9 passengers
Crew: 1
Production: not available

Above: A Bell 204 starts its turbine engine on a grass strip in Bermuda
Right: An Agusta-Bell 204B equipped with a personnel hoist at the Paris Air Show of June 1965. The Bell helicopters which are known loosely as Huey, from their original military HU designation, are among the most widely used civil and military aircraft of any kind. Service-trained pilots are readily available to fly them

Bell 205

FIRST FLIGHT 1962

THE Bell 205 helicopter is a development of the Model 204 with an uprated version of the 204's Lycoming LTC1 turboshaft, a longer fuselage, increased cabin volume and area, and a number of other detail improvements to add to payload and performance while at the same time reducing maintenance requirements. The first development of the Model 205 was for military use.

Initial civil production of the 205 was of the Model 205A-1 version, derived from the UH-1H but fitted with the civil version of the UH-1H's engine, the 1400-shp T5313A turboshaft, derated to 1250 shp for take-off. The 205A-1 was designed for easy conversion into several configurations. As a passenger carrier, the 205A-1 can carry up to 14 people in addition to the pilot. In the air-freight role, the type's cargo capacity is 7.02 m³ (248 cu ft), including a small hold in the boom, and freight is loaded through doors on each side of the fuselage, each presenting an opening of 2.34 m by 1.24 m (7 ft 8 in by 4 ft 1 in). The doors are about knee height which makes for easy loading of stretchers or cargo and, like the 204, they can be moved back along the fuselage to reveal the complete interior.

As a flying crane, the 205A-1 can lift weights up to 2268 kg (5000 lb), and as an aerial ambulance, the helicopter can accommodate up to six litters and one or two medical attendants.

As with the military versions of the 205, the civil 205A-1 has a standard fuel tankage which can be supplemented with an auxiliary capacity when needed. Standard tankage is five rubber fuel cells

Below: An Agusta-Bell 205; this Italian-built version has been sold to Iran, Kuwait, Morocco, Saudi Arabia, Spain, Turkey, the United Arab Emirates and Zambia. It can be delivered with an external cargo hook, auxiliary fuel tanks, rescue hoist, floats and skis

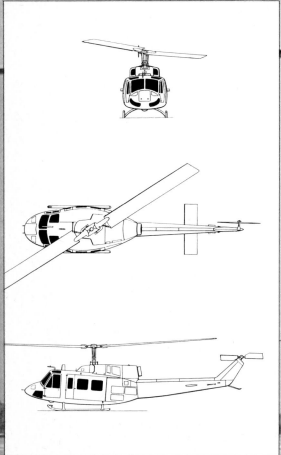

205A-1

Type: utility helicopter
Maker: Bell Helicopter Textron; Costruzioni Aeronautiche Giovanni Agusta
Rotor diameter: 14.63 m (48 ft)
Length: 12.65 m (41 ft 6 in) fuselage
Height: 4.39 m (14 ft 4¾ in)
Main rotor disc area: 168.06 m² (1809 sq ft)
Weight: maximum 4763 kg (10 500 lb); empty 2370 kg (5226 lb)
Powerplant: one 1400-shp Lycoming T5313A turboshaft

Performance: maximum speed 204 km/h (127 mph) at sea level; range at 2438 m (8000 ft) 553 km (344 miles)
Payload: 2268 kg (5000 lb); seats for up to 14 passengers
Crew: 1
Production: not available

holding 814 litres (179 Imp gal), to which can be interconnected two extra cells for an additional 682 litres (150 Imp gal) of fuel.

The 205A-1 is also built under licence in Italy by Agusta, as the Agusta Bell AB 205A-1. This model is almost identical with the Bell 205A-1, but is powered by the 1400-shp Lycoming T5313B turboshaft, derated to 1250 shp for take-off, and has a number of improvements. Fuselage length is 12.78 m (41 ft 11 in) compared with the 205A-1's 12.65 m (41 ft 6 in), and maximum speed is 222 km/h (138 mph) compared with 204 km/h (127 mph). As in the Bell 205A-1, there is in the tail boom a 0.8-m³ (28⅓-cu ft) baggage compartment, and the type can readily be converted.

Bell is unusual in the design of medium-size helicopters in opting for a main rotor comprising only two broad-chord blades. In the case of the 205A-1 these blades are interchangeable, and built up of extruded aluminium spars and laminates. The rotor turns at up to 324 revolutions per minute, and is stabilized by an end-weighted bar above and at right angles to the main blades, each of which has a chord of 53.34 cm (21 in).

The Bell 205A-1 can be used on water by adding optional inflatable landing floats, and for the search-and-rescue role a medium-capacity winch can be fitted. The evolution of the Bell 212 and 214 helicopters can be traced back to the Models 204 and 205 respectively, making this family numerically the most important helicopter ever.

Bell 214B

FIRST FLIGHT 1974

THE Bell 214B BigLifter is the civil version of the Model 214A utility helicopter produced for the Iranian army, itself developed in 1972 and 1973 from the Model 214 Huey Plus. The BigLifter was announced on January 4, 1974 for delivery beginning 1975. Unfortunately, US Federal Aviation Administration Type Approval of the 214B was not received until January 27, 1976.

The 214B BigLifter is derived essentially from the 204 and 205, and was specifically designed to better the lift capacity of any contemporary civil helicopter of the same power. The key to the type's considerable lifting ability is the use of a 2930-shp Lycoming T5508D turboshaft (the civil version of the T55-LTC4B-8D turboshaft powering the 214A and its search-and-rescue derivative, the 214C), flat-rated to 2250 shp maximum output. The rotor and transmission are identical with those of the 214A, the transmission being capable of accepting up to 2050 shp at take-off and 1850 shp for continuous running.

The rotor system is of an advanced type, the blades having swept tips and the hub featuring elastomeric bearings on the flapping axis. The twin-blade tail rotor has a hub which needs no lubrication. Other advanced features of the type are the use of an automatic flight-control system, with the capability of altitude maintenance and augmented stability; dual hydraulic systems; a nodalized suspension (Bell's patented 'Noda-Matic' concept of 1972, by which the fuselage is suspended from points of no relative motion in the engine mounting) to reduce fuselage vibration by

about 80%; and an engine decking that is also used as a maintenance platform for the engine, transmission and rotor hub.

The 214B BigLifter carries to an extreme the Bell design philosophy of a twin-blade wide-chord main rotor, each of the blades having a chord of no less than 88.9 cm (35 in). The transmission and rotor-drive systems are well proved by earlier use in the 214A, after development in the experimental KingCobra gunship helicopter.

Although it is intended mainly as a weight-lifter, the 214B can carry up to 14 passengers in addition to its crew of two. As a weight-lifter, however, the 214B can carry up to 1814 kg (4000 lb) internally, or up to 3175 kg (7000 lb) externally on its cargo hook, which is cleared for flight with loads weigh-

Above: A Bell 214B BigLifter of Heliswiss, a Swiss helicopter operator which was formed in 1953. The firm now specializes in the transport of passengers and freight in the Alps. Other work includes aerial advertizing, ambulance and crop dusting and spraying
Right: A Heliswiss BigLifter transports a workmans' shelter using its external cargo sling

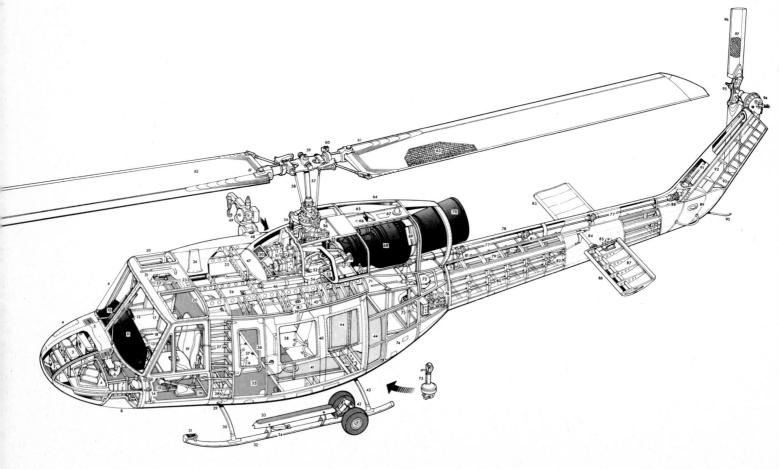

ing up to 3629 kg (8000 lb). This weight-lifting capacity is also useful in the agricultural role, in which up to 3629 kg (8000 lb) of chemicals or 3023 litres (665 Imp gal) of liquid can be uplifted. The considerable liquid-carrying capability of the 214B is also useful for fire-fighting.

The only current version of the Bell 214B is the Model 214B-1, which is intended for different certification standards, and is thus limited in the internal load-carrying role to a maximum take-off weight of 5670 kg (12 500 lb).

The Bell 214A is the military version supplied to the Iranian army as the Isfahan, while the Model 214C is the search-and-rescue variant operated by the Iranian air force.

On April 29, 1975, three days after delivery to Iran of the first production 214A, this machine was used to set up five records for altitude and time-to-height. The records were for a maximum altitude of 9071 m (29 760 ft), maximum sustained altitude in horizontal flight also of 9071 m and times of 1 min 58 sec to 3000 m (9842 ft), 5 min 13.2 sec to 6000 m (19 685 ft) and 15 min 5 sec to 9000 m (29 526 ft).

Before the overthrow of the Iranian royal dynasty, an agreement was signed for Bell and Iranian Helicopter Industry (IHI) to co-produce the 214A, after which IHI was to have built some 350 of an improved variant, the Model 214ST (Stretched Twin), with a coupled turboshaft powerplant and greater size. This scheme has now been abandoned, and with it has been lost the short-term chance of Bell producing a civil model based on it.

Bell 214B

1 Pitot tube
2 Batteries
3 Radio and electronics compartment
4 Access doors
5 Air grilles
6 Ventilation system
7 Yaw-control pedals
8 Downward vision window
9 Laminated glass windshield
10 Windscreen wipers
11 Instrument panel shroud
12 Pilot's cyclic control stick
13 Co-pilot's cyclic control stick
14 Cockpit door hinge release handle
15 Co-pilot's collective stick
16 Cockpit floor
17 Pilot's seat, military armoured type
18 Centre console
19 Co-pilot's seat commercial type
20 Cockpit eyebrow windows
21 Temperature probe
22 Rotor brake control
23 Overhead control panel
24 Antenna
25 Cabin roof construction
26 Main passenger/cargo compartment
27 Fuselage side panel construction
28 Heater duct
29 Position light
30 Landing skid gear forward cross tube
31 Cockpit step
32 Landing skid gear
33 Cabin entry step
34 Step jack
35 Cabin floor
36 Hinged forward cabin door panel
37 Rearward facing seats
38 Forward facing seats
39 Left navigation light housing
40 Main cabin sliding cargo door
41 Underfloor fuel tank
42 Ground handling wheels (removable)
43 Landing skid gear aft cross tube
44 Fuel tanks
45 Transmission oil sump
46 Ventilation duct
47 Transmission housing front fairing
48 Right navigation light
49 Rescue winch/hoist
50 Air-intake grille
51 Hydraulic equipment
52 Nodal beam gearbox mounting
53 Engine left intake
54 Gearbox (main and tail rotor drives)
55 Engine reduction gearbox
56 Main rotor control linkage (cyclic and collective)
57 Main rotor mast
58 Main rotor blade pitch control tubes
59 Pivoted rotor head mounting
60 MIR hub grip oil reservoir
61 MIR blade doublers
62 Main rotor blades
63 Honeycomb construction
64 Engine cowlings
65 Intake duct particle separator
66 Generator cooling intake
67 Anti-collision light
68 Lycoming T550-8D turboshaft engine
69 Intake particle separator exhaust duct
70 Exhaust ejector
71 Engine tripod mounting leg
72 Fire extinguisher bottle
73 Oil-cooler fan
74 Rear avionics and electrical compartment
75 Cargo hook
76 Rear radio and electronics racks
77 Tail rotor drive shaft
78 Tail rotor drive shaft cover
79 Bearing cooling air duct
80 Tail boom construction
81 Tail rotor drive shaft bearings
82 Elevator control bell crank
83 Right elevator
84 Elevator horn
85 Radio compass
86 Left elevator
87 Elevator construction
88 Intermediate gearbox
89 Rear navigation light
90 Tail skid
91 Tail rotor transmission shaft
92 Fin construction
93 Cambered section fin
94 Tail rotor gearbox
95 Tail rotor pitch control
96 Two-blade tail rotor
97 Honeycomb blade construction

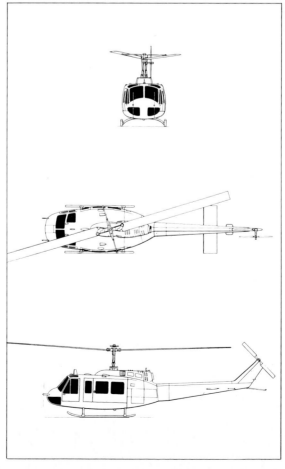

214B BigLifter

Type: heavy-lift helicopter
Maker: Bell Helicopter Textron
Rotor diameter: 15.24 m (50 ft)
Length: 12.92 m (42 ft 4¾ in) fuselage
Height: 4.52 m (14 ft 10 in)
Main rotor disc area: 182.4 m² (1963 sq ft)
Weight: maximum 7258 kg (16 000 lb); empty 3380 kg (7450 lb)
Powerplant: one 2930-shp Lycoming T5508D turboshaft
Performance: maximum cruising speed 259 km/h (161 mph); range not available
Payload: minimum 3175 kg (7000 lb); seats for up to 14 passengers
Crew: 2
Production: not available

Bell 206 JetRanger

FIRST FLIGHT 1966

THE origins of the Bell 206 JetRanger series of civil utility helicopters lie in a 1960 US Army requirement for an LOH (light observation helicopter). The Bell 206A JetRanger was basically the civil version of the OH-58A, the first flying on January 10, 1966, powered by the 317-shp Allison 250-C18 turboshaft, the civil version of the T63-A-700 used for the Bell OH-4 military prototypes.

In 1970 Bell produced for initial delivery in the spring of 1971 the uprated 206B JetRanger II powered by the 400-shp Allison 250-C20 turboshaft. This powerplant was introduced with minimal airframe modifications to meet the needs of operators in 'hot and high' circumstances.

Thus while the 206B is only 8 km/h (5 mph) faster than the 206A at sea level, despite an

increase in power of 93 shp, at 3048 m (10 000 ft) the speed difference is 46.7 km/h (29 mph). Two other facets of this improvement are an increase in hovering weight of 181 kg (400 lb) at the same altitude, and a hovering ceiling in ground effect raised to 3444 m (11 200 ft).

Model 206A helicopters can be brought up to 206B standard by using conversion kits developed by Bell and Allison, the former for airframe modification, and the latter to improve the 250-C18 to 250-C20 standard. An indication of the success of the 206A and 206B is given by the production total of more than 4000 civil and military examples by January 1975. One year later, in January 1976, Bell announced a programme in conjunction with the Collins Radio Group to

Above: A Bell 206A JetRanger which first flew in December 1970 and is operated by BEAS Oxford for CSE

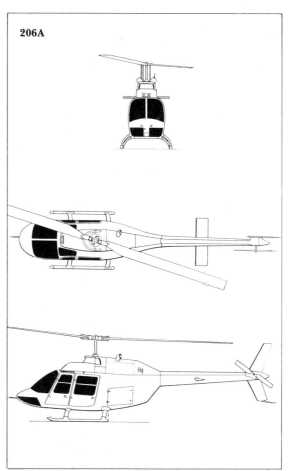

206A

Bell Model 206B JetRanger III

Type: general-purpose light helicopter
Maker: Bell Helicopter Textron; Costruzioni Aeronautiche Giovanni Agusta
Rotor diameter: 10.16 m (33 ft 4 in)
Length: 9.5 m (31 ft 2 in) fuselage
Height: 2.91 m (9 ft 6½ in)
Main rotor disc area: 81.1 m² (873 sq ft)
Weight: maximum 1451 kg (3200 lb); empty 717 kg (1580 lb)
Powerplant: one 420-shp Allison 250-C20B turboshaft
Performance: maximum speed 225 km/h (140 mph) at sea level; range with maximum fuel and maximum payload at 1525 m (5000 ft) 608 km (378 miles)
Payload: approx 476 kg (1050 lb); seats for up to 4 passengers
Crew: 1
Production: minimum 10 000 by 1980 (all versions)

Above: One of four Bell 206Bs operated in 1980 by British Caledonian from bases at Shoreham, Cranfield, Edinburgh and Falmouth. The machines were formerly part of Ferranti Helicopters before a take-over in 1979

develop an IFR (Instrument Flight Rules) system for the 206B, with the object of permitting single-pilot certification by automatic control of attitude (pitch and roll axes) and by selected heading maintenance. This helped maintain the popularity of the 206, of which more than 5000 had been built by January 1977, some 2200 of these going to commercial operators.

On February 7, 1977, Bell announced a new model of the helicopter, the 206B JetRanger III. The main difference between this and the Jet-Ranger II is the use of the 420-shp Allison 250-C20B turboshaft, with further improvement in 'hot and high' performance: hovering ceiling in ground effect is increased to 3871 m (12 700 ft), and cruising speed at 3048 m (10 000 ft) is boosted by

9.7 km/h (6 mph). A retrofit kit to improve Jet-Ranger IIs to JetRanger III standard is readily available, and production of the JetRanger II thus ended in the summer of 1977, the JetRanger III taking over.

The other main producer of the 206 is Agusta in Italy, which has produced the Agusta Bell AB 206A JetRanger I, the AB 206B JetRanger II and is currently producing the AB 206B JetRanger III. Compared with the Bell-built models, the Italian helicopters are slightly heavier and marginally worse in performance. Agusta produce the 206 for several armed forces, as do Bell, in a variety of forms: for example, the Swedish navy's HKP 6 variant has longer landing skid legs to allow the installation of under-fuselage weapon racks.

Boeing Vertol 107
FIRST FLIGHT 1962

MOST Model 107 helicopters, (the civil development of the CH-46 Sea Knight combat assault helicopter) currently in service have been built by Kawasaki Heavy Industries. They acquired manufacturing rights for the 107-II in 1961, the first KV-107/II flying in May 1962.

All KV-107/II variants have the same basic configuration and structure: a tandem-rotor layout with the forward blades rotating anti-clockwise and the rear blades clockwise; a semi-monocoque fuselage; a non-retractable tricycle undercarriage; and the twin units of the powerplant located on each side of the rear rotor pylon. The main rotors are each three-bladed units, each blade consisting of a D-section leading-edge steel spar, with a trailing edge of aluminium ribs covered by glassfibre or aluminium skinning. The two units are located on well-faired pylons at each end of the rectangular-section fuselage, which is constructed of aluminium alloy, and has a loading ramp built into the undersurface of the unswept rear fuselage on utility models.

The main units of the undercarriage extend below the rear-fuselage sponsons, which house some 1323 litres (291 Imp gal) of fuel. The engines comprise two 1250-shp General Electric CT58-110-1 turboshafts, built by the parent company or under licence in Japan by Ishikawajima-Harima; both engines drive into the rear transmission, which is connected by shaft with the forward rotor to ensure synchronization and continued rotation of both rotor units in the event of engine failure.

None of the basic utility version, the KV-107/II-1, has yet been built, but production of the KV-107/II-2 airliner model has reached 11. This helicopter has two crew, a stewardess and 25 passengers seated three-abreast (two to the right and one to the left of the aisle) in eight rows with two double seats at the rear of the cabin. A baggage container in the lower rear fuselage can carry up to 680 kg (1499 lb) of luggage. Other civil models are the KV-107/II-7 VIP transport for up to 11 passengers (one built) and the KV-107/IIA-17 (one built) for long-range transport of passengers or freight (up to 24 passengers, or up to 12 passengers and 2268 kg [5000 lb] of freight).

All KV-107/II variants can be produced to KV-107/IIA standard, with two 1400-shp CT58-140-1 turboshafts, either US- or Japanese-built, and 3785 litres (833 Imp gal) of fuel.

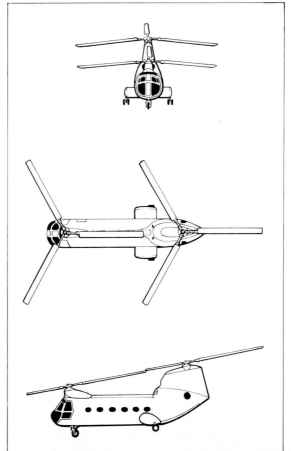

Model 107 (KV-107/II-2)

Type: airliner helicopter
Maker: Boeing Vertol Co; Kawasaki Heavy Industries
Rotor diameter: 15.24 m (50 ft)
Length: 13.59 m (44 ft 7 in) fuselage
Height: 5.09 m (16 ft 8½ in)
Main rotor disc area: 364.6 m² (3925 sq ft)
Weight: maximum 9706 kg (21 400 lb); empty 4868 kg (10 732 lb)
Powerplant: two 1250 shp General Electric CT58-110-1 or Ishikawajima-Harima CT58-IHI-110-1 turboshafts
Performance: maximum speed 253 km/h (157 mph) at sea level; range with a payload of 3000 kg (6614 lb) 175 km (109 miles)
Payload: seats for up to 25 passengers
Crew: 2
Production: 11 (KV-107/II-2)

Top: The prototype Boeing Vertol 107 in the livery of New York Airways
Above: New York Airways operated seven 107s as 25-seaters from July 1962. They linked New York's airports with the PanAm buildings and other city locations

LongRanger, Bell 206L

FIRST FLIGHT 1974

THE Bell 206L LongRanger was announced on September 25, 1973 to meet the civil operators' requirement for a turbine-powered medium-lift helicopter. Based on the JetRanger II, the Long-Ranger introduced a 63.5-cm (25-in) fuselage stretch to provide accommodation for five passengers in addition to the two crew, the 420-shp Allison 250-C20B turboshaft with a continuous rating of 370 shp, a new rotor and a new transmission able to handle up to 428 shp.

Most importantly, however, the LongRanger marked the debut in service of Bell's newly developed Noda-Matic suspension, in which the fuselage is hung from nodal points (points of no relative motion) in the engine mounting, thus greatly reducing cabin vibration. At the same time the introduction of elastomeric bearings in the rotor-blade hinges greatly reduced noise.

The fuselage stretch of the LongRanger increases cabin volume from the 1.39 m³ (49 cu ft) of the JetRanger II to 2.35 m³ (83 cu ft), while careful design has allowed optimum use of this volume. In passenger configuration there are two angled aft-facing seats and three forward-facing seats. The forward seat on the left side is constructed to allow its back to be folded down so making possible the loading of long items which cannot be transported in any other helicopter of the same class. Loading is facilitated by left-sided double doors with an opening 1.52 m (5 ft) wide.

The first 206L LongRanger flew on September 11, 1974, and US Federal Aviation Administration certification was received in 1975.

Left: A Bell LongRanger of Dominion Pegasus working as a flying crane on a construction site in Toronto
Below: A Bell 206 of the German operator Benteler

206L-1 LongRanger II

Type: general-purpose light helicopter
Maker: Bell Helicopter Textron
Rotor diameter: 11.28 m (37 ft)
Length: 12.46 m (40 ft 10½ in) overall
Height: 2.91 m (9 ft 6½ in)
Main rotor disc area: 99.9 m² (1075 sq ft)
Weight: maximum 1837 kg (4050 lb); empty 978 kg (2156 lb)
Powerplant: one 500-shp Allison 250-C28B
Performance: maximum speed 241 km/h (150 mph) at sea level; range at 1525 m (5000 ft) 621 km (386 miles)
Payload: 907 kg (2000 lb); seats for up to 5 passengers
Crew: 2
Production: minimum 250

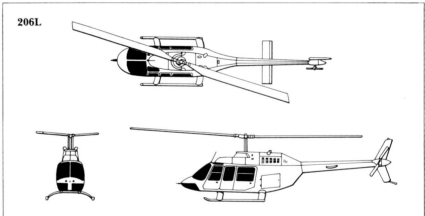

206L

D-HEHB

BENTELER

Bell 222

FIRST FLIGHT 1976

IN APRIL 1974 Bell announced that it was about to start the development of the first twin-turbine light helicopter to be produced in the United States. Construction of the first of five prototypes began on September 1 of the same year.

The first of these Bell 222 prototypes flew on August 13, 1976, and soon showed itself to have very useful commercial aspects, thanks to extensive consultations between the manufacturer and possible operators. These factors include carefully designed glazing on the lower sides of the flight-deck to facilitate landings on rooftops, and a widening and heightening of the rear part of the passenger cabin to increase comfort in high-density passenger configuration.

The Bell 222 has good performance, the result largely of careful streamlining, low structure weight and ample power. The fuselage has particularly fine lines, and is a semi-monocoque structure of light alloy, with a fail-safe structure in highly stressed areas. Light alloy honeycomb panels are used only to a limited extent. The tail unit is a light alloy cantilever structure with a two-part swept vertical fin to the right and the two-blade stainless steel rotor to the left. A fairly substantial tailplane with small endplate fins of swept configuration is located half-way along the tail structure, between the fin and fuselage proper. Under the rotor assembly towards the bottom of the fuselage is a pair of sponsons, light alloy and honeycomb cantilever units, into which the mainwheels of the hydraulically-actuated tricycle undercarriage re-

Above: The Bell 222 was the first commercial light twin-engined helicopter to be built in the USA (it was preceded by Germany's BO 105)

Bell 222

1 Electronics cooling air grille
2 Hinged nose compartment access panel
3 Weather radar scanner
4 Radar mounting
5 Battery
6 Radio and electronics racks
7 Nosewheel doors
8 Nosewheel
9 Downward vision window
10 Rudder/yaw pedals
11 Instrument panel shroud
12 Windscreen wipers
13 Windscreen panels
14 Optional electrically heated, birdproof windscreens
15 Overhead electrical control panel
16 Rotor brake lever
17 Pilot's seat
18 Collective-pitch control column
19 Engine throttles
20 Cyclic-pitch control column
21 Footboards
22 Cockpit door
23 Forward emergency floatation bag (optional)
24 Floatation bag stowage
25 Sliding seat rails
26 Safety harness
27 Co-pilot's seat
28 Sliding side window panel
29 Cockpit overhead window
30 Right vertical control duct
31 Pitot tubes
32 Fresh-air intake door
33 Glassfibre top decking fairings
34 Rotor control rods
35 Access panel
36 Honeycomb skin panels
37 Fuselage forward frame construction
38 Three-abreast main cabin seating
39 Folding outboard seat (each side) for access to rear seats
40 Cabin passenger door
41 Door latch
42 Cabin heater duct
43 Cabin floor level
44 Folding maintenance step
45 Noda-Matic anti-vibration main gearbox mounting

46 Control system duplex hydraulic jacks
47 Rotor blade control hinge links
48 Right engine air intake
49 Rotating swash plate assembly
50 Main rotor mast
51 Blade control rods
52 Pivoted rotor head mounting
53 Flexible titanium yoke
54 Pitch control horns
55 Blade root attachments
56 Spar doublers
57 Stainless-steel rotor blade spar
58 Honeycomb construction
59 Glassfibre skins
60 Stainless-steel leading edges
61 Right engine cowlings
62 Anti-collision light
63 Engine and transmission oil coolers
64 Rotor brake
65 Main transmission gearbox
66 Bevel drive gearbox
67 Hydraulic pump
68 Three-abreast rear seat row
69 Folding seat backs for access to baggage compartment
70 Main fuel tanks
71 Gearbox vibration damper
72 Left engine air intake
73 Engine drive shaft
74 Engine intake duct
75 Fireproof bulkhead
76 Intake separator screen
77 Oil-cooler air outlet
78 Engine mounting deck
79 Lycoming LTS 101-650C-2 turboshaft engine
80 Intake by-pass duct
81 By-pass air-cooled exhaust ejector
82 Cooling air grilles
83 Exhaust pipes
84 Engine and transmission aft fairing
85 Tail rotor transmission shaft
86 Right fixed tailplane
87 Tailplane fixed inverted slot
88 Right fixed fin
89 Transmission shaft bearings
90 Spin shaft housing
91 Main rotor
92 Rotor blade tab
93 Tailfin construction
94 Fin tip fairing
95 Tail navigation light

96 Tail rotor gearbox
97 Blade pitch control
98 Two-bladed tail rotor
99 Tail skid
100 Ventral fin
101 Tailcone ring frames
102 Communications aerial
103 Left tailplane endplate fin
104 Tailplane construction
105 Fixed slot
106 Tail rotor control rod
107 Tailcone joint ring
108 Fuselage frame and stringer construction
109 Tail rotor control rod hydraulic jack
110 Baggage compartment floor, door on right side
111 Air-outlet grille
112 Air-conditioning plant
113 Maintenance step
114 Fuel filters, filler cap on right side
115 Sponson fuel tank
116 Stub wing/sponson construction
117 Main undercarriage wheel well
118 Landing taxiing lamp
119 Long range fuel tank in optional extended tip
120 Glassfibre tip fairing
121 Left navigation light
122 Flotation bag stowage in optional extended tip
123 Left mainwheel
124 Emergency floatation bag (optional)
125 Alternative skid landing gear

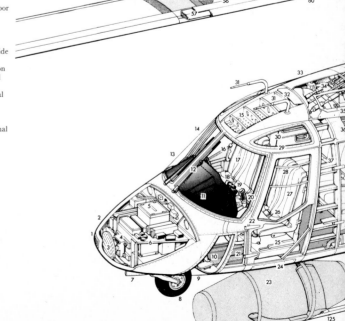

tract. The wheels have a free-fall extension capability for emergency use, and water-activated emergency floats are available as a customer option.

The two-blade main rotor is of typical Bell design, with wide blades; construction is advanced, however, with the blades made of stainless steel and glassfibre. The rotor hub is completely dry and features conical elastomerics. The transmission is rated at 850 shp for twin-engined operation, and at 675 shp for single-engined operation. The pylon is a focused unit with Noda-Matic suspension to ensure low fuselage vibration levels from the turning of the rotor. Power is provided by two Avco Lycoming LTS 101-650C2 turboshafts mounted side-by-side in a streamlined pack behind the rotor pylon. The engines are each rated at 675 shp maximum for 2½ min, 630 shp for 30 min and 590 shp for continuous running.

The internal space can be divided in a number of ways to suit operator requirements. The standard seating arrangement is for a pilot and up to seven passengers in a 2-3-3 layout (or for a pilot, co-pilot and six passengers in the same layout); alternatively, a high-density layout of 2-2-3-3 seating is possible. The total volume available, including the crew area, is 5.52 m³ (195 cu ft), and the passenger area is 2.01 m (6 ft 7 in) long, with a maximum width of 1.41 m (4 ft 7½ in) and a maximum height of 1.3 m (4 ft 3 in). There is a baggage hold of 1.05 m³ (37 cu ft) immediately aft of the passenger cabin, which is entered through either of two doors on each side of the fuselage just forward of the undercarriage sponsons. Each of these sponsons

contains a fuel bladder, and a third bladder is located in the fuselage to provide a total tankage of 714 litres (157 Imp gal). The versatility of the Bell 222 is enhanced by the provision as an optional extra of a 1814-kg (4000-lb) cargo hook for external loads.

The Bell 222 is one of the most interesting civil helicopters to have appeared in recent years, and fully reflects modern concern with safety considerations. The twin-engined layout is particularly important in this respect, and the ample power reserve of the type is indicated by the fact that the Bell 222's single-engined service ceiling is 1951 m (6400 ft), the same altitude as the type's twin-engined hovering ceiling out of ground effect.

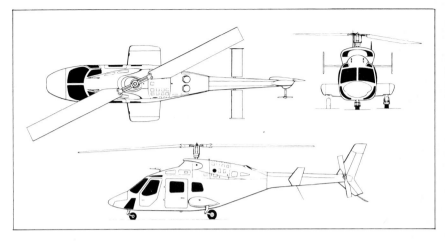

Model 222

Type: general-purpose light helicopter
Maker: Bell Helicopter Textron
Rotor diameter: 12.12 m (39 ft 9 in)
Length: 10.98 m (36 ft 0¼ in) fuselage
Height: 3.51 m (11 ft 6 in)
Main rotor disc area: 115.29 m² (1241 sq ft)
Weight: maximum 3470 kg (7650 lb); empty 2064 kg (4550 lb)
Powerplant: two 675-shp Avco Lycoming LTS 101-650C2 turboshafts
Performance: maximum speed 265 km/h (165 mph) at sea level; range 644 km (400 miles)
Payload: up to 9 passengers
Crew: 1 to 2
Production: 137 ordered by 1980

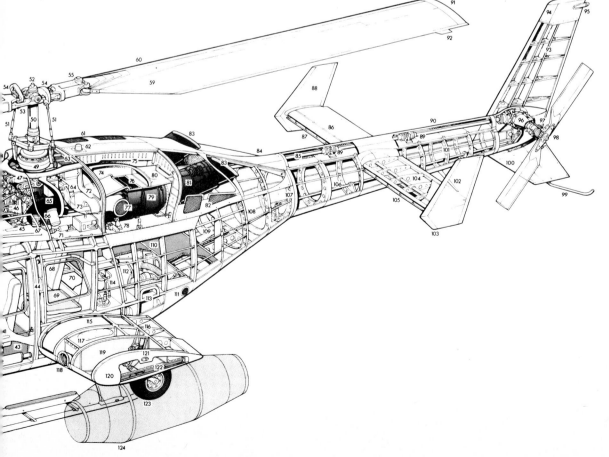

Ka-25K, Kamov

FIRST FLIGHT 1965

Left: The Kamov Ka-25K showing its cockpit in the chin position, which is a feature used for manoeuvring when the machine is employed as a flying crane. A second set of controls in this cockpit allow the pilot to work close to landing zones

THE Kamov Ka-25K (*kran* or crane) is a civil development of the Ka-25 military helicopter, which has the NATO reporting name Hormone. Like its military counterpart, the Ka-25K is based on a rotor system of two three-blade co-axial contra-rotating rotors on a tall mast.

The Ka-25K has an extensively glazed gondola. This is unoccupied except during loading and unloading operations, when the second pilot lowers himself from the main cockpit into the rearward-facing seat in this chin gondola. Here he is ideally situated to command the aircraft with a second set of controls.

The use of a co-axial rotor assembly eliminates the need for an anti-torque tail rotor, and keeps the overall dimensions of the helicopter as small as possible. In the case of the Ka-25K, the rotors, transmission and powerplant are mounted above the fuselage as a powerpack, and can be removed in only one hour. The engines, a pair of 900-shp Glushenkov GTD-3 turboshafts, are mounted side-by-side forward of the transmission.

Although intended primarily as a flying crane, the Ka-25K can also be used as a conventional transport helicopter. In this role the chin gondola is removed, and the load is accommodated in the large hold. The floor has nine lash-down points for freight, which can be loaded through a sliding door in the left side.

Alternatively, up to 12 passengers can be carried on tip-up seats along the sides of the hold. For external loads, the freight sling is led through a hatch in the cabin floor.

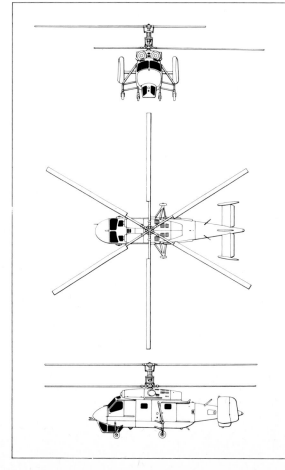

Ka-25K

Type: flying crane and utility helicopter
Maker: Kamov Design Bureau
Rotor diameter: (each) 15.74 m (51 ft 8 in)
Length: 9.83 m (32 ft 3 in) fuselage
Height: 5.37 m (17 ft 7½ in)
Main rotor disc area: (total) 389.2 m² (4886 sq ft)
Weight: maximum 7300 kg (16 094 lb); empty 4400 kg (9700 lb)
Powerplant: two 900-shp Glushenkov GTD-3 turboshafts
Performance: maximum speed 220 km/h (137 mph); range 650 km (405 miles)
Payload: up to 12 passengers; up to a weight of 2000 kg (4409 lb)
Crew: 2
Production: not available

Ka-26, Kamov
FIRST FLIGHT 1965

THE Kamov Ka-26, which has the NATO codename Hoodlum, was announced in January 1964 as a light commercial helicopter with twin-turbine powerplant and a design making it easily convertible to meet the requirements of several roles. The primary task envisaged for the Ka-26, however, was agricultural.

The main need for such a helicopter was in remote areas, and so the Kamov design bureau opted for its standard co-axial contra-rotating twin rotor configuration, but powered by a pair of 325-hp Vedeneev M-14V-26 radial piston engines because of the need for minimum fuel consumption. To leave the area under the transmission and rotor assemblies free for the payload, the engines were installed in pods at the ends of shoulder-mounted stub wings, the engines and transmission being connected by drive shafts with flexible couplings.

The first prototype flew in 1965, and state trials were successfully completed in the same year, allowing it to enter limited production during 1966.

The compact size and manoeuvrability of the Ka-26 proved a great asset for agricultural work, and the pod-and-boom design of the fuselage highly effective. The fuselage forward of the stub wings is a minimal pod with the crew cabin at the front, while the glassfibre tail unit is carried on twin booms and has conventional flying controls.

The design thus leaves the area under the engines and on the centre of gravity free for the payload. For agricultural work a 900-kg (1984-lb) hopper can be fitted, the load being spread by spray-bars or dust-spreaders under the hopper and

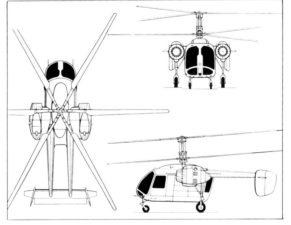

aft of the tail assembly. For passenger operations the Ka-26 can be fitted with a detachable pod for six passengers on tip-up seats, and for freight work this pod can be used to carry up to 700 kg (1543 lb).

The Ka-26 is thus a valuable general-purpose helicopter, despite the 'obsolescent' feature of piston engines. The greater weight of these units compared with turbines has been compensated by the use of lightweight materials in the airframe. Each of the interchangeable rotor blades, for example, is made of plastic, and weighs only 25 kg (55 lb); and much of the fuselage is made of aluminium panels sandwiched in glassfibre. Apart from saving weight, such features also reduce the problem of metal corrosion from the chemicals carried in the agricultural role.

Ka-26

Type: general-purpose light helicopter
Maker: Kamov Design Bureau
Rotor diameter: 13 m (42 ft 8 in)
Length: 7.75 m (25 ft 5 in) fuselage
Height: 4.05 m (13 ft 3½ in)
Main rotor disc area: 265.46 m² (2857 sq ft)
Weight: maximum 3250 kg (7165 lb); empty (passenger) 2100 kg (4630 lb)
Powerplant: two 325-hp Vedeneev M-14V-26 7-cylinder air-cooled radial engines
Performance: maximum speed 170 km/h (105 mph); range with 7 passengers 400 km (248 miles)
Payload: 1100 kg (2425 lb); seats for up to 7 passengers
Crew: 1 to 2
Production: minimum 650

Above: A Ka-26 fitted with a 900-kg (1984-lb) hopper directly beneath the engine. Like the Ka-25 it has twin contra-rotating rotors which means extreme compactness

A109A, Agusta

FIRST FLIGHT 1971

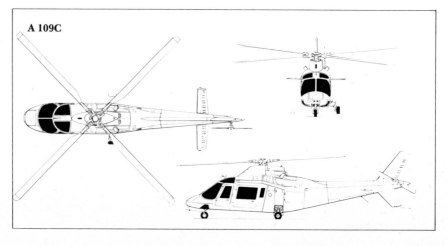

Above: An Italian-registered
Agusta 109; though the type
has a wide range of military
applications it is also popular
as an executive transport
Left: An A 109A comes in to
land during a sales promotion
demonstration. This machine
is finished in a company livery

A 109A

Type: general-purpose
helicopter
Maker: Costruzioni
Aeronautiche Giovanni
Agusta
Rotor diameter: 11 m (36 ft
1 in)
Length: 10.73 m (35 ft 2½ in)
fuselage
Height: 3.32 m (10 ft 10¾ in)
Main rotor disc area: 95 m²
(1023 sq ft)
Weight: maximum 2600 kg
(5730 lb); empty 1415 kg
(3120 lb)
Powerplant: two 420-shp
Allison 250-C20B turboshafts
Performance: maximum
cruising speed 266 km/h
(165 mph); range at sea level
565 km (351 miles)
Payload: seats for up to 7
passengers
Crew: 1 to 2
Production: minimum 130
(orders)

WHILST Agusta had experienced continued
success in its licence-building operations, it
decided in the late 1960s to undertake the design of
its own high-performance twin-turbine helicopter,
under the designation A 109A. The key to the
type's performance was careful design of the highly
streamlined fuselage and engine/transmission-
/rotor-hub assembly, combined with relatively low
structure weight and two moderately powerful
turboshafts.

Agusta produced three flying prototypes of the A
109A, the first of these flying on August 4, 1971.
Both Italian and American certification of the type,
including operation by a single pilot in IFR
(Instrument Flight Rules) conditions, were
achieved on June 1, 1975 and production examples
of the A 109A began in 1976 (to US customers) and
1977 (European customers).

The fuselage of the A 109A is of conventional
pod-and-boom type, with a semi-monocoque
structure of light aluminium alloy. Construction is
in four main sections: nose, cockpit, cabin and tail
boom. The cockpit is extensively glazed, with small
panels in the forward cockpit floor to facilitate
difficult landings, such as those on rooftops and in
restricted areas.

Passenger accommodation is for six people in the
main cabin, and a seventh in the cockpit if the
aircraft is flown by a single pilot. The cabin
accommodation comprises two three-seat rows,
and entrance to the cabin is gained by large doors
on each side of the compartment. To the rear of the
seats is a large baggage compartment, with a

volume of 0.52 m³ (18.4 cu ft). The passenger cabin
measures 1.62 m (5 ft 3¾ in) in length, 1.42 m (4 ft
8 in) in width and 1.29 m (4 ft 2¾ in) in height, and
as the front row of seats can be removed, this gives
a fair volume of freight space also. As a flying
ambulance the A 109A can carry two stretchers
and two medical attendants.

The powerplant comprises a pair of Allison 250-
C20B turboshafts, each rated at 420 shp for take-off
and 385 shp maximum for continuous running,
with maximum and normal cruise ratings of 370
shp and 346 shp respectively available for twin-
engined flight. These engines are neatly located aft
of the transmission and rotor mast, separated from
each other and the passenger compartment by
firewalls, and are well faired into the upper line of

A 109C

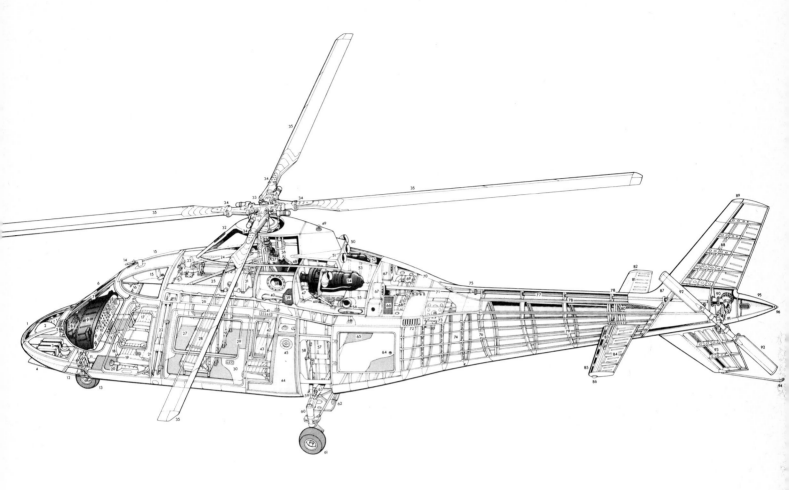

the fuselage. During development other engines were considered including the Turboméca Astazou XII, the Astazou X, and the Continental T67-T-1 for use in the service versions. The fuel, totalling 550 litres (121 Imp gal), is located in the lower rear fuselage. The four-blade main rotor is fully articulated, and is positioned on a short rotor mast projecting only slightly upwards from the fairing concealing the main transmission assembly.

The tricycle undercarriage is fully retractable, with hydraulic actuation for the nosewheel forward and the mainwheels upward into the fuselage. The conventional hydraulic actuation is supplemented by a hydraulic emergency system.

In 1977 Agusta carried out trials with a four-float gear for water operations. These floats were produced by Air Cruiser, an American firm based in New Jersey, but nothing has so far come of the experiment. Agusta is also considering an improved version, the A 119, with accommodation for 10 passengers and the pilot.

The A 109 is also produced in two versions for the military: the A 109 for army use can carry up to seven passengers, with an armament of two machine-guns and two rocket-launcher pods, and an alternative of four HOT or TOW (tube-launched, optically-tracked, wire-guided) anti-tank missiles; the A 109 for naval use can carry ECM (electronic counter measures) and MAD (magnetic anomaly detector) equipment, and be fitted with two torpedoes or anti-shipping missiles, such as the AS.12 or AM.10, used in conjunction with a high-power search radar.

A 109A

1 Nose compartment
2 Nosewheel well
3 Radio and electronics rack
4 Nosewheel door
5 Ventilation duct
6 Windscreen
7 Windscreen wipers
8 Battery
9 Instrument panel shroud
10 Instrument panel
11 Toe-brake torque pedals
12 Downward vision window
13 Castoring (45° either side of centre) nosewheel
14 Pitot head
15 Cockpit roof windows
16 Cockpit roof engine control panel
17 First pilot's seat
18 Collective-pitch control column (optional left side and standard right side)
19 Co-pilot/passenger tracked seat
20 Cyclic-pitch control (optional and standard side)
21 Cockpit door (left and right)
22 Control rod duct
23 Pitch control linkage mechanism
24 Gearbox mounting struts
25 Cabin roof (honeycomb panel)
26 Roof beam construction
27 Passenger cabin floor
28 Triple-seat bench (two aft-facing individual seats optional)
29 Cabin side window
30 Cabin door (left and right)
31 Oil tank
32 Rotor head fairing
33 Fully-articulated rotor head
34 Blade attachment (bonded doubler plates and bonded-and-bolted grip plates)
35 Four-bladed main rotor (bonded aluminium blades with honeycomb core)
36 Pitch control jacks
37 Main reduction gearbox
38 Engine air intake
39 Air-intake grille
40 Push-pull control rods
41 Cabin air vent
42 Cabin rear window
43 Rear triple-seat bench
44 Left L-shaped bladder-type two-compartment fuel cell
45 Fuel filler cap
46 Engine mounting struts
47 Engine transmission shaft
48 Coupling gearbox
49 Anti-collision light
50 Engine exhaust pipes
51 Exhaust pipe box fairing
52 Right engine bay
53 Engine compartment stainless-steel firewall
54 Allison 250-C20B turboshaft engine
55 Left engine bay
56 Generator cooling duct
57 Main undercarriage bay
58 Undercarriage door mechanism
59 Undercarriage leg top forks
60 Main leg strut
61 Mainwheel
62 Mainwheel doors
63 Retraction jack
64 Baggage compartment door
65 Baggage compartment floor (honeycomb panel)
66 Air-intake grille
67 Oil-cooler fans
68 Engine oil cooler
69 Transmission oil cooler
70 Fuselage top fairing
71 Tail rotor drive shaft
72 Oil-cooler air vent
73 Control rod hinge joint
74 Rear fuselage frame construction
75 Spine shaft housing
76 Tailcone joint
77 Tail rotor transmission shaft
78 Transmission shaft bearings
79 Tailcone construction
80 Elevator hinge control
81 Right elevator
82 Right navigation light
83 Elevator hinge shaft
84 Elevator construction
85 Left elevator
86 Left navigation light
87 Fin root fairing
88 Fin construction
89 Fin tip fairing
90 Tail rotor gearbox
91 Tail rotor control mechanism
92 Two-bladed semi-rigid tail rotor
93 Ventral fin construction
94 Tail skid
95 Tailcone fairing
96 Rear navigation light

Enstrom

FIRST FLIGHT 1962

THE R J Enstrom Corporation was established in 1959 to produce and then market in developed form an experimental light helicopter designed by Rudolph Enstrom. The experimental machine first flew on November 12, 1960, and resulted in a development programme to evolve the F-28 production model, the prototype of which first flew in 1962.

Production of the F-28 began in 1963, and a limited number of this type were built before the improved F-28A appeared in 1968. In October of that year Enstrom was bought by the Purex Corporation as part of its Pacific Airmotive Aerospace subsidiary. The new owners continued development of the F-28 type, producing the F-28B with a turbocharged piston engine, and the T-28 with a turbine engine.

In January 1971 the Purex Corporation sold the Enstrom helicopter company to F Lee Bailey, and under this new ownership, the Enstrom Helicopter Corporation restarted manufacture of the definitive F-28A light helicopter with the 500th helicopter delivered during June 1977.

The F-28A is an interesting but in no way remarkable light helicopter, its useful performance depending on light structure weight and careful streamlining rather than brute power. The forward fuselage, consisting of the extensively glazed compartment for the pilot and two passengers seated side-by-side on a bench seat, is made of light alloy and glassfibre. The centre section of the fuselage, accommodating the engine, transmission and fuel tanks, as well as providing anchorage points for the

Above: An Enstrom F-28A at Teterboro Airport, New Jersey. The F-28 is used for traffic control, search and rescue and communications work
Left: An F-280 Shark improved version with larger fuel capacity
Below: The Shark has been widely sold and versions are now available with a turbocharged engine. Enstrom have also developed their own wet and dry agricultural chemical-spraying equipment with spraybooms and quick-fill hoppers

steel-tube undercarriage skids, is more substantially built of steel tube. The rear fuselage, carrying small vertical tail surfaces and the two-blade teetering tail rotor of bonded light alloy construction, is a semi-monocoque structure basically conical in shape and built of aluminium.

The 205-shp Lycoming HIO-360-C1B piston engine is located in the centre fuselage, and fed from two fuel tanks with a total usable capacity of 151.4 litres (33.3 Imp gal). The engine's output is led through a right-angle reduction gearbox to drive the main rotor through a Poly V-belt drive. The main rotor is situated at the top of a tall rotor mast, and is a three-blade fully articulated unit with blades of bonded light alloy construction.

Since its inception, the basic F-28 has been the subject of numerous improvement programmes, with the result that in 1980 there were seven models currently in production or under development. The first of these is the basic F-28A. The Model 280 Shark is an improved F-28A, with revised nose contours of better aerodynamic shape, a larger dorsal fin, horizontal tail surfaces, and increased standard fuel capacity.

The F-28C is based on the F-28A, but is powered by the 205-shp Lycoming HIO-360-E1AD piston engine fitted with a Rajay 301 E-10-2 turbocharger; unlike the F-28A and 280 Shark, the F-28C introduces a tail rotor on the left side of the tail rotating in the opposite direction to the rotors of its two preceding models. The Model 280C Shark is basically the F-28C equivalent of the 280 Shark.

The F-28F Falcon is based on the F-28C but incorporates a one-piece windscreen and pedestal-type instrument panel to improve the pilot's downward view; maintenance has been simplified, and power is provided by a 225-shp Lycoming engine. The Model 280L Hawk is a four-seat development of the 280C Shark. Finally, the Model 480 Eagle is a development of the 280L Hawk, with seating for five and power provided by the Allison 250-C20B turboshaft.

Although the Enstrom helicopters are intended mainly for light passenger operations, the F-28C and Model 280C can be used in the agricultural role with two side-mounted chemical hoppers and their associated spraybooms. Liquid chemical capacity is 340 litres (75 Imp gal), and powder chemical capacity $0.5\,\mathrm{m}^3$ (17.7 cu ft).

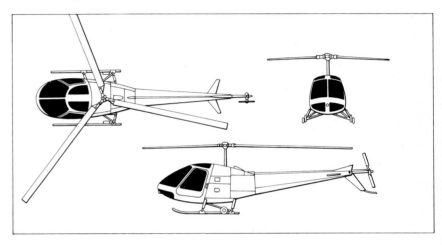

Enstrom F-28A

Type: light helicopter
Maker: Enstrom Helicopter Corporation
Rotor diameter: 9.75 m (32 ft)
Length: 8.94 m (29 ft 4 in)
Height: 2.79 m (9 ft 2 in)
Main rotor disc area: 74.69 m² (804 sq ft)
Weight: maximum 975 kg (2150 lb); empty 657 kg (1450 lb)
Powerplant: one 205-hp Lycoming HIO-360-C1B 4-cylinder horizontally-opposed air-cooled engine
Performance: maximum cruising speed 161 km/h (100 mph) at sea level; range 381 km (237 miles)
Payload: seats for 2 passengers
Crew: 1
Production: minimum 340

Puma, Aérospatiale

FIRST FLIGHT 1965

CURRENTLY one of the world's most important military helicopters, the Aérospatiale SA 330 Puma was designed in the early 1960s to meet a French army requirement for a twin-turbine tactical transport. The success of the SA 330 Puma was also assured by the commercial success of the type in securing world-wide orders.

Two prototypes of the SA 330 were built, the first of these flying on April 15, 1965. The two prototypes undertook a rigorous trials programme, supplemented by six pre-production helicopters, the last of which flew on July 30, 1968.

The first commercial models were the SA 330F passenger and SA 330G freight carriers. The first example of the type flew on September 26, 1969, the model receiving its French certificate of airworthiness on October 12, 1970 and its US Federal Aviation Administration Type Approval for single-pilot IFR (Instrument Flight Rules) operation in A and B conditions on June 23, 1971. The Puma was the world's first helicopter to achieve such FAA certification, thanks to the all-weather day and night aspects of its original military specification. British certification was finally achieved on June 4, 1975.

The initial military versions for the British and French armies were powered by two 1328-shp Turboméca Turmo IIIC$_6$ turboshafts, but the SA 330F and SA 330G introduced the 1435-shp Turmo IVA fitted with air intake anti-icing equipment. The engines are located side-by-side, but separated by a firewall, forward of the main transmission assembly above the payload area and

Above: An SA 330J Puma on a demonstration flight in the French mountains
Above right: G-BERG, *Delphinius*, one of ten Pumas in service with Bristow Helicopters. The Puma is the first helicopter to be cleared for all-weather operation outside the USSR
Left: An SA 330J Puma lands on the helicopter pad of the marine exploration ship *Talisman*

well away from the extensive fuel tankage. This latter comprises 1544 litres (340 Imp gal) in four main tanks and one auxiliary flexible tank under the fuselage floor. Extra range can be bestowed by additional fuel carried in four auxiliary tanks in the cabin (1900 litres [418 Imp gal]) and two external tanks (700 litres [154 Imp gal]).

The SA 330F can be fitted with a number of interior layouts depending on specific role: 8-, 9- or 12-seat executive, 17-seat commuter, or 20-seat high-density configurations are possible. With each of these there are provisions for baggage and a lavatory at the rear of the cabin. Access to the cabin is by means of an airstair door, which is removable for the loading of bulkier items into the baggage compartment. The SA 330G can carry its

freight load in a stripped-out interior, or up to 3000 kg (6614 lb) in an external sling running through a hatch in the cabin floor.

From the end of 1973 production SA 330Gs were fitted with an uprated powerplant, consisting of a pair of 1575-shp Turmo IVC turboshafts. This powerplant is also used on the current civil model of the Puma, the SA 330J.

Apart from the engines, the main difference between the SA 330F and SA 330G compared with the SA 330J is the latter's more advanced rotor. Each blade on the earlier models consisted of an extruded aluminium-alloy spar, machined to form a leading edge and with metal pockets bonded to the spar to form a trailing edge. On the SA 330J each blade is of composite construction and slightly increased chord, based on a glassfibre spar and trailing edge, with a glassfibre skin over an inner skin of carbon fibre and a honeycomb core, and with a stainless steel protective cap over the leading edge. The increase in power, coupled with the revised rotor blades, allows an increase in maximum weight from the 6700 kg (14771 lb) of the SA 330F and SA 330G to the 7400 kg (16314 lb) of the SA 330J, with a consequent increase in payload.

On April 25, 1978 the SA 330J became the first western helicopter to be certificated for all-weather flight even in icing conditions. This is possible because of the provision of weather radar, thermal de-icing of the main rotor blades, thermal anti-icing of the tail rotor blades, and lengthened air intakes to ensure adequate air supply in all conditions.

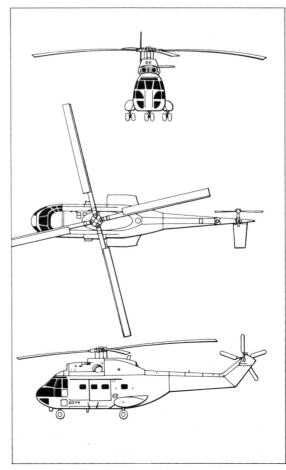

SA 330J

Type: transport helicopter
Maker: Société Nationale Industrielle Aérospatiale; Westland Helicopters Ltd
Rotor diameter: 15 m (49 ft 2½ in)
Length: 14.06 m (46 ft 1½ in) fuselage
Height: 5.14 m (16 ft 10½ in)
Main rotor disc area: 177 m² (1905 sq ft)
Weight: maximum 7400 kg (16314 lb); empty 3766 kg (8303 lb)
Powerplant: two 1575-shp Turboméca Turmo IVC turboshafts
Performance: maximum cruising speed 258 km/h (160 mph); range 550 km (341 miles)
Payload: 3500 kg (7716 lb); seats for up to 20 passengers
Crew: 1 to 2
Production: minimum 650 (civil and military orders)

Gazelle, Aérospatiale

FIRST FLIGHT 1967

THE SA 341 Gazelle is of wholly French design, although it is one of the helicopters produced jointly by Aérospatiale in France and by Westland in Great Britain, as part of a 1967 agreement.

The first civil model was the SA 341G, powered by the Astazou IIIA turboshaft. This was intended as a utility helicopter with seating for five people. Behind the bench seat is a baggage compartment with a volume of 0.45 m³ (16 cu ft). The rear seat can also be neatly folded down into the floor to leave the space for freight between the front seats and the rear bulkhead unobstructed. Overall, the cabin measures 2.2 m (7 ft 2½ in) in length, with a maximum width and height of 1.32 m (4 ft 4 in) and 1.21 m (3 ft 11¾ in) respectively.

The single Turboméca Astazou IIIA turboshaft,

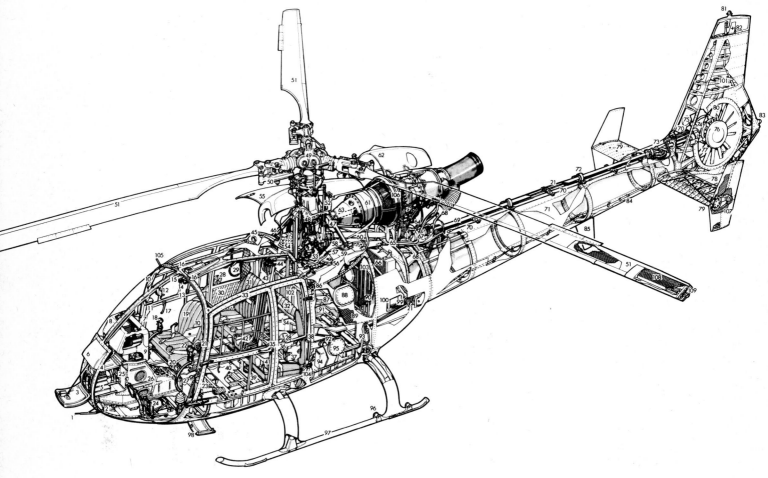

SA 341 Gazelle

1 Pitot head
2 Landing light
3 Battery access panel (open)
4 Circuit breaker panel
5 Battery
6 Cabin ventilating air intake
7 Cabin ventilating air control lever
8 Instrument panel shroud
9 Instrument panel
10 Handgrip (assisting entry/exit)
11 Standby compass
12 Rear view mirror
13 Transmission brake control lever
14 Fuel flow control lever
15 Fuel shut-off lever
16 Cabin heating system ducts
17 Door pull (both forward doors)
18 Pilot's cyclic pitch stick
19 Pilot's seat
20 Collective lever with control box
21 Tail rotor control cable relay
22 Co-pilot's cyclic pitch stick
23 Co-pilot's collective pitch stick
24 Co-pilot's directional control

25 Pilot's directional control assembly
26 Control pedestal and radio control panel
27 Left front door jettison lever
28 Ventilator with rotational adjuster
29 Roof-mounted intercom connectors
30 Padded interior trim
31 Single passenger seat
32 Double passenger seat
33 Circuit breaker panel
34 Cargo compartment access
35 Left front door
36 Left rear door
37 First aid kit stowage
38 Left rear door jettison linkage
39 Hinged passenger seat base/cushion
40 Passenger seat floor recess
41 Dynamotor and transmitter/receiver
42 Mixing unit (rotor controls)
43 Main rotor controls
44 Transmission platform main rotor control linkage
45 Stale air extractor duct

46 Main gearbox mounting 'V' strut
47 Engine to main gearbox coupling
48 Main gearbox
49 Main rotor head (semi-articulated)
50 Friction type drag damper
51 Bölkow-type rotor blades
52 Pitch change control assembly
53 Control linkage to pitch change assembly
54 Hydraulic pack
55 Right main gearbox cowling
56 Mounting plate damper
57 Transmission platform
58 Transmission disc-brake
59 Main gearbox mounting rear strut
60 Transmission shaft (main gearbox to intermediate gearbox)
61 Reduction gear housing
62 Right engine cowling
63 Clutch and free-wheel unit
64 Fuel flow control assembly
65 Engine mounting strut
66 Oil cooler
67 Intermediate gearbox
68 Oil-cooler warm air extraction duct

69 Transmission shaft to tail rotor gearbox
70 Hydraulic lines to tail rotor gearbox
71 Tail boom
72 Transmission shaft bearing
73 Tail rotor control rod
74 Tail rotor gearbox
75 Tail rotor gearbox filler cap
76 Tail rotor hub
77 Tail rotor blades
78 Main stabilizer ventral fin
79 Stabilizer/tailplane
80 Tail rotor hub/fairing support strut
81 Tail beacon
82 Upper UHF aerial
83 Navigation light
84 Conduit for tail electronics leads
85 Lower UHF/VHF aerial
86 Securing (anchorage) ring
87 Fuel tank
88 Fuel tank access panel
89 Honeycomb sandwich centre section structure
90 Oil-cooler compartment air intake

91 Distribution box
92 Left side navigation light
93 Landing gear damper (hydraulic)
94 Medical kit container
95 Left access panel to cargo hold
96 Air temperature (exterior) gauge
97 Landing gear
98 Access panel to underfloor section
99 Foot hold with anti-slip surface
100 Hand hold (to aid access to cowling/transmission platform)
101 Main stabilizer fin
102 Forward bulkhead
103 Aft bulkhead
104 Passenger safety belt anchorage point
105 Air temperature (exterior) gauge
106 Turboméca Astazou III turboshaft
107 Honeycomb and wood endplate fin structure (metal skinned)
108 Honeycomb structure of main rotor blade(s)
109 Adjustable weights assembly (fine balance dynamically) in tip of each main rotor blade

delivering 590 shp at take-off and for continuous running, is located above and behind the cabin, and is fed from a 445-litre (98-Imp gal) tank in the fuselage, with the optional addition of a 90-litre (20-Imp gal) tank underneath the baggage compartment and/or a 200-litre (44-Imp gal) ferry tank in the cabin. The main rotor, a conventional semi-articulated three-blade unit (with each blade built up round a glassfibre-reinforced plastic spar with a laminated skin and honeycomb core) is driven through a reduction-gear transmission. The rear rotor is of the Aérospatiale 'Fenestron' type, with 13 light alloy blades set as a shrouded fan in the fin, and driven by a shaft running along the top of the tail boom.

In January 1975 the SA 341G became the first helicopter in the world to be certificated for single-pilot operation under IFR (Instrument Flight Rules) Category I conditions, later extended to Category II conditions, with ceiling down to 30 m (98 ft) and forward vision down to 365 m (1197 ft). This is made possible by the installation of a Sperry flight director connected with servo-dampers.

The SA 341 Gazelle has been developed into the SA 342 Gazelle by the installation of the Turboméca Astazou XIVH turboshaft, rated at 870 shp. The SA 342J is the civil counterpart of the SA 342L military helicopter, and though its speed performance is almost identical with that of the SA 341G, service ceiling is slightly inferior and range marginally superior.

Left: An Aérospatiale SA 341G Gazelle of Electricité de France flies engineers to check power line installations
Below: A Westland SA 341 at a small city heliport. As an executive transport it can carry up to four passengers with hand baggage

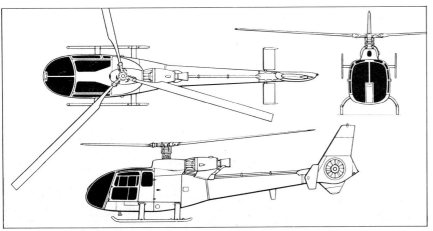

SA 341G

Type: utility helicopter
Maker: Société Nationale Industrielle Aérospatiale; Westland Helicopters Ltd
Rotor diameter: 10.5 m (34 ft 5½ in)
Length: 9.53 m (31 ft 3³⁄₁₆ in) fuselage
Height: 3.15 m (10 ft 2⅝ in)
Main rotor disc area: 86.5 m² (931 sq ft)
Weight: maximum 1800 kg (3968 lb); empty 917 kg (2022 lb)
Powerplant: one 590-shp Turboméca Astazou IIIA turboshaft
Performance: maximum cruising speed 264 km/h (164 mph) at sea level; range with 500-kg (1102-lb) payload 360 km (223 miles)
Payload: seats for up to 4 passengers
Crew: 1 to 2
Production: minimum 800 (civil and military orders)

AS 350 Ecureuil, Aérospatiale

FIRST FLIGHT 1974

THE Aérospatiale AS 350 Ecureuil (squirrel) and AStar are basically similar apart from their powerplants, and are intended as successors to the best-selling Alouette series of light general-purpose helicopters.

The object was to produce a basic type with attractive commercial prospects derived from low flying and maintenance costs, combined with customer appeal in the form of low vibration and noise levels. Right from the beginning, the AS 350 was seen in two basic forms: for the North American market the AS 350C AStar, powered by the Avco Lycoming LTS 101-600A turboshaft; and for other markets the AS 350B Ecureuil, powered by the Turboméca Arriel.

The first prototype to fly, on June 27, 1974, was powered by the Lycoming LTS; the second, which flew on February 14, 1975, was Arriel-powered. The prototypes fully vindicated the designers' expectations, but revealed the need for refinement of the basic concept. However, US Federal Aviation Administration Type Approval for the AS 350C AStar was secured on December 21, 1977. French certification of the AS 350B Ecureuil preceded this slightly, being awarded on October 27, 1977, allowing production deliveries to begin in March 1978. By this time, Aérospatiale's order book for the AS 350 had passed the 300 mark, the orders having been placed by some 100 operators in 14 countries. The company achieved a production rate of seven Ecureuils and 16 AStars per month by February 1980.

The two different engines can be installed with

minimal alteration to the basic airframe, and the key to the AS 350's success is that it fulfilled its objectives of low cost, ease of maintenance and reduction of 'nuisance' factors. Apart from careful detail design, the single factor which contributes most to ease of maintenance is the simple main transmission: this consists of one main epicyclic gear train, with only nine gear wheels and nine bearings compared with the 22 and 23 respectively found in the SA 318C Alouette II. Airframe maintenance is also simplified by the construction: light alloy pressings covered with a skinning mainly of thermoformed plastic.

The rotor system also helps to cut down maintenance problems, and is instrumental in reducing noise and vibration levels. The rotor hub is of

Above: An Aérospatiale AS 350 Ecureuil (Squirrel) at a flying club in Britain
Below left: An AS 350 fitted with floats for water operations
Below right: The AS 350C AStar is the US-built version. It is powered by an Avco Lycoming turboshaft, but has a performance very similar to the AS 350 Ecureuil

Aérospatiale's new Starflex type: a glassfibre structure with a single ball joint (of rubber and steel sandwich construction) replaces what would otherwise have been a unit with three hinges, and needs no maintenance. The rotor blades are produced entirely mechanically, and each is of glassfibre construction with a sheathing of stainless steel over the leading edge.

Standard accommodation provides for two bucket seats forward for the pilot and co-pilot/passenger, with the space behind these occupied by two double bench seats or three armchair seats in the de luxe model.

The baggage compartment has a single large door on the right-hand side of the fuselage, and the compartment's ceiling is reinforced to make a maintenance platform for the rotor head. The AS 350C was superseded in 1978 by the AS 350D.

Aérospatiale's latest development of the AS 350 design is the AS 355E Ecureuil 2 or Twinstar, with a powerplant comprising two Allison 250-C20F turboshafts each rated at 420 shp for take-off and at 370 shp for continuous running, combined with an uprated transmission, able to handle 590 shp instead of 529 shp.

Performance, except in altitude, is roughly the same as that of the AS 350, but though the AS 355E is more expensive than its single-engined counterparts, it has attractions in the form of twin-engined safety, allowing night and urban operations. By the end of 1979 there were two AS 355E prototypes flying, and Aérospatiale had received orders for some 200 of the type.

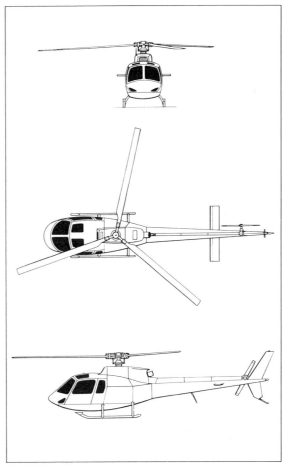

AS 350

Type: general-purpose helicopter
Maker: Société Nationale Industrielle Aérospatiale
Rotor diameter: 10.69 m (35 ft 0¾ in)
Length: 10.91 m (35 ft 9½ in) fuselage
Height: 3.08 m (10 ft 1¼ in)
Main rotor disc area: 89.75 m² (966 sq ft)
Weight: maximum 1950 kg (4300 lb); empty 1045 kg (2304 lb) (AS 350B), 1070 kg (2359 lb) (AS 350D)
Powerplant: one 641-shp Turboméca Arriel turboshaft (AS 350B Ecureuil); one 592-shp Avco Lycoming LTS 101-600A turboshaft (AS 350D AStar)
Performance: maximum cruising speed 232 km/h (144 mph) (AS 350B), 230 km/h (143 mph) (AS 350D) at sea level; range at sea level 710 km (441 miles) (AS 350B), 760 km (472 miles) (AS 350D)
Payload: 750 kg (1653 lb); seats for up to 5 passengers
Crew: 1 to 2
Production: minimum 350 (orders)

BK 117, MBB/Kawasaki

FIRST FLIGHT 1979

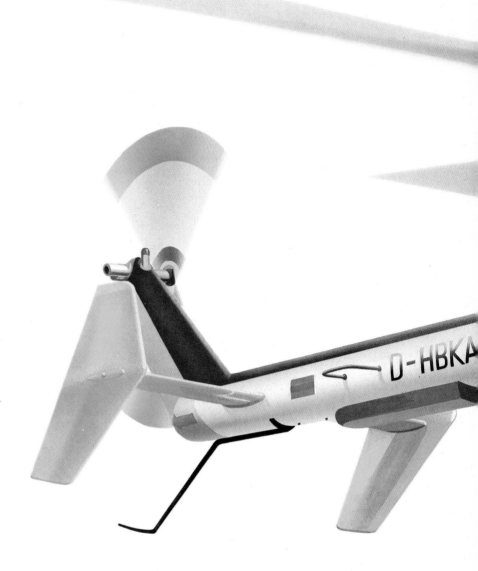

DEVELOPMENT of the BK 117 general-purpose medium helicopter was formally agreed on February 25, 1977 after two years of negotiations between the West German Messerschmitt-Bölkow-Blohm consortium and the Japanese manufacturer Kawasaki Heavy Industries. Both partners had considerable helicopter experience.

The project agreed by the partners was for an 8- to 10-seat utility and multirole helicopter to replace the separate BO 107 and KH-7 designs being worked on in Germany and Japan, with costs being shared equally by the two consortia and their respective governments. The main responsibilities were allocated as follows: to MBB went the main and tail rotors, tail boom, tail unit, hydraulic system, controls (power amplified) and integration of systems; to Kawasaki went the undercarriage, fuselage, transmission and the smaller items of equipment.

Initial planning called for four prototypes, two to be built by MBB at Munich and two by Kawasaki at Gifu, to be ready by mid 1979. Of each pair of prototypes, one was to be for static testing, and the other for flight trials. By December 1979, however, both German prototypes were complete, but only one of the Japanese helicopters.

The relationship of the BK 117 to the BO 105 is evident in a number of ways. A number of accessories are identical with those of the BO 105, the hydraulic system has been converted from that of the BO 105, and the main rotor is essentially that of the BO 105 scaled up to meet the requirements of the larger BK 117. This rotor is a four-blade rigid unit with a titanium hub and GRP (glassfibre-reinforced plastic) blades. The factor which obviously connects the BK 117 with the KH-7 is the transmission, which is derived from that of the 7- to 10-seat Japanese helicopter project, which was to have been powered by a pair of 590-shp Lycoming turboshafts.

The powerplant of the BK 117 comprises a pair of Avco Lycoming LTS 101-650B-1 turboshafts, each rated at 600 shp for take-off and 550 shp for continuous running. Tankage for 605 litres (133 Imp gal) of fuel is accommodated in the lower fuselage.

Accommodation is for a single pilot and up to five passengers in the initial executive model. Cabin volume is 3.22 m³ (114 cu ft), so there is ample room for passenger growth to the planned seven in the standard commuter and offshore-support versions, and to nine in the high-density model. On each side of the cabin is a rearward-sliding door, with inbuilt folding steps on the left side. Behind the passenger compartment, and entered by means of clamshell doors at the rear of the fuselage, is a freight compartment with a volume of 1.34 m³ (47 cu ft).

The manufacturers now confidently expect the BK 117 to have received its German, Japanese and US certificates of airworthiness for VFR (Visual Flight Rules) operation by the end of 1980, and deliveries of the first of an initial batch of 60 BK 117s to begin in 1981. Certification for IFR (Instrument Flight Rules) is anticipated by the end of 1981, allowing the type to be used for the growing offshore support role. The proposed autopilot for

308

the IFR-equipped BK 117 is of Newmark manufacture.

The prospects of the German and Japanese venture appear excellent, not least as the BK 117 will apparently cost purchasers some US $100 000 less than the competing Aérospatiale SA 365C Dauphin 2 and Bell 222. Moreover, several military versions of the basic type are also being considered.

The first flight of the BK 117 was made by the second prototype D-HBKA in Germany on June 13, 1979. Four prototypes are being built, one each for airframe tests and Federal Aviation Regulation ground testing, plus a flying prototype for each country. A total of 48 had been sold by the summer of 1979.

Above: The second prototype of the BK 117 which made its first flight in Germany in June 1979. This joint German/Japanese design has an edge over its competitors since it is intended to be cheaper. Part of this is because the development costs were shared by the governments of the two nations

BK 117

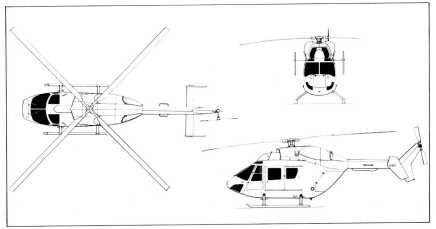

Type: general-purpose helicopter

Maker: Messerschmitt-Bölkow-Blohm GmbH; Kawasaki Heavy Industries

Rotor diameter: 11 m (36 ft 1 in)

Length: 9.88 m (32 ft 5 in) fuselage

Height: 3.84 m (12 ft 7¼ in)

Main rotor disc area: 95 m² (1023 sq ft)

Weight: maximum 2800 kg (6173 lb); empty 1520 kg (3351 lb)

Powerplant: two 600-shp Avco Lycoming LTS 101-650B-1 turboshafts

Performance: (estimated) maximum cruising speed 264 km/h (164 mph); range 545 km (338 miles)

Payload: seats for up to 9 passengers

Crew: 1

Production: 48 ordered by summer 1979

S-76 Spirit, Sikorsky
FIRST FLIGHT 1977

Above: A British Airways
Spirit on oil rig service; with
its all-weather capability it is
ideal for this role. Sikorsky see
it as a high-performance
reliable machine which is
suitable for 'off-the-shelf' sale
to military buyers

HAVING concentrated its efforts on the military helicopter market since the end of World War II, Sikorsky announced in January 1975 that it was developing a twin-turbine all-weather helicopter intended mainly for the civil market. Before and during this period the company investigated a number of design alternatives in conjunction with likely users, and before metal had first been cut on the new 14-seat design, Sikorsky had secured a useful number of orders.

The building of four prototypes of the new S-76 (numbered out of Sikorsky sequence in honour of the United States of America's bicentennial in 1976) began in May 1976. The design clearly reflected the company's experience with the S-70 combat assault squad helicopter being developed for the United States Army as the UH-60A Black Hawk.

The first prototype to fly was in fact the second aircraft, the initial flight taking place on March 13, 1977. The aircraft had been designed from the beginning to meet the US Federal Aviation Regulations Part 29 Category A Instrument Flight Rules (IFR) to allow immediate operations in support of offshore oil exploration and production, night flying and routes which took the type over built-up areas. So provision had been made for full instrumentation, an autopilot and weather radar, and the S-76 was awarded its US Federal Aviation Administration Type Approval for IFR flight during 1978, with deliveries of production aircraft beginning during the second half of the year.

The S-76 Spirit makes extensive use of design

features and technology developed for the S-70. This tendency is nowhere more apparent than in the dynamic system: the rotor, for example, is a scaled-down version of that of the S-70, and of advanced concept and structure. Each of the four main rotor blades is built up round a titanium spar, a titanium leading-edge cover with a nickel abrasion strip, and a honeycomb trailing edge of glassfibre and nylon. The whole blade is pressurized to provide, via gauges, indication of the blade's structural integrity. The rotor hub contains non-lubricated elastomeric bearings and special vibration absorbers.

The twin-engine powerplant is neatly faired into the upper fuselage behind the rotor shaft, and comprises a pair of 650-shp Allison 250-C30 turbo-

310

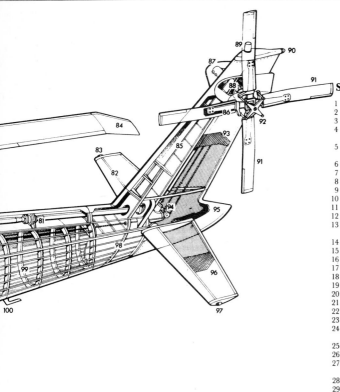

S-76 Spirit

1 Pitot tubes
2 Radome
3 Weather radar scanner
4 Forward optional floatation bags, inflated
5 Radio and electronics equipment bay
6 Nose compartment access panels
7 Radar control unit
8 Nosewheel
9 Downward vision windows
10 Rudder pedals
11 Instrument panel shroud
12 Windscreen wipers
13 Optional electrically-heated windscreen panels
14 Pilot's seat
15 Electrical fuse panels
16 Cyclic pitch control column
17 Safety harness
18 Co-pilot's seat
19 Door emergency release handle
20 Collective-pitch control lever
21 Seat mounting rails
22 Foward entry doorway
23 Door latch
24 Four-abreast bench seat, 14-seat utility layout
25 Passenger seat lap-straps
26 Central control run duct
27 Overhead engine throttle and fuel controls
28 Fresh-air scoop
29 Temperature probe
30 'Kevlar' plastic fuselage fairings
31 Stability augmentation system
32 Aluminium honeycomb fuselage
33 Cabin window panel
34 VOR aerial
35 Interior floor level
36 Left main entry doorway
37 Optional external cargo hook
38 Floor beam construction
39 Right main entry door
40 Cabin roof air ducting
41 Control system links
42 Access panel
43 Hydraulic reservoir
44 Rotor head fairing
45 Main rotor head (elastomeric, non-lubricated bearings)

46 Blade pitch angle control horns
47 Hydraulic dampers
48 Blade root attachment joints
49 Bifilar vibration damper
50 Hydraulic reservoir
51 Rotor control swash plate
52 Main rotor gearbox
53 Gearbox mounting beam
54 Cabin rear-row bench seat
55 Forward fuel tank bay
56 Cabin rear bulkhead
57 Fuel filler cap
58 Forward fuel tank
59 Aft fuel tank
60 Baggage compartment door
61 Fuel tank access panel
62 Baggage compartment floor
63 Hydraulic pump
64 Engine combining gearbox
65 Left engine air intake
66 Engine and gearbox oil coolers
67 Exhaust fairing
68 Engine exhaust ducts
69 Engine bay fireproof bulkhead
70 Engine mounting struts
71 Allison 250-C30 turboshaft engine
72 Cooling air intake
73 Fire extinguisher bottle
74 'Kevlar' plastic tail fairing
75 Hollow titanium blade spar
76 Nomex honeycomb core
77 Leading-edge erosion strip
78 Glassfibre blade skins
79 Dorsal spine fairing
80 Tail rotor drive shaft
81 Shaft bearings
82 Right fixed tailplane
83 Right navigation light
84 Swept blade tips
85 Tailfin construction
86 Graphite composite tail rotor spars
87 Tail rotor hydraulic actuator
88 Tail rotor gearbox
89 Anti-collision light
90 Tail navigation light
91 Glassfibre tail rotor blades
92 Pitch control spider
93 Honeycomb trailing-edge panels
94 Tail rotor shaft bevel drive gearbox
95 'Kevlar' tailcone fairing
96 Left tailplane honeycomb construction
97 Left navigation light

98 Tailfin sloping bulkheads
99 Tail boom frame and stringer construction
100 Communications aerials
101 Tail boom access panel
102 Optional air-conditioning plant
103 Tail boom attachment joint frame
104 Electrical equipment bay
105 Battery
106 Honeycomb undercarriage door panel
107 Retraction strut
108 Main undercarriage leg strut
109 Tie-down ring
110 Left mainwheel
111 Aft optional floatation bag, inflated

shafts, the Series IV model of the widely used Allison 250. This has a more advanced single-stage compressor to handle a greater mass flow at an increased pressure ratio. Among the numerous detail improvements of this model is a dual ignition system to comply with FAR Part 29 requirements. The fuel tankage, in the fuselage, has a capacity of 1030 litres (266½ Imp gal), and there is also provision for long-range tanks as an optional extra.

The fuselage itself is a well streamlined unit of composite structure: a glassfibre nose, cabin section of light alloy honeycomb, light alloy semi-monocoque tail and cantilever pylon, with Kevlar fairings. The undercarriage is a tricycle unit with short legs, thus keeping the fuselage close to the ground. All three units are hydraulically actuated, the nosewheel retracting rearwards and the two main units inwards.

Basic accommodation is provided for 14. Arrangement is for the pilot and co-pilot at the front, with the 12 passengers seated behind them in three four-abreast rows. Baggage is contained in a compartment to the rear of the passenger accommodation, this compartment having a volume of 1.19 m³ (42 cu ft). Sikorsky have also proposed a number of executive layouts for the passenger cabin, all featuring considerable comfort and luxury for the occupants, who vary in number from four upwards. For the carriage of external loads the S-76 can be fitted with a hook of 2268-kg (5000-lb) capacity.

After a delay in the start of production many Spirits were operating by 1980.

S-76 Spirit

Type: general-purpose all-weather helicopter
Maker: Sikorsky Aircraft Division, United Technologies Corporation
Rotor diameter: 13.41 m (44 ft)
Length: 13.44 m (44 ft 1 in) fuselage
Height: 4.41 m (14 ft 5¾ in)
Main rotor disc area: 116.77 m² (1257 sq ft)
Weight: maximum 4399 kg (9 700 lb); empty 2241 kg (4942 lb)
Powerplant: two 650-shp Allison 250-C30 turboshafts
Performance: maximum cruising speed 269 km/h (167 mph); range with 12 passengers 748 km (465 miles)
Payload: 2268 kg (5000 lb); seats for up to 12 passengers
Crew: 2
Production: minimum 220 (orders)

Kania, PZL

FIRST FLIGHT 1979

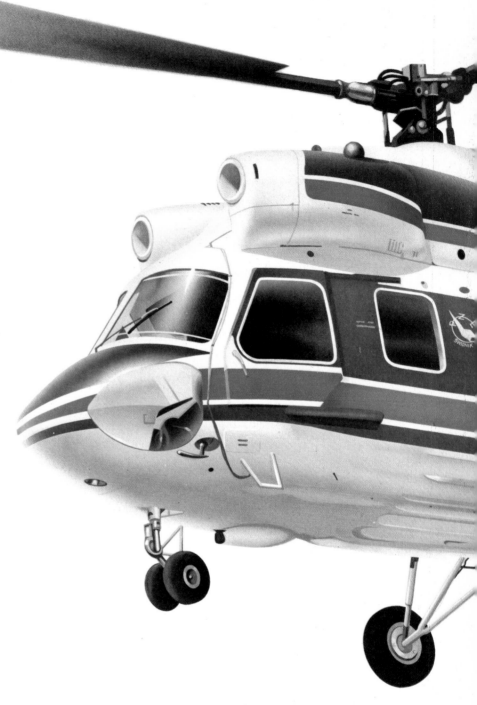

THE Kania is an example of the interest shown by the Communist bloc in trying to sell its aeronautical products to the western world. On August 12, 1978, for example, the Polish aircraft export agency Pezetel signed an agreement with the Spitfire Helicopter Company of Media, Pennsylvania for the latter to sell in western markets the Mil Mi-2 general-purpose helicopter built by WSK-PZL Swidnik as the Taurus II. At the same time, thought was given to the production of an Mi-2 variant with American engines, and this has emerged as the Kania (or Kitty Hawk).

The engine selected for the Kania is the ubiquitous Allison 250 turboshaft. WSK-PZL Swidnik have worked closely with the Detroit Diesel Allison Division of the General Motors Corporation on the installation of the two 250-C20B turboshafts, to ensure optimum location at minimum weight. Each of the engines is rated at 420 shp for take-off and 30 min, 400 shp maximum continuous running, and 370 shp maximum cruising power. Fuel tankage remains unaltered, compared with that of the Mi-2, at 600 litres (132 Imp gal), with provision for another 480 litres (105½ Imp gal) in optional auxiliary tanks.

Accommodation is provided at the front of the cabin for a pilot and co-pilot or passenger, on separate seats, with eight more passengers seated on two three-abreast benches and one double or two single seats at the rear of the cabin. The Kania is intended as a general-purpose helicopter, and so the seating is removable to allow the carriage of freight, agricultural equipment and litters. Access to the cabin is gained by a small door on each side of the forward fuselage, and a larger door on the left side of the passenger compartment's rear. To suit the type to western markets, the Kania is provided with a comprehensive array of western avionics. These include dual instrument lighting systems, pilot's cabin extension light and an adjustable landing light. Among the optional avionics are a King KWX-50 digital weather radar, and a KRA-10 radar altimeter. Standard instrumentation includes King KX-175BE com/nav, KR-85 digital Automatic Direction Finding equipment and KT-76 transponder. An interesting optional feature is a 16k VA AC generator for de-icing the pilot's windscreen and cabin heating and air conditioning.

The smaller size of the Allison 250-C20B, compared with the Isotov GTD-350P used on the Mi-2, has made possible a smaller engine installation, and the opportunity has also been taken to recontour the nose. Rotor diameter has been increased by 6 cm (2⅓ in) compared with the 14.5 m (47 ft 6¾ in) of the Mi-2. The overall effect has been a reduction in empty weight of 262 kg (578 lb), though maximum take-off weight falls by only 150 kg (331 lb).

. Despite the lower power of the American engines, the performance of the Kania is comparable with that of the Mi-2 except in range, where the Kania appears to be superior by a small margin.

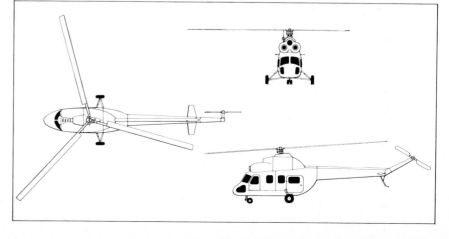

Kania

Type: general-purpose light helicopter
Maker: WSK-PZL-Swidnik
Rotor diameter: 14.56 m (47 ft 9¼ in)
Length: 11.95 m (39 ft 2½ in) fuselage
Height: 3.75 m (12 ft 3½ in)
Main rotor disc area: 166.5 m² (1792 sq ft)
Weight: maximum 3550 kg (7826 lb); empty 2140 kg (4718 lb)
Powerplant: two 420-shp Allison 250-C20B turboshafts
Performance: (estimated) maximum cruising speed 210 km/h (130 mph); range 497 km (309 miles)
Payload: seats for up to 9 passengers
Crew: 1 to 2
Production: under development

Above: Originally the American market version of the Kania was to be named the Kitty Hawk, but this has recently been changed to Taurus. It is a joint venture by WSK-PZL Swidnik and the Detroit Diesel Allison Division of the General Motors Corporation, and intended to be a general-purpose machine capable of carrying passengers or freight

Dauphin, Aérospatiale

FIRST FLIGHT 1972

T HE Aérospatiale SA 360 Dauphin was developed from the late 1960s as a replacement for the highly successful Alouette III general-purpose helicopter, and the first of its two prototypes flew on June 2, 1972. Initially the powerplant was a 980-shp Turboméca Astazou XVI turboshaft, but after some 180 test flights this was replaced by a 1050-shp Astazou XVIIIA.

Deliveries of production aircraft began in 1976, and the type has attracted a steady stream of customers. The first prototype, in its re-engined form, established three class records for speed with payload during May 1973.

The rotor is a four-blade unit, each blade being made up of a polyester leading-edge spar, with an inner covering of carbon fibre and an outer skin of glassfibre over a honeycomb core, plus a sheathing of stainless steel to protect the leading edge. The tail rotor is a 13-blade unit of the 'Fenestron' shrouded type, set into the vertical fin.

Accommodation is for ten people in all: seated at the front of the cabin are the pilot and co-pilot or passenger; behind them are the other eight passengers, seated four-abreast in two rows, each row being provided with a door on each side of the fuselage. To the rear of this compartment is the baggage space, with a volume of $1\,m^3$ (35 cu ft) and its own door on the right-hand side. The SA 360 can also be fitted with an extra row of four seats on the rear bulkhead, in place of space for hand baggage and coats. Also possible are executive configurations for four or six passengers.

The SA 360 can also be used in the mixed-payload role, with only one row of four seats, in the forward position, and space for $2.5\,m^3$ (88 cu ft) or 1420 kg (3131 lb) of freight behind it. Options are a 1300-kg (2866-lb) cargo sling for external loads, and a 272-kg (600-lb) rescue hoist.

An unusual feature of the SA 360 is the fact that it can be produced with a neatly spatted non-retractable tailwheel undercarriage, or with twin metal skids. Skis and floats can be fitted.

Developments of the SA 360 include the SA 361H with a 1400-shp Astazou XXB and a Starflex rotor head (a glassfibre structure with a single ball joint), intended mainly for military customers and fitted for armament capability; and the SA 365C Dauphin 2 twin-engined variant with two 650-shp Turboméca Arriel turboshafts and Starflex rotor hub. The first Dauphin 2 flew on January 24, 1975.

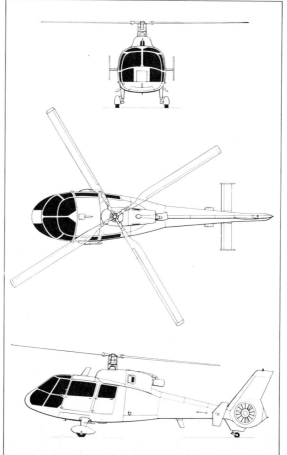

SA 360

Type: general-purpose helicopter
Maker: Société Generale Industrielle Aérospatiale
Rotor diameter: 11.5 m (37 ft 8¾ in)
Length: 10.98 m (36 ft) fuselage
Height: 3.5 m (11 ft 6 in)
Main rotor disc area: $103.87\,m^2$ (1118 sq ft)
Weight: maximum 3000 kg (6614 lb); empty 1580 kg (3483 lb)
Powerplant: one 1050-shp Turboméca Astazou XVIIIA turboshaft
Performance: maximum cruising speed 275 km/h (171 mph) at sea level; range 680 km (423 miles)
Payload: 1420 kg (3131 lb); seats for up to 8 passengers
Crew: 2
Production: minimum 100 (orders for SA 360 and SA 365)

Top left: An SA 365 runs its engine prior to take-off
Top: An Aérospatiale Dauphin comes in to land in a clearing during a demonstration flight
Above: The SA 365 can accommodate up to 13 passengers without baggage

314

R22, Robinson

FIRST FLIGHT 1975

Left: The compact Robinson R22 which was designed with an emphasis on low noise, minimum maintenance and low operating costs. The cyclic control stick can be used from either seat

R22

Type: light helicopter
Maker: Robinson Helicopter Co
Rotor diameter: 7.67 m (25 ft 2 in)
Length: 6.3 m (20 ft 8 in) fuselage
Height: 2.67 m (8 ft 9 in)
Main rotor disc area: 46.21 m² (498 sq ft)
Weight: maximum 590 kg (1300 lb); empty 346 kg (762 lb)
Powerplant: one 150-hp Lycoming O-320-A2B 4-cylinder horizontally-opposed air-cooled piston engine
Performance: cruising speed 174 km/h (108 mph); range 386 km (240 miles)
Payload: seat for 1 passenger
Crew: 1
Production: not available

THE Robinson Helicopter Company was established in the early 1970s to design, produce and market a light helicopter able to compete in terms of purchase price and operating costs with contemporary light planes of the two- to four-seat category. The design of the helicopter to meet this requirement, the Robinson R22, began in July 1973.

From the inception of the programme, great emphasis was placed on providing the type with the simplest and easiest methods of maintenance, low operating noise levels and maximum aerodynamic and mechanical efficiency. Two prototypes were built, the first flying on August 28, 1975, and the second taking to the air in the spring of 1977. Deliveries of production helicopters began during the second half of 1978.

The R22 is a very clean helicopter, of interesting but not advanced construction. The fuselage, which sits on a pair of simple skids, is of steel-tube and light-alloy construction, covered with light alloy and glassfibre panels. The tail boom is a monocoque structure, and the simple tail unit is a light alloy cantilever structure.

The powerplant consists of a single Lycoming O-320-A2B piston engine, located in a semi-exposed position in the lower fuselage behind the cabin, where it helps to keep the helicopter's centre of gravity low while simultaneously it receives adequate air cooling. The engine is normally rated at 150 hp but is derated to 124 hp, and drives the rotors by means of a belt drive. The drive systems use flexible couplings requiring no maintenance.

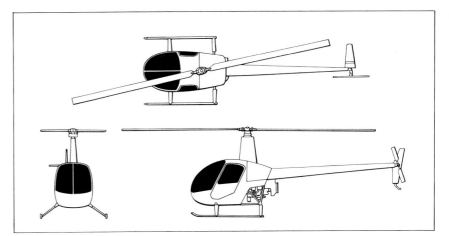

The main rotor, which sits above a well-faired tail-rotor mast, is a semi-rigid two-blade unit with a triple-hinged low-vibration underslung hub. Each blade is of bonded metal using a stainless steel leading edge and light alloy skin over a light alloy honeycomb core. The two-blade tail rotor is bonded of light alloy.

The accommodation is for two people, seated well back from the two-piece windscreen on individual seats. There is a small baggage space under each of these seats, and a door on each side to ensure easy access. The cyclic control stick is located between the seats so that either occupant can fly the machine, and is pivoted to simplify entry and exit. Avionics are simple, and optional to meet customer requirements.

315

V-12, Mil
FIRST FLIGHT 1968

THE Mil V-12 (M-12), which was allotted the NATO reporting name Homer, is currently the world's largest helicopter, but does not appear to have progressed past the development phase. This is presumably because of technical problems rather than performance deficiencies, for the V-12 holds many world records for payload and payload-to-altitude.

The origins of the V-12 lie with a 1965 Soviet air force requirement for a heavy-lift helicopter able to carry major missile components. These would be brought into remote missile site areas by fixed-wing aircraft, notably the Antonov An-22, and then lifted from the airfield to the launch site by the new helicopter.

There also existed a civil requirement for such a machine, principally for use in developing Siberia which is resources-rich but communications-poor. The military specification, calling for a tandem-rotor configuration using dynamic system components from existing helicopters, was paramount, however, as evidenced by the fact that the V-12 has the same basic hold dimensions as the An-22: 4.4 m by 4.4 m (14 ft 5½ in by 14 ft 5½ in), with length only 4.85 m (15 ft 11 in) less than that of the An-22 at 28.15 m (92 ft 4¼ in).

Although the requirement called for a tandem-rotor layout, Mil received early permission to concentrate instead on a twin side-by-side rotor configuration, which the design bureau claimed as having better reliability, fatigue life and stability. Thus the V-12, which first flew in the second half of 1968, appeared with a fuselage resembling that of a

V-12

Type: general-purpose heavy helicopter
Maker: Mil Design Bureau
Rotor diameter: 35 m (114 ft 10 in)
Span: 67 m (219 ft 10 in) over rotors
Length: 37 m (121 ft 4½ in) fuselage
Height: 12.5 m (41 ft)
Main rotor disc area: 1924.22 m² (20 712 sq ft)
Weight: maximum 105 000 kg (231 483 lb); empty not available
Powerplant: four 6500-shp Soloviev D-25VF turboshafts
Performance: maximum speed 260 km/h (161 mph); range with 35 400-kg (78 043-lb) payload 500 km (311 miles)
Payload: 40 000 kg (88,184 lb); seats for up to 50 passengers
Crew: 6
Production: not available

fixed-wing aircraft, from whose top spring two inversely tapered wings carrying the twin dynamic systems at their tips. Each of these dynamic systems is very closely related to that of the Mi-6 helicopter: it comprises two 6500-shp Soloviev D-25VF turboshafts, uprated from the 5500 shp of the Mi-6's Soloviev D-25V by the addition of a zero stage to the compressor and by an increase of operating temperature.

The two engines are located side-by-side with twin intakes, and drive five-bladed metal rotors. The left rotor rotates anti-clockwise and the right unit clockwise; the two units are connected by transverse shafting to ensure synchronization and the continued rotation of both units in the event of engine failure at either wingtip. The lower part of each cowling can be dropped to form a working platform for mechanics. Fuel is housed in two cylindrical tanks mounted externally on the lower fuselage sides. The main units of the fixed tricycle undercarriage are supported by a plethora of struts bracing the wings and running from the lower fuselage, wings and engines.

Although the V-12 could accommodate large numbers of passengers, tip-up seats are provided for only 50; the reason for this is that the type is intended mainly for heavy-lift work, with accommodation only for drilling crews, missile crews etc. The main freight hold has overhead rails for a moving crane which has four loading points, each rated at 2500 kg (5512 lb), or can alternatively lift a single item of up to 10 000 kg (22 046 lb). The bottom of the rear fuselage comprises an inbuilt loading ramp, with large clamshell doors forming the rear fuselage aft of this point.

The first prototype crashed, apparently as a result of engine failure, during 1969, but the second prototype established seven world records the same year. On February 22, the V-12 lifted a payload of 31 030 kg (68 408 lb) to 2951 m (9682 ft), breaking the records for maximum payload carried to 2000 m (6562 ft). On August 6, a load of 40 204.5 kg (88 634 lb) was lifted to an altitude of 2255 m (7398 ft), which constituted a new payload record for 2000 m (6562 ft), and payload-to-height records for 35 000 kg (77 161 lb) and 40 000 kg (88 184 lb).

Despite these impressive performances, little has recently been heard of the V-12, and technical problems have presumably led to its abandonment.

Top left and left: The Mil V-12 as it appeared at the 1971 Paris Air Show at Le Bourget
Above: The V-12, or Mi-12, has a six-man flight crew – pilot, co-pilot, flight engineer and electrician in the nose, and a navigator and radio operator in the upper cockpit

Boeing 234
FIRST FLIGHT 1980

THE Boeing Vertol 234LR Commercial Chinook is the civil derivative of the highly successful Models 114 and 234, used by the US Army as the CH-47 Chinook medium-transport military helicopter series.

The Model 114, military designation CH-47A, was itself a development of the Boeing Vertol 107 tandem-rotor helicopter, this latter also being the developed form of a concept pioneered by the Piasecki Helicopter Corporation.

The civil 234LR was announced in the summer of 1978 as a contender in the market for offshore oilfield support helicopters, with the ability to undertake other commercial operations. Although modelled closely on the CH-47C variant of the basic design, the 234LR is designed to carry up to 44 passengers over ranges of approximately 925 km (575 miles). To meet this requirement the 234LR is fitted with cabin windows similar to those of the Boeing 727 airliner, airliner seats at 84-cm (33-in) pitch, overhead baggage lockers, and a number of other 'airliner' features.

Other alterations compared with the military 234 are the inclusion of civil versions of the engines (in the form of Avco Lycoming AL 5512 turbo-shafts, each with a take-off rating of about 4075 shp), and a new fuel system with pressure-refuelling capability, and glassfibre rotor blades. Although the 234LR will undoubtedly offer operators considerable advantages (for example one 234LR could replace three of the Sikorsky S-61Ns currently used for most offshore support operations), there are problems: the cost of the 234LR is likely to rise

318

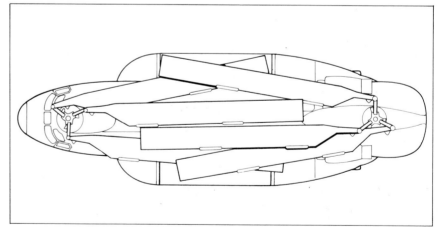

by some 40% before the type enters service in 1982, and the related engine used in the Bell 214B BigLifter (the Lycoming T5508D) has run into severe difficulties.

The two engines are located in pods on each side of the rear rotor pylon, the rotors being driven in counter-rotating directions by a series of interconnected shafts which ensure that each engine drives both rotors in the event of the other failing. In the military model the transmission is rated at 7200 shp for twin-engined operation, and at 4600 shp for single-engined flight, but this will presumably be further strengthened on the 234LR, which has more power and greater take-off weight (23 133 kg [51 000 lb] with an external load compared with 20 865 kg [46 000 lb]).

Top: The Boeing Vertol 234; British Airways planned to operate their six machines on support missions for gas and oil rigs in the North Sea from the summer of 1981
Above: The rotor stowage reduces the width from a diameter of 18.29 m (60 ft) to 3.78 m (12 ft 5 in)
Above right: Checking the glassfibre rotor blades at the Boeing Vertol plant at Morton, Philadelphia

The keynote of the 234LR's projected success is its great versatility: apart from a payload of up to 44 passengers, the helicopter can carry an internal load of some 9526 kg (21 000 lb) in the cabin, which is 9.19 m (30 ft 2 in) long, 2.51 m (8 ft 3 in) wide, and 1.98 m (6 ft 6 in) high. Alternatively, a maximum payload of 13 290 kg (29 300 lb) can be carried externally with the helicopter in its utility configuration.

With an internal payload the 234LR's maximum take-off weight is 21 318 kg (47 000 lb), compared with 23 133 kg (51 000 lb) with an external payload. Fuel load can also be altered considerably: in the utility version, maximum capacity is 1826 kg (4026 lb); in the long-range layout, this capacity is increased to 6361 kg (14 024 lb).

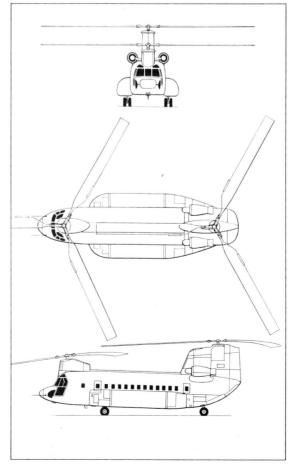

234LR

Type: transport and resources-support helicopter
Maker: Boeing Vertol Co
Rotor diameter: 18.29 m (60 ft)
Length: 16.08 m (52 ft 9 in) fuselage
Height: 5.68 m (18 ft 7¾ in)
Main rotor disc area: 525.37 m² (5655 sq ft)
Weight: maximum 23 133 kg (51 000 lb); empty 9144 kg (20 160 lb)
Powerplant: two 4075-shp Avco Lycoming AL5512 turboshafts
Performance: (estimated) maximum cruising speed 278 km/h (173 mph); range with 44 passengers 1010 km (627 miles)
Payload: 13 290 kg (29 300 lb); seats for up to 44 passengers
Crew: 2
Production: under development

Mk II, Spitfire

FIRST FLIGHT 1978

THE Spitfire Helicopter Company became associated with the Enstrom Helicopter Corporation in January 1975 when it began to develop, under the designation Spitfire Mk I, a turbine-engined light helicopter based on the Enstrom F-28A. Apart from its turbine engine, the Spitfire Mk I also introduced a conventional reduction-gear transmission instead of Enstrom's arrangement of multiple belts, thus making a saving in structure weight of 91 kg (200 lb) and economizing on fuselage space which could then be used for auxiliary fuel or extra freight. Prototype construction began in January 1976, and a number of pre-production helicopters were begun in February 1977.

The Spitfire Mk II is basically an improved version of the Mk I, with more power and a slight increase in size to allow the carriage of three passengers rather than two. Although the rating of the Allison 250-C20B remains substantially unaltered, its take-off power has been increased slightly to cater for the greater take-off weight of the Mk II (1134 kg [2500 lb] compared with 1043 kg [2300 lb]). The empty weight of the Mk II at 601 kg (1325 lb) is only 34 kg (75 lb) greater than the Mk I's 567 kg (1250 lb). The fuselage length of the Mk II has been increased slightly, with overall length rising from 8.96 m (29 ft 4¾ in) to 9.3 m (30 ft 6 in).

Accommodation in the Mk I is provided for the pilot and two passengers seated side-by-side on a bench seat, but in the Mk II seating is for the pilot and three passengers side-by-side on a wider bench seat. Baggage space on the Mk II consists of a 0.57-

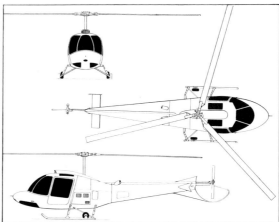

cm³ (20-cu ft) compartment aft of the cabin, with loading doors on each side of the fuselage.

Despite the Mk II's greater weights, it appears to be marginally superior to the Mk I in performance: cruising speed is up 16 km/h (10 mph), while rate of climb and service ceiling remain unaltered. The first Spitfire Mk II flew in the second half of 1978, and will probably enter production in 1981.

The company's future plans include the Mk III, a four-seat helicopter with stub wings to help offload the rotor in forward flight, thus enhancing performance; and the Mk IV, derived from the Mk III but with larger wings and an auxiliary propulsion engine in the rear of the fuselage, plus the unusual feature of the torque-control tail rotor replaced by ducted fans at each wingtip.

Mk II

Type: light helicopter
Maker: Spitfire Helicopter Co
Rotor diameter: 9.75 m (32 ft)
Length: 9.3 m (30 ft 6 in) fuselage
Height: 2.79 m (9 ft 2 in)
Main rotor disc area: 74.69 m² (804 sq ft)
Weight: (estimated) maximum 1134 kg (2500 lb); empty 601 kg (1325 lb)
Powerplant: one 420-shp Allison 250-C20B turboshaft
Performance: (estimated) maximum speed 217 km/h (135 mph)
Payload: seats for up to 3 passengers
Crew: 1
Production: under development

Top: The Spitfire Mk II. Optional extras will eventually include a cargo hook, stretchers, survey and agricultural equipment.

Index

Page numbers in bold refer to the
main entry of the aircraft

A109A, Agusta, *298–99*
A300B, Airbus Industrie, *158–69*, *170*
A310, Airbus Industrie, *170–73*
Aermacchi/Lockheed AL.60 Conestoga, see AL.60
Aerospace Fletcher, see Fletcher
Aérospatiale, see Alouette III, AS 350 Ecureuil,
     AStar, Concorde, Corvette, Dauphin, Gazelle,
     Lama, Puma, SA 321F Super Frelon
Aerovan, Miles, *199*
Ag-Cat, Gulfstream America, *209*
Agusta A109A, see A109A
Airbus Industrie, see A300B, A310
AirCruiser Bellanca, see Bellanca
Air Tractor AT-301, *241*
Airtruk, Transavia, *240*
AL.60 Conestoga, Aermacchi/Lockheed, *227*
Alouette III, Aérospatiale, *271*, *274*
An-2, Antonov, *202*
An-10, Antonov, *86*
An-14, Antonov, *232*
An-24, Antonov, *100*
An-72, Antonov, *104–05*
Antonov, see An-2, An-10, An-14, An-24, An-72
Arava, IAI, *237*
AS 350 Ecureuil, Aérospatiale, *306–07*
AStar, Aérospatiale, *306*
AT-301 Air Tractor, see Air Tractor
Avco Aerostructures, *124*, *127*
Avro Lancastrian jet, see Lancastrian jet
Avro 740, *54*, *60*
Avro Canada Jetliner, see Jetliner
Ayres Thrush Commander, see Thrush Com-
     mander

B-29 Superfortress, Boeing, *22*
B-47 Stratojet, Boeing, *10*, *44*
B-52 Stratofortress, Boeing, *10*
BAC One-Eleven, see One-Eleven
BAe 125, British Aerospace, *214–15*
BAe 146, British Aerospace, *124–25*
Bandeirante, Embraer, *236*
BB-152, VEB, *44*
Beaver, de Havilland Canada, *200*
Beech 18, *204–05*
Beech Super King Air, see Super King Air
Bell 47, *257*
Bell 204, *285*
Bell 205, *286–87*
Bell 206 JetRanger, *290–91*
Bell 206L, see LongRanger
Bell 214B, *288–89*
Bell 222, *294–95*
Bellanca AirCruiser, *196*
BK 117, MBB/Kawasaki, *308–09*
Boeing, see B-29, B-47, B-52, YC-14
Boeing 234, *318–19*
Boeing 377 Stratocruiser, *10*
Boeing 707, *10–17*, *138*
Boeing 720, *18–20*

Boeing 727, *60–64*, *126*
Boeing 737, *76–81*
Boeing 747, *52*, *138–47*
Boeing 757, *126–27*
Boeing 767, *126*, *181–85*
Boeing Vertol 107, *292*
Brantly, *282*
Bristol 171, *260*
Bristol 173, *261*
Bristol 192, *261*
Bristol 200, *54*, *60*
Bristol 223, *109*
Bristol Aircraft, *186*
Bristol Siddeley, *110*
British Aeroplane Company, *260*
British Aerospace, see BAe 125, BAe 146, Con-
     corde, Harrier, Nimrod
British Aircraft Corporation One-Eleven, see One-
     Eleven

Camel, see also Tu-104, Tupolev
Canadair, see Challenger, CL-215
Caravelle, Aérospatiale, *28–33*
Cessna, see Citation, Conquest
Challenger, Canadair, *124*, *250*
Chase XCG-20A, see XCG-20A
Cheyenne, Piper, *246*
Citation, Cessna, *242–43*
CL-215, Canadair, *233*
Clod, see An-14, Antonov
Colt, see An-2, Antonov
Comet 1, de Havilland, *6–9*
Comet 4, de Havilland, *34–37*
Commander 700, Rockwell, *254*
Concorde, Aérospatiale/British Aerospace, *109–
     17*, *118*, *186*
Conquest, Cessna, *247*
Consolidated PB2Y Coronado, see PB2Y
Constellation, Lockheed L-749, see L-749
Convair, see CV-880, CV-990
Cooker, see Tu-110, Tupolev
Cookpot, see Tu-124, Tupolev
Coronado, Consolidated PB2Y, see PB2Y
Corvette, Aérospatiale, *244*
Courier, Helio, *206*
Curtiss Robin, see Robin
CV-880, Convair, *45–47*
CV-990, Convair, *48–49*

Dassault Mystère, see Mystère
Dassault-Breguet, see Falcon, Falcon 10, Falcon
     20, Falcon 50, Mercure, Mirage
Dauphin, Aérospatiale, *314*
DC-3, Douglas, *97*, *98*
DC-7, Douglas, *38*
DC-8, Douglas, *38–43*
DC-9, McDonnell Douglas, *70–75*
DC-9 Super 80, McDonnell Douglas, *122–3*
DC-10, McDonnell Douglas, *148–57*
de Havilland, see Comet 1, Comet 4, DH.121
de Havilland Australia Drover, see Drover
de Havilland Canada, see Beaver, DHC-3 Otter
Delta, Fairey, *110*
DH.121, de Havilland, *54*, *60*
DHC-3 Otter, de Havilland Canada, *203*

Right: A Boeing 747

Dornier Skyservant, see Skyservant
Douglas, see DC-3, DC-8
Dromader, PZL, **251**
Drover, de Havilland Australia, **201**

Edgar Percival E.P.9, see E.P.9
Electra, Lockheed L-188, see L-188
Embraer, see Bandeirante, Xingu
Enstrom, **300–01**
E.P.9, Edgar Percival, **208**
Ernst Heinkel Flugzeugbau, *97*

F27 Friendship, Fokker, *92*
F28 Fellowship, Fokker, **92–96**, *128*
F29, Fokker, **128**
F + W, *102*
Fairchild FC.2, see FC.2
Fairchild Hiller FH-1100, see FH-1100
Fairchild-Republic, *127*
Fairey Delta, see Delta
Falcon, Dassault-Breguet, *102*
Falcon 10, Dassault-Breguet, **218**
Falcon 20, Dassault-Breguet, **217**
Falcon 50, Dassault-Breguet, **219**
FC.2, Fairchild, **194**
Fellowship, Fokker F28, see F28
FH-1100, Fairchild Hiller, **259**
Fletcher, Aerospace, **207**
Focke-Wulf, *97*
Fokker, see F27 Friendship, F28 Fellowship, F29
Foxjet ST-600, see ST-600
Friendship, Fokker F27, see F27

GAF Nomad, see Nomad
Gazelle, Aérospatiale, **304–05**
General Dynamics, *20, 45*
Government Aircraft Factories Nomad, see Nomad
Grumman Widgeon, see Widgeon
Gulfstream I, Gulfstream American, **222**
Gulfstream II, Gulfstream American, **235**
Gulfstream American, see Ag-Cat, Gulfstream I, Gulfstream II

HAL, see Hindustan Aeronautics Limited
Handley Page 115, *110*
Hansa, MBB HFB 320, see HFB 320
'Hare', see Mi-1, Mil
Harrier, British Aerospace, *44*
Hawker Siddeley Trident, see Trident
Helio Courier, see Courier
HFB 320 Hansa, MBB, **230**
Hiller 360, **258**
Hindustan Aeronautics Limited, *271*
'Hip', see Mi-8P, Mil
'Horner', see V-12, Mil
'Hoodlum', see Ka-26, Kamov
'Hook', see Mi-6, Mil
'Hoplite', see Mi-2, Mil
'Hormone', see Ka-25K, Kamov
'Horse', see Yak-24A, Yakovlev
Hughes 300, **283**
Hughes 500, **284**
Hydrogen-fuelled airliners, **190–91**

IAI, see Israel Aircraft Industries
IAR-827, **253**
ICX Aviation, *99*
Il-2, Ilyushin, *193*
Il-10, Ilyushin, *193*
Il-12, Ilyushin, *98*
Il-14, Ilyushin, *26, 99*
Il-18, Ilyushin, *86, 100*
Il-62, Ilyushin, **90–91**, *106*
Il-76, Ilyushin, **106–08**
Il-86, Ilyushin, *101*, **174–80**
Ilyushin, see Il-2, Il-10, Il-12, Il-14, Il-18, Il-62, Il-76, Il-86
Israel Aircraft Industries, see Arava, Westwind

Jetliner, Avro Canada, **4–5**
JetRanger, see Bell 206
JetStar, Lockheed, **210**
Junkers, *188*

Ka-25K, Kamov, **296**
Ka-26, Kamov, **297**
Kamov, see Ka-25K, Ka-26
Kania, PZL, **312–13**
Kawasaki Heavy Industries, see BK 117
KC-135, Boeing, *12, 18*
Kruk, PZL, **252**

L-188 Electra, Lockheed, *8*
L-749 Constellation, Lockheed, *7*
L-1011 TriStar, Lockheed, **129–37**, *148, 190*
Lama, Aérospatiale, **271–73**
Lancastrian jet, Avro, *2*
Learjets, **220–21**
Li-2, Lisunov, *98*
Lisunov Li-2, see Li-2
Little Rock Airmotive, *217*
Lockheed, see AL.60 Conestoga, JetStar, L-188 Electra, L-749 Constellation, L-1011 TriStar
LongRanger, Bell 206L, **293**

M-15 Belphegor, PZL, **256**
MBB, see Messerschmitt-Bölkow-Blohm
McDonnell Douglas, see DC-9, DC-9 Super 80, YC-15
McKinnon Enterprises, **198**
Mercure, Dassault-Breguet, *102*
Messerschmitt-Bölkow-Blohm, see BK 117, HFB 320 Hansa
Mi-1, Mil, **275**
Mi-2, Mil, **276**
Mi-4, Mil, *268*
Mi-6, Mil, **277–79**
Mi-8P, Mil, **280**
MiG-21, Mikoyan-Gurevich, *118*
Mikoyan-Gurevich MiG-21, see MiG-21
Mil, see Mi-1, Mi-2, Mi-4, Mi-6, Mi-8P, V-12
Miles Aerovan, see Aerovan
Mirage III, Dassault-Breguet, *102*
Mitsubishi MU-2, see MU-2
Mk II, Spitfire, **320**
MU-2, Mitsubishi, **228–29**
Mystère, Dassault, *102*

Right: A Kamov Ka-26
Bottom left: a PZL-104 Wilga
Bottom right: A Sikorsky S-51

NASA/Boeing QSRA, *189*
National Aerospace Laboratory Q/STOL, *189*
Navajo, Piper, *225*
Nene-Lancastrian, Vickers-Armstrongs, *1*
Nene Viking, Vickers-Armstrongs, *1*, *3*
Nimrod, British Aerospace, *37*
Nomad, GAF, *245*
Noorduyn Norseman, see Norseman
Norseman, Noorduyn, **197**

One-Eleven, BAC, **65–69**, *70, 76, 82*

P.136, Piaggio, *216*
P.166, Piaggio, **216**
Pawnee, Piper, **238**
PB2Y Coronado, Consolidated, *48*
Piaggio, see P.136, P.166
Pilatus Turbo-Porter, see Turbo-Porter
Piper, see Cheyenne, Navajo, Pawnee
Po-2, Polikarpov, **193**
Puma, Aérospatiale, **302–03**
PZL, see Dromader, Kania, Kruk, M-15 Belphegor, Wilga

R22, Robinson, **315**
Raisbeck Corporation, *211*
Robin, Curtiss, **195**
Robinson R22, see R22
Rockwell, see Commander 700, Sabreliner, Turbo Commander

S-51, Sikorsky, **262**
S-55, Sikorsky, **263**, *264*
S-58, Sikorsky, **264–65**
S-61N, Sikorsky, **266–67**
S-76, Spirit, Sikorsky, **310–11**
SA 321F Super Frelon, Aérospatiale, *281*
Saab-Scania, *124*
Sabreliner, Rockwell, **211**
Shorts Skyvan, see Skyvan
Sikorsky, see S-51, S-55, S-58, S-61N, S-76 Spirit
Skyservant, Dornier, **248**
Skyvan, Shorts, **231**
Slew-winged airliners, **192**
Société de Constructions Aéro Navales, *198*
Spirit, Sikorsky S-76, see S-76
Spitfire MkII, see Mk II
SST Projects and Advanced Transports, **186–89**
ST-600, Foxjet, **255**
Stratocruiser, Boeing 377, see Boeing 377
Stroukoff Aircraft, *21*
Sud-Aviation Super Caravelle, see Super Caravelle
Super 80, McDonnell Douglas DC-9, see DC-9 Super 80
Super Caravelle, Sud-Aviation, *109*
Super Frelon, Aérospatiale SA 321F, see SA 321F
Super King Air, Beech, **226**

Tay Viscount, Vickers-Armstrongs, *3*
Thrush Commander, Ayres, **239**, *251*
Transavia Airtruk, see Airtruk
Turbo Commander, Rockwell, **212–13**

Trident, Hawker Siddeley, **54–59**, *60*
TriStar, Lockheed L-1011, see also L-1011
Tu-4, Tupolev, *22*
Tu-16, Tupolev, *22, 24, 25*
Tu-104, Tupolev, **22–24**, *25, 26, 33, 82, 86*
Tu-110, Tupolev, **25**
Tu-124, Tupolev, **26–27**, *82, 84, 86*
Tu-134, Tupolev, **82–85**, *86, 100*
Tu-144, Tupolev, *86, 109*, **118–21**, *186*
Tu-154, Tupolev, **86–89**, *106, 174*
Tupolev, see Tu-4, Tu-16, Tu-104, Tu-110, Tu-124, Tu-134, Tu-144, Tu-154
Turbo-Porter, Pilatus, **224**

V-12, Mil, **316–17**
V.1000, Vickers, *50*
Vanguard, Vickers-Armstrongs, *35, 54*
VC7, Vickers, *50*
VC10/Super VC10, Vickers, **50–53**, *90*
VEB, see Vereinegung Volkseigener Betriebe Flugzeugbau
Vereinegung Volkseigener Betriebe Flugzeugbau BB-152, see BB-152
VFW 614, **97**
VFW-Fokker, *92, 93, 97*
Vickers, see V.1000, VC7, VC10
Vickers-Armstrongs, see Nene-Lancastrian, Nene Viking, Tay Viscount, Vanguard, Viscount
Viscount, Vickers-Armstrong, *36*

Westland Whirlwind Series 3, see Whirlwind Series 3
Westwind, IAI, **234**
Whirlwind Series 3, Westland, **270**
Widgeon, Grumman, **198**
Wilga, PZL, **223**

X-Avia, Yakovlev, *99*
XCG-20A, Chase, *21*
Xingu, Embraer, **249**

Yak-16, Yakovlev, *98*
Yak-24A, Yakovlev, **268–70**
Yak-40, Yakovlev, **98–99**, *100*
Yak-42, Yakovlev, *84*, **100–01**, *104*
Yakovlev, see X-Avia, Yak-16, Yak-24A, Yak-40, Yak-42
YC-14, Boeing, *104, 105*
YC-15, McDonnell Douglas, *105*

Right: A Piper Pawnee flies low over a field during spraying operations

Picture credits